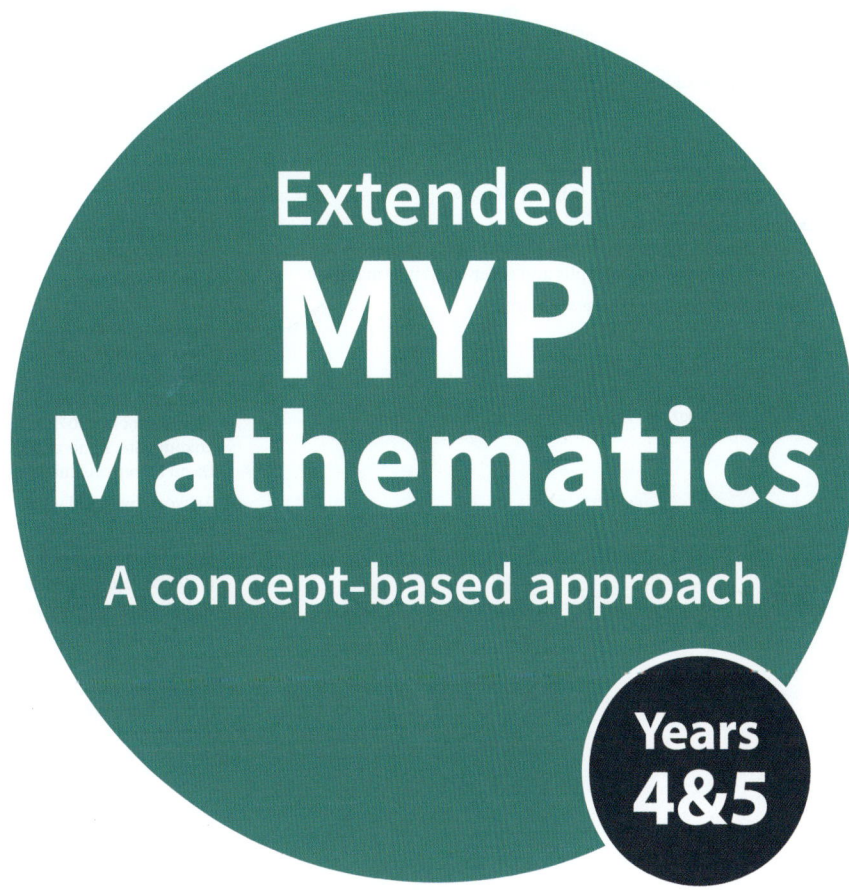

Extended

MYP Mathematics

A concept-based approach

Years 4&5

Rose Harrison
Clara Huizink
Aidan Sproat-Clements
Marlene Torres-Skoumal

OXFORD
UNIVERSITY PRESS

OXFORD
UNIVERSITY PRESS

Great Clarendon Street, Oxford, OX2 6DP, United Kingdom

Oxford University Press is a department of the University of Oxford. It furthers the University's objective of excellence in research, scholarship, and education by publishing worldwide. Oxford is a registered trade mark of Oxford University Press in the UK and in certain other countries

© Oxford University Press 2021

British Library Cataloguing in Publication Data
Data available

978-1-382-01092-4

7 9 10 8

The manufacturing process conforms to the environmental regulations of the country of origin.

Printed in the UK by Bell and Bain Ltd, Glasgow

Acknowledgements

The publisher and authors would like to thank the following for permission to use photographs and other copyright material:

Cover: Boris SV/Getty Images. Photos

p4: fintastique/iStockphoto; **p15:** FotoDuets/Shutterstock; **p16:** ManuKro/iStockphoto; **p20:** Evan Lorne/Shutterstock; **p21:** gillmar/Shutterstock; **p25:** Antony McAulay/Shutterstock; **p26:** Chris King/OUP; p27(b): Elnur/Shutterstock; **p28:** Patrik Mezirka/Shutterstock; **p46:** Martin Valigursky/Shutterstock; **p72:** Kanate/Shutterstock; p73(t): AshTproductions/Shutterstock; p73(m): Janelle Lugge/Shutterstock; p73(b): Piotr Krzeslak/Shutterstock; **p74:** K.Wanvisa/Shutterstock; **p85:** Tina Rencelj/Shutterstock; p101(t): njaj/Shutterstock; p101(ml): Eric Milos/Shutterstock; p101(m): Anton Starikov/Shutterstock; p101(mr): tgunal/Shutterstock; p101(bl): NASA; p101(bm): NASA; p101(br): NASA; **p102:** Typhoonski/Dreamstime; **p123:** Dorling Kindersley ltd / Alamy Stock Photo; **p126:** Peacefully7/Shutterstock; **p127:** sebaturek/Shutterstock; **p128:** PEPPERSMINT/Shutterstock; **p132:** sisqopote/Shutterstock; **p137:** Jacek Chabraszewski/Shutterstock; **p143:** Dionisvera/Shutterstock; **p144:** Boris Sosnovyy/Shutterstock; **p145:** Eric Isselee/Shutterstock; **p146:** Monkey Business Images/Shutterstock; **p147:** Jonathan Lenz/Shutterstock; **p148:** LeventeGyori/Shutterstock; **p151:** DuPo/Shutterstock; **p152:** Mana Photo/Shutterstock; **p166:** Vitalliy/Shutterstock; **p175:** Gail Johnson/Shutterstock; **p186:** Dmitry Kalinovsky/Shutterstock; **p192:** WDG Photo/Shutterstock; **p197:** Meunierd/Shutterstock; **p200:** Lilu2005/Shutterstock; **p205:** Andrey Yurlov/Shutterstock; **p213:** iurii/Shutterstock; **p214:** szefei/Shutterstock; **p215:** Amra Pasic/Shutterstock; **p231:** Pablo Caridad/Shutterstock; **p239:** SandiMako/Shutterstock; p242(t): greenland/Shutterstock; **p242:** Clara Huizink; p243(t): Clara Huizink; p243(ml): Clara Huizink; p243(mr): Clara Huizink; **p244:** Pixbilder/Dremstime; **p248:** Dagamarhijmans/Dreamstime; p256(t): wavebreakmedia/Shutterstock; p256(b): XYZ/Shutterstock; p257(t): Pop Paul-Catalin/Shutterstock; p257(b): Rose Harrison; **p258:** Ales Liska/Shutterstock; **p263:** Eugene Sim/Shutterstock; **p266:** Moose Henderson/123RF; **p269:** Damsea/Shutterstock; p270(t): injun/Shutterstock; p270(b): Marco Tomasini; **p273:** Christian Delbert/Shutterstock; **p274:** Dmitry Pichugin/Shutterstock; **p289:** Noolwlee/Shutterstock; **p303:** Monkey Business Images/Shutterstock; **p306:** StudioM1/iStock; p307(t): Claudio Divizia/Shutterstock; p307(b): Ted Kinsman/Science Photo Library; **p308:** kokouu/iStockphoto; **p311:** Claudio Divizia/Shutterstock; **p333:** Scott David Patterson/Shutterstock; **p350:** perspectivestock/Shutterstock.

Artwork by Jon Mackay, Thomson Digital, and Q2A Media Services Pvt. Ltd.

Every effort has been made to contact copyright holders of material reproduced in this book. Any omissions will be rectified in subsequent printings if notice is given to the publisher.

The 'in cooperation' logo signifies that the content in the print book has been reviewed by the IB to ensure it fully aligns with the revised MYP framework. The extra online resources found in the digital book offer additional support but are not published in cooperation with the IB.

Contents

Launch answers and other digital resources for this book

Introduction

Introduction for students

Studying mathematics is a fundamental part of a balanced education: understanding mathematics can help make sense of the world around us, exploring it can give both the thrill of exploration and the rewards of discovery, and engaging in mathematics can give insightful reflections.

Our aim writing this book was to create a journey of knowing, understanding, investigating and communicating mathematics. The MYP 4&5 Extended book is designed to take you on this wondrous journey and to help your analytical reasoning and problem-solving skills that contribute to strengthening your logical, abstract and critical thinking. All these skills are necessary to participate successfully in an ever-changing world.

Introduction for teachers

We believe that mathematics aims to equip all students with the knowledge, understanding and intellectual capabilities to progress to further study, as well as to prepare them for their life journey, which is why we wanted to showcase authentic examples of how mathematics is useful and relevant to students' lives and encourage them to apply it to new situations. In addition, we wanted them to experience the elegance and beauty of pure mathematics. To achieve this, we entwined content, concepts and contexts throughout the units for the right balance of new and consolidation material, both in the printed book and the extra digital resources.

This second edition of the MYP Mathematics 4&5 Extended book is fully aligned with the latest MYP Mathematics framework, for first teaching in 2020. Unlike the first edition, this book is structured by unit, making it easier for you to use it in the classroom.

How to get the most out of this resource

We also wanted to give you more teaching resources which is why this new edition comes with an enhanced digital online book. Wherever you see this icon, you are able to launch supporting resources:

Launch additional digital resources for this unit

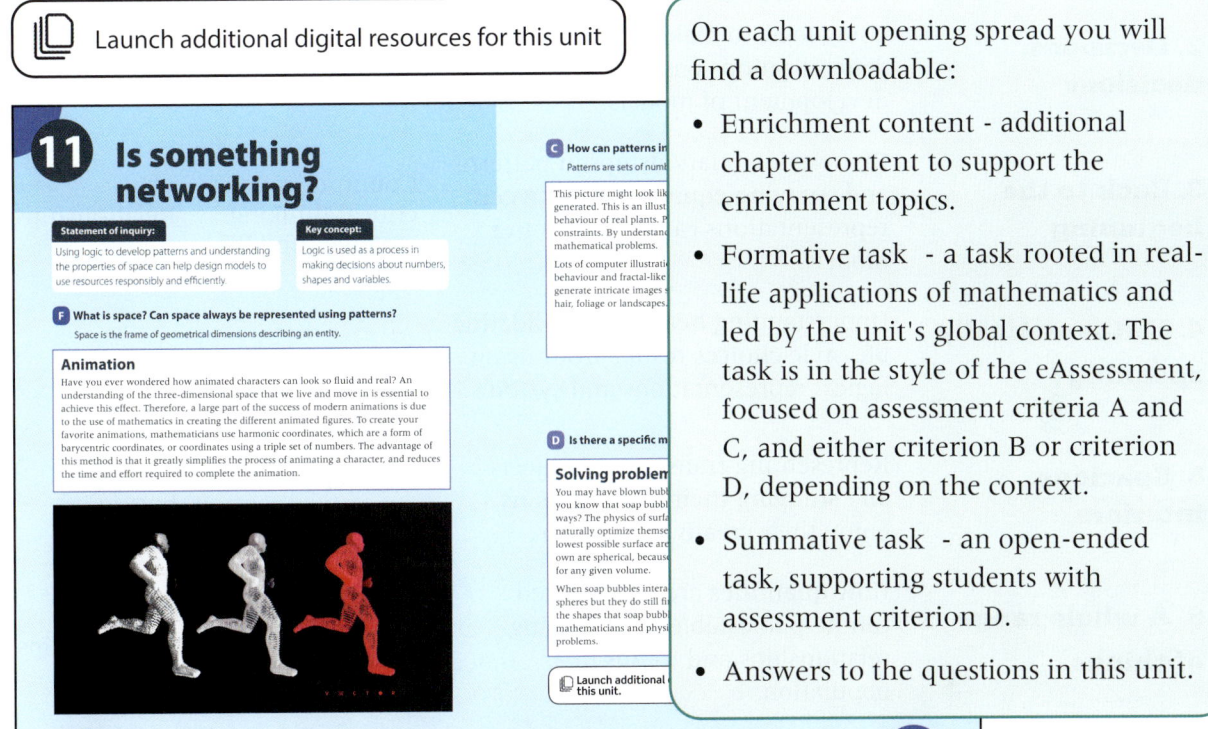

On each unit opening spread you will find a downloadable:

- Enrichment content - additional chapter content to support the enrichment topics.

- Formative task - a task rooted in real-life applications of mathematics and led by the unit's global context. The task is in the style of the eAssessment, focused on assessment criteria A and C, and either criterion B or criterion D, depending on the context.

- Summative task - an open-ended task, supporting students with assessment criterion D.

- Answers to the questions in this unit.

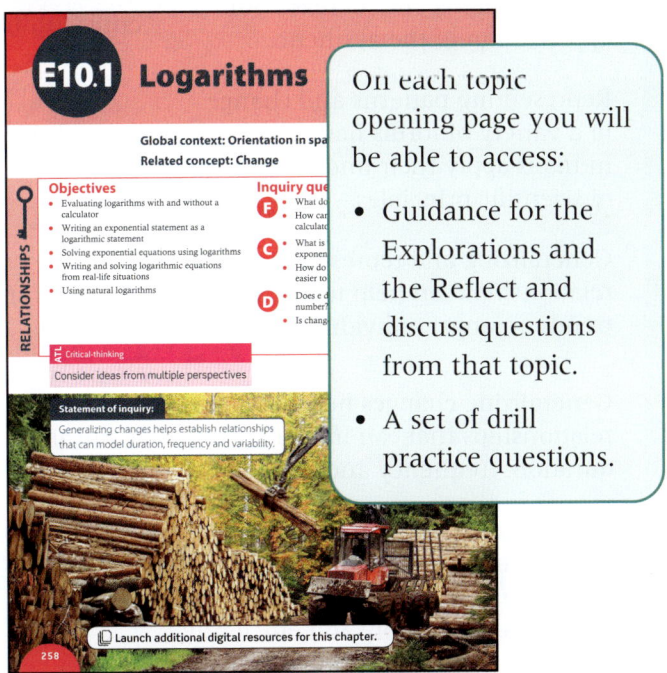

On each topic opening page you will be able to access:

- Guidance for the Explorations and the Reflect and discuss questions from that topic.

- A set of drill practice questions.

Unit	Statement of inquiry	ATL cluster(s)	Key concept
1. Being specific	Representing numbers in different forms to simplify them can help understand human-made systems.	Organization, communication, critical thinking	Form
2. Decisions, decisions	Using logic to make and validate generalizations enhances the development of models.	Critical thinking, transfer	Logic
3. Back to the beginning	Discovering relationships in patterns and studying equivalence between representations can lead to better models.	Communication, critical thinking, creative thinking	Relationships
4. Mathematically speaking	Understanding health and validating life-style choices results from using logical representations and systems.	Communication	Logic
5. Spacious interiors	Representing transformed objects and studying their form helps us enjoy their creativity in space.	Creative thinking	Form
6. A whole range of things	How quantities are represented can help to establish underlying relationships and trends in a population.	Communication, critical thinking	Relationships
7. How do they measure up?	Systems use logic to validate generalizations and increase our appreciation of the aesthetic.	Communication, critical thinking	Logic
8. What comes next?	Representing patterns and change in a variety of forms has helped humans apply their understanding of scientific principles.	Critical thinking, transfer	Form
9. So, what do you think?	Generalizing and representing relationships can help to clarify trends amongst individuals.	Critical thinking	Relationships
10. Go ahead and log in!	Generalizing changes helps establish relationships that can model duration, frequency and variability.	Critical thinking	Relationships
11. Is something networking?	Using logic to develop patterns and understanding the properties of space can help design models to use resources responsibly and efficiently.	Critical thinking	Logic

Related concepts	Global context	Exploration
Simplification, representation, quantity, approximation	Globalization and sustainability	Exploring different ways of measuring human-made systems
Generalization, validity, models	Scientific and technical innovation	Exploring the natural world by developing realistic models
Representation, patterns, equivalence	Scientific and technical innovation	Exploring systems and methods to create models
Validity, representation, systems	Identities and relationships	Exploring personal and physical health and good lifestyle choices
Representation, space	Personal and cultural expression	Exploring the ways in which we reflect on, extend and enjoy our creativity
Representation, quantity, generalization	Globalization and sustainability	Exploring trends and the impact of decision-making on the environment
Approximation, generalization, systems, models, space	Personal and cultural expression	Exploring the appreciation of the aesthetic.
Patterns, change, equivalence	Scientific and technical innovation	Exploring how humans apply their understanding of scientific principles to real-life situations
Generalization, representation	Identities and relationships	Exploring trends and characteristics amongst individuals
Change, validity, models	Orientation in space and time	Exploring scales and modelling duration, frequency and variability
Pattern, space	Fairness and development	Exploring the use of resources in a responsible and efficient manner

1 Being specific

F What is an approximation? What is a human-made system?

An approximation is a quantity or a representation that is nearly, but not exactly, correct.

Estimating

Using a model can help you calculate reasonable estimates.

The average human body is about 60% water.

- Modelling your body as a cylinder, calculate an estimate for the volume of water in your body.

- How could you improve your model to make your estimate more accurate?

C How does simplifying lead to better results?

Simplification is the process of reducing something to a less complicated form.

Simplified Chinese

Many traditional characters in the Chinese language are very complex, making the written language hard to learn. From 1949, in an effort to increase literacy, simplified Chinese was introduced. Simplified Chinese is probably easier to learn, because it has fewer strokes per character. Pinyin is the conversion of Chinese characters to a Roman script, based on pronunciation.

The table here shows the Pinyin, Simplified and Traditional characters for three nouns and three verbs.

English	Pinyin	Simplified character(s)	Traditional character(s)
Mathematics	shù xué	数学	數學
To count	shù	数	數
To learn	xué	学	學
Book	shū	书	書
Horse	mǎ	马	馬
To thank	xiè	谢	謝

D **Can approximations ever be exact? Do more representations make understanding easier?**

Representation in symbols

Maps contain symbols that represent features of the landscape or terrain. Which of the symbols below do you recognize? Are they ones that are used in places other than maps?

Global context: Globalization and sustainability

Exploration: Explore different ways of measuring human-made systems

⬚ Launch additional digital resources for this unit.

E1.1 Laws of exponents and rational exponents

Global context: Globalization and sustainability

Related concept: Simplification

FORM

Objectives

- Evaluating numerical expressions with a positive or negative fractional exponent
- Writing numerical expressions with fractional exponents as radicals
- Using the rules of indices to simplify expressions that contain radicals and/or fractional exponents

Inquiry questions

F
- How do you evaluate a number with a fractional exponent?
- How do you use the rules of indices to simplify expressions with fractional exponents?

C
- How are the rules of indices and the rules of radicals related?
- How do the rules of indices help simplify radical expressions?

D
- Can expressions with decimal exponents be simplified?
- Is simpler always better?

ATL Critical-thinking

Analyse complex concepts and projects into their constituent parts and synthesize them to create new understanding

📖 **Launch additional digital resources for this chapter.**

Statement of inquiry:

Representing numbers in different forms to simplify them can help understand human-made systems.

You should already know how to:

• use the multiplicative rule for exponents	**1** Simplify: **a** $(x^3)^2$ **b** $(2^4)^2$ **c** $(2x^2)^3$
• use the rules of radicals to simplify expressions	**2** Simplify completely: **a** $\sqrt{45}$ **b** $\dfrac{\sqrt{128}}{\sqrt{8}}$ **c** $\sqrt{60} \times \sqrt{3}$

• evaluate expressions with negative exponents	**3** Evaluate, leaving your answer as a fraction where necessary:
	  a 4^{-1} **b** 6^{-2} **c** 2^{-3}
	  d $\left(\dfrac{1}{2}\right)^{-1}$ **e** $\left(\dfrac{2}{3}\right)^{-1}$ **f** $\left(\dfrac{2}{5}\right)^{-2}$

F Fractional exponents

- How do you evaluate a number with a fractional exponent?
- How do you use the rules of indices to simplify expressions with fractional exponents?

For any positive real number x, and integer n, where $n \neq 0$, $x^{\frac{1}{n}} = \sqrt[n]{x}$.

Example 1

Evaluate:

a $\left(\dfrac{9}{25}\right)^{\frac{1}{2}}$ **b** $\left(\dfrac{1}{8}\right)^{-\frac{1}{3}}$ **c** $\left(\dfrac{7}{81}\right)^{-\frac{1}{2}}$

a $\left(\dfrac{9}{25}\right)^{\frac{1}{2}} = \sqrt{\dfrac{9}{25}} = \dfrac{3}{5}$

b $\left(\dfrac{1}{8}\right)^{-\frac{1}{3}} = 8^{\frac{1}{3}} = \sqrt[3]{8} = 2$ —————— Using the multiplicative rule for exponents, $(x^a)^b = x^{ab}$: $\left(\dfrac{1}{8}\right)^{-\frac{1}{3}} = \left(\left(\dfrac{1}{8}\right)^{-1}\right)^{\frac{1}{3}} = 8^{\frac{1}{3}}$

c $\left(\dfrac{7}{81}\right)^{-\frac{1}{2}} = \left(\dfrac{81}{7}\right)^{\frac{1}{2}} = \dfrac{9}{\sqrt{7}} = \dfrac{9\sqrt{7}}{7}$ —————— Here, the denominator has been rationalized.

Practice 1

1 Work out the value of:

  a $\left(\dfrac{1}{4}\right)^{\frac{1}{2}}$ **b** $\left(\dfrac{1}{16}\right)^{-\frac{1}{4}}$ **c** $\left(\dfrac{1}{8}\right)^{\frac{1}{3}}$ **d** $\left(\dfrac{1}{25}\right)^{-\frac{1}{2}}$

  e $\left(\dfrac{4}{9}\right)^{\frac{1}{2}}$ **f** $27^{-\frac{1}{3}}$ **g** $\left(\dfrac{4}{25}\right)^{-\frac{1}{2}}$ **h** $\left(\dfrac{27}{1000}\right)^{-\frac{1}{3}}$

2 Simplify and leave your final answer as a power of x:

a $(4x)^{\frac{1}{2}}$ **b** $(27x^3)^{\frac{1}{3}}$ **c** $(8x^6)^{-\frac{1}{3}}$ **d** $\left(\dfrac{x^4}{100}\right)^{-\frac{1}{2}}$

e $x^{-\frac{1}{2}} \times x^{\frac{1}{2}}$ **f** $x^{\frac{1}{3}} \div x^{\frac{1}{2}}$ **g** $x^{\frac{1}{4}} \times x^{-\frac{1}{2}}$ **h** $(9x^2)^{-\frac{1}{2}} \times 9x^2$

> Assume that $x \neq 0$ for all expressions.

Problem solving

3 Write each of these using exponents instead of the radicals.

a $\dfrac{1}{\sqrt{x}}$ **b** $\sqrt[3]{x}$ **c** $\dfrac{1}{\sqrt[4]{x}}$

4 Solve:

a $\left(\dfrac{1}{x}\right)^{-\frac{1}{3}} = 2$ **b** $\left(\dfrac{y}{9}\right)^{-\frac{1}{2}} = 0.3$

- -

Using the multiplicative rule for exponents $(x^a)^b = x^{ab}$:

$$(x^{\frac{1}{2}})^3 = x^{\frac{3}{2}} \qquad\qquad\qquad (x^4)^{\frac{1}{3}} = x^{\frac{4}{3}}$$

Reflect and discuss 1

What do expressions with fractional exponents like $x^{\frac{2}{3}}$ or $x^{\frac{4}{3}}$ mean?

ATL

Exploration 1

1 Copy and complete this table:

Using integer and unit fractional exponents	Using a radical	Using fractional exponents
$\left(x^{\frac{1}{2}}\right)^3$	$(\sqrt{x})^3$	$x^{\frac{3}{2}}$
$\left(x^{\frac{1}{2}}\right)^5$		
$(x^3)^{\frac{1}{2}}$	$\sqrt{x^3}$	
	$\sqrt[3]{x^4}$	
		$x^{\frac{2}{5}}$
		$x^{\frac{2}{3}}$

> A unit fraction has numerator 1.

2 Simplify $\left(x^{\frac{1}{3}}\right)^2$ and $(x^2)^{\frac{1}{3}}$. Are $\left(x^{\frac{1}{3}}\right)^2$ and $(x^2)^{\frac{1}{3}}$ equivalent?

Generalize your result for $\left(x^{\frac{1}{n}}\right)^m$ where m and n are integers and $n \neq 0$.

3 Copy and complete, using your result from step **2**:

$$(\sqrt[n]{x})^{\square} = \left(x^{\frac{1}{n}}\right)^{\square} = x^{\frac{m}{n}} = (x^m)^{\square} = \sqrt[n]{x^{\square}}$$

Reflect and discuss 2

- Did everyone in the class get the same results for the last two rows in the table in Exploration 1?
- Is there more than one way of writing $x^{\frac{2}{3}}$ and $x^{\frac{3}{4}}$ in the other two columns?

> For any positive real number x, and integers m and n, where $n \neq 0$,
>
> $$x^{\frac{m}{n}} = (\sqrt[n]{x})^m = \sqrt[n]{x^m}$$

Example 2

Simplify $16^{\frac{3}{4}}$ without using a calculator.

$16^{\frac{3}{4}} = (16^{\frac{1}{4}})^3$ —————————— Split the exponent into a unit fraction and an integer.

$\quad = (2)^3$ ————————————————— $16^{\frac{1}{4}} = \sqrt[4]{16} = 2$

$\quad = 8$

Reflect and discuss 3

You could also simplify $16^{\frac{3}{4}}$ like this: $16^{\frac{3}{4}} = (16^3)^{\frac{1}{4}}$. Complete the calculation and verify that this gives the same answer as Example 2.

Which was easier – this method, or the one in Example 2? Explain why.

Write a hint to help you simplify expressions with fractional exponents.

Exploration 2

In the definition of rational powers, the base x is a positive real number. You will investigate why this restriction is important.

1 Rewrite $\sqrt{-8}$ as a rational power, that is, in the form $(-8)^{\frac{1}{n}}$.

2 Is it possible to find:
   i the square root of -8
   ii the fourth root of -8? Why or why not?

3 Find $\sqrt[3]{-8}$.

4 Rewrite $\sqrt[3]{-8}$ as a rational power, that is, in the form $(-8)^{\frac{1}{n}}$.

5 What subset of the real numbers must n be in for the nth root of a negative number to exist?

6 Consider that $(-8)^{\frac{1}{3}} = (-8)^{\frac{2}{6}}$. What kind of a number is the 6th root of a negative number? Does it exist?

7 Hence, explain why the definition of rational powers insists that the base must be a positive number.

Practice 2

1 Simplify these expressions without using a calculator.

   a $8^{\frac{2}{3}}$ **b** $27^{\frac{4}{3}}$ **c** $25^{\frac{3}{2}}$ **d** $64^{\frac{2}{3}}$ **e** $125^{\frac{2}{3}}$ **f** $343^{\frac{2}{3}}$

Problem solving

2 Write each of these using exponents instead of the radicals.

   a $\sqrt[3]{x^2}$ **b** $(\sqrt[4]{x})^3$ **c** $(\sqrt{x})^3$ **d** $\sqrt{x^5}$

3 Simplify these. Where applicable, leave your final answer as a power of x.

   a $(x^{\frac{2}{3}})^2$ **b** $x^{\frac{1}{3}} \times x^4$ **c** $x^{\frac{1}{2}} \times x^{\frac{2}{3}}$ **d** $(3^4)^{\frac{1}{2}}$ **e** $(x^{\frac{2}{5}})^{\frac{2}{3}}$ **f** $(32^2)^{\frac{2}{5}}$

ATL

Example 3

Simplify $\left(\dfrac{27}{8}\right)^{-\frac{2}{3}}$

$\left(\dfrac{27}{8}\right)^{-\frac{2}{3}} = \left(\dfrac{8}{27}\right)^{\frac{2}{3}}$

$= \left(\left(\dfrac{8}{27}\right)^{\frac{1}{3}}\right)^2$

$= \left(\dfrac{2}{3}\right)^2$

$= \dfrac{4}{9}$

Using the multiplicative rule for exponents, $(x^a)^b = x^{ab}$, gives:

$\left(\dfrac{27}{8}\right)^{-\frac{2}{3}} = \left(\left(\dfrac{27}{8}\right)^{-1}\right)^{\frac{2}{3}}$

$x^{\frac{m}{n}} = (x^{\frac{1}{n}})^m$

ATL

Reflect and discuss 4

The method in Example 3 dealt with the negative sign in the exponent first, by taking the reciprocal. Confirm that taking the cube root first, or squaring first, all give the same final answer. Which method is easiest?

If necessary, add to the hint you wrote in Reflect and discuss 3, to help you simplify expressions with fractional exponents.

Practice 3

1 Find the value of each expression. Leave your answer as a simplified fraction.

   a $25^{-\frac{3}{2}}$ **b** $16^{-\frac{3}{4}}$ **c** $\left(\dfrac{9}{16}\right)^{-\frac{3}{2}}$

   d $\left(\dfrac{1}{64}\right)^{-\frac{4}{3}}$ **e** $\left(\dfrac{36}{25}\right)^{-\frac{3}{2}}$ **f** $\left(\dfrac{81}{16}\right)^{-\frac{3}{4}}$

2 Simplify these expressions completely.

   a $125^{\frac{1}{4}} \times 125^{\frac{1}{12}}$ **b** $16^{\frac{1}{6}} \times 16^{\frac{1}{12}}$ **c** $49^{\frac{3}{2}} \times 343^{\frac{1}{3}}$

   d $8^{\frac{3}{4}} \div 8^{\frac{1}{12}}$ **e** $27^2 \div 27^{\frac{2}{3}}$ **f** $45^{\frac{1}{2}} \div 15^{\frac{1}{2}}$

Problem solving

3 Write down an equivalent expression that contains fractional exponents:

   a 2   **b** 5   **c** $\dfrac{1}{2}$ **d** $\dfrac{2}{3}$

4 Simplify:

   a $3^2 \times 9^{-2}$ **b** $4^{\frac{1}{4}} \times 2^{\frac{3}{2}}$ **c** $3^{\frac{1}{2}} \times 27^{\frac{1}{2}}$ **d** $16^{\frac{1}{3}} \div 2^{\frac{1}{3}}$

> In question **4**, first write both numbers as powers of the same base.
> For example:
> $3^2 \times 9^{-2} = 3^2 \times (3^2)^{-2}$

C   Rules of indices and radicals

- How are the rules of indices and the rules of radicals related?
- How do the rules of indices help simplify radical expressions?

Writing a radical as an exponent can help you simplify some expressions.

Example 4

Write $32\sqrt{2}$ as a power of 2.

$$32\sqrt{2} = 2^5 \times 2^{\frac{1}{2}}$$ Write each number as a power of 2, then simplify.

$$= 2^{\frac{11}{2}}$$

Exploration 3

1 Use the rules of radicals to simplify:

   a $\sqrt{8} \times \sqrt{2}$ **b** $\dfrac{\sqrt{8}}{\sqrt{2}}$

2 Here are the expressions from step **1** written using exponents. Simplify them by writing 8 as a power of 2, and using the rules of exponents:

   a $8^{\frac{1}{2}} \times 2^{\frac{1}{2}}$ **b** $8^{\frac{1}{2}} \div 2^{\frac{1}{2}}$

3 Justify why the two methods for simplifying expressions with square roots are equivalent.

4 Use the rules of exponents to show that for $a, b \geq 0$, $\sqrt[3]{ab} = \sqrt[3]{a} \times \sqrt[3]{b}$. Generalize your findings.

> Write down a rule for the nth root of ab.

5 Use the rules of exponents to show that for $a \geq 0$ and $b > 0$, $\sqrt[4]{\dfrac{a}{b}} = \dfrac{\sqrt[4]{a}}{\sqrt[4]{b}}$. Generalize your findings.

> Why can b not equal 0?

6 Use the rules of exponents to show that $\sqrt[n]{a^n} = a$, where $a \geq 0$, $n > 0$.

For $a, b \geq 0$: $\sqrt[n]{ab} = \sqrt[n]{a} \times \sqrt[n]{b}$.

For $a \geq 0, b > 0$: $\sqrt[n]{\dfrac{a}{b}} = \dfrac{\sqrt[n]{a}}{\sqrt[n]{b}}$.

For $a \geq 0, n > 0$: $\sqrt[n]{a^n} = a$.

Practice 4

1 Write as a single power of 2:

   a $8\sqrt{2}$ **b** $4\sqrt[3]{2}$ **c** $\dfrac{16}{\sqrt{2}}$ **d** $\dfrac{\sqrt[3]{2}}{4}$

Problem solving

2 Write as powers of prime numbers:

   a $\sqrt[3]{7} \times \sqrt[5]{7}$ **b** $\sqrt{9} \times \sqrt[4]{9}$ **c** $\dfrac{\sqrt[3]{8}}{\sqrt[4]{8}}$ **d** $\dfrac{2\sqrt[4]{8}}{\sqrt{2^3}}$

> In part **b**, first write 9 as a power of 3.

3 Write as products of powers of prime numbers:

   a $\sqrt{6}$ **b** $\sqrt[3]{14}$ **c** $\sqrt[4]{162}$ **d** $\sqrt[4]{100}$

   e $\sqrt[4]{50}$ **f** $\sqrt[6]{72}$

Objective C: Communicating

iii. move between different forms of mathematical representation

In Q4, write radical expressions as exponents to simplify them.

---

4 Write these expressions as powers of prime numbers. Use the rules of exponents to simplify. Give your answers as powers of prime numbers.

   a $\sqrt{2} \times \sqrt[3]{2}$ **b** $\sqrt[3]{9} \times \sqrt[4]{9}$ **c** $\sqrt[5]{7} \times \sqrt[10]{7}$ **d** $\dfrac{\sqrt{6}}{\sqrt[3]{6}}$

   e $\dfrac{\sqrt[3]{4}}{\sqrt[5]{4}}$ **f** $\dfrac{\sqrt[n]{10}}{\sqrt[m]{10}}$ **g** $\sqrt[n]{a} \times \sqrt[m]{a}$ **h** $\dfrac{\sqrt[n]{a}}{\sqrt[m]{a}}$

> In parts **g** and **h**, assume a is prime.

Reflect and discuss 5

Use the rules of exponents to justify why these expressions cannot be simplified:

   $\sqrt[3]{4} \times \sqrt[5]{3}$ $\sqrt[4]{144} \times \sqrt{125}$ $\dfrac{\sqrt{5}}{\sqrt[3]{2}}$ $\dfrac{\sqrt[4]{64}}{\sqrt{27}}$

Write a general rule for when you can simplify products and quotients of radicals.

When radicals have the same radicand but different indices, write them with fractional exponents to simplify them. For example:

- $\sqrt[n]{a} \times \sqrt[m]{a} = a^{\frac{1}{n}} \times a^{\frac{1}{m}} = a^{\frac{1}{n}+\frac{1}{m}} = a^{\frac{n+m}{nm}}$

- $\dfrac{\sqrt[n]{a}}{\sqrt[m]{a}} = \dfrac{a^{\frac{1}{n}}}{a^{\frac{1}{m}}} = a^{\frac{1}{n}-\frac{1}{m}} = a^{\frac{n-m}{nm}}$

> The radicand is the number under the root sign.

Example 5

Simplify $\dfrac{\sqrt[4]{8}}{\sqrt{2}}$

$\dfrac{\sqrt[4]{8}}{\sqrt{2}} = \dfrac{\sqrt[4]{2^3}}{\sqrt{2}}$ ——————————— Write the radicands as exponents with the same base.

$= \dfrac{2^{\frac{3}{4}}}{2^{\frac{1}{2}}}$

$= 2^{\frac{3}{4}-\frac{1}{2}}$

$= 2^{\frac{1}{4}}$ ——————————— Give the answer as a radical, with prime number radicand.

$= \sqrt[4]{2}$

When radicals have different radicands, but one is a power of the other, write them as exponents with the same base to simplify them.

Example 6

Write $10\sqrt{5} \times 3\sqrt[3]{75}$ as a simplified radical, by expressing the radicands as powers of prime numbers.

$10\sqrt[3]{5} \times 3\sqrt[3]{75} = 10 \times \sqrt[3]{5} \times 3 \times \sqrt[3]{25 \times 3}$ ——————————— Write the radicands as multiples of primes.

$= 10 \times 3 \times \sqrt[3]{5} \times \sqrt[3]{5^2} \times \sqrt[3]{3}$

$= 30 \times 5^{\frac{1}{3}} \times 5^{\frac{2}{3}} \times 3^{\frac{1}{3}}$ ——————————— Write radicands using exponents.

$= 30 \times 5^1 \times 3^{\frac{1}{3}}$

$= 150\sqrt[3]{3}$

Practice 5

1 Simplify these completely, leaving your answer as a simplified radical.

a $\sqrt{2} \times \sqrt[3]{2} \times \sqrt[6]{2}$ **b** $\sqrt[3]{3^2} \times \sqrt[4]{3} \times \sqrt[12]{3}$ **c** $\dfrac{\sqrt{5}}{\sqrt[3]{5}}$ **d** $\dfrac{\sqrt[3]{11}}{\sqrt{11}}$ **e** $\dfrac{\sqrt{7^3}}{\sqrt{7}}$

f $\dfrac{\sqrt[3]{3^4}}{\sqrt{3}}$ **g** $3\sqrt{2} \times 5\sqrt[3]{2}$ **h** $5\sqrt{3^3} \times 2\sqrt[4]{3}$ **i** $\dfrac{2\sqrt{5}}{\sqrt[3]{5}}$ **j** $\dfrac{4\sqrt{3^5}}{8\sqrt{3}}$

2 Write as simplified radicals, with prime power radicands.

a $\dfrac{4}{\sqrt[3]{2}}$ **b** $\sqrt[4]{12} \times \sqrt[3]{3}$ **c** $\sqrt{12} \times \sqrt[3]{18}$ **d** $\dfrac{\sqrt[3]{16}}{\sqrt{2}}$ **e** $\dfrac{\sqrt[3]{7}}{\sqrt{343}}$

f $\dfrac{\sqrt[4]{125}}{\sqrt[3]{5}}$ **g** $\dfrac{4\sqrt{6}}{\sqrt{3}}$ **h** $\dfrac{5\sqrt[4]{125}}{\sqrt[4]{5}}$ **i** $\dfrac{\sqrt[3]{81}}{\sqrt[3]{24}}$ **j** $\sqrt[5]{49} \times \sqrt[5]{343}$

Problem solving

3 Solve these equations, where the unknown is always a power of 3.

a $\dfrac{\sqrt{27}}{x} = \sqrt{3}$ **b** $\dfrac{y}{3} = \dfrac{1}{\sqrt[3]{9}}$ **c** $\dfrac{\sqrt[3]{9}}{z} = \sqrt[6]{3}$

D Other exponents

- Can expressions with decimal exponents be simplified?
- Is simpler always better?

A rational number is a number that can be written as a fraction.

Exploration 4

1 Convert these decimals into fractions:

   a 0.1   **b** 0.375   **c** 1.6   **d** $0.\dot{3}$

2 Write the decimal exponents as fractions, and hence write these expressions as radicals:

   a $5^{0.75}$ **b** $5^{0.1}$ **c** $5^{0.375}$ **d** $5^{1.6}$ **e** $5^{0.\dot{3}}$ **f** $5^{0.8}$

3 Use your answers to step **2** to justify why any number with a finite decimal exponent can be written as a radical.

You cannot *evaluate* an expression like 3^{π} or $5^{\sqrt{2}}$ without a calculator, because the exponents are irrational numbers. However, you can *simplify* expressions like $3^{\pi} \times 3^4$ or $(7^{\pi})^2$, using the rules for exponents. Examples:

$$3^{\pi} \times 3^4 = 3^{\pi+4}$$

$$(7^{\pi})^2 = 7^{2\pi}$$

Reflect and discuss 6

The definition of a radical is this: $\sqrt[n]{a} = x$ means that $a = x^n$.

Suggest why it is difficult to evaluate $\sqrt[\pi]{a}$.

Practice 6

1 Write these expressions as radicals of powers of prime numbers:

   a $9^{0.2}$ **b** $16^{1.25}$ **c** $100^{1.5}$

   d $(3^2)^{0.3}$ **e** $4^{1.5}$ **f** $10\,000^{0.75}$

Problem solving

2 Evaluate $32^{0.2}$. Explain your method.

3 Copy and complete:

   a $4^{0.2} \times 4 = 2^{\square}$ **b** $27^{0.2} \times 81^{0.1} = 3^{\square}$ **c** $32^{0.4} \times 16^{0.5} \times 64^{0.1} = 2^{\square}$

4 Solve $x^{0.1} = 2$.

5 Simplify:

   a $\dfrac{27^{0.4}}{3^{0.2}}$ **b** $\dfrac{6^2 \times 2^{0.6}}{9 \times 4^{0.8}}$

Summary

For any positive real number x, and integer n, where $n \neq 0$, $x^{\frac{1}{n}} = \sqrt[n]{x}$.

For any positive real number x, and integers m and n, where $n \neq 0$, $x^{\frac{m}{n}} = (\sqrt[n]{x})^m = \sqrt[n]{x^m}$.

For $a, b \geq 0$: $\sqrt[n]{ab} = \sqrt[n]{a} \times \sqrt[n]{b}$.

For $a \geq 0, b > 0$: $\sqrt[n]{\dfrac{a}{b}} = \dfrac{\sqrt[n]{a}}{\sqrt[n]{b}}$.

For $a \geq 0, n > 0$: $\sqrt[n]{a^n} = a$.

The radicand is the number under the root sign.

When radicals have the same radicand but different indices, write them with fractional exponents to simplify them.

For example:

$$\sqrt[n]{a} \times \sqrt[m]{a} = a^{\frac{1}{n}} \times a^{\frac{1}{m}} = a^{\frac{n+m}{nm}}$$

$$\frac{\sqrt[n]{a}}{\sqrt[m]{a}} = \frac{a^{\frac{1}{n}}}{a^{\frac{1}{m}}} = a^{\frac{1}{n} - \frac{1}{m}} = a^{\frac{n-m}{nm}}$$

When radicals have different radicands, but one is a power of the other, write them as exponents with the same base to simplify them.

When radicals have different radicands, but one is *not* a power of the other, then they can not be simplified into one radical.

Mixed practice

1 Work out the value of:

  a $\left(\dfrac{1}{9}\right)^{\frac{1}{2}}$ **b** $\left(\dfrac{1}{9}\right)^{-\frac{1}{2}}$ **c** $25^{-\frac{1}{2}}$ **d** $\left(\dfrac{1}{27}\right)^{-\frac{1}{3}}$

  e $\left(\dfrac{9}{16}\right)^{\frac{1}{2}}$ **f** $\left(\dfrac{25}{100}\right)^{-\frac{1}{2}}$ **g** $\left(\dfrac{8}{125}\right)^{-\frac{1}{3}}$

2 Simplify:

  a $(49x^6)^{\frac{1}{2}}$ **b** $(64x^3)^{-\frac{1}{3}}$ **c** $(4x^4)^{-\frac{1}{2}} \times 3x$

3 Work out the value of:

  a $10000^{\frac{3}{4}}$ **b** $1000^{\frac{2}{3}}$ **c** $27^{-\frac{2}{3}}$ **d** $9^{-\frac{3}{2}}$

4 Find the value of each of these expressions. Leave your answers as rational numbers.

  a $\left(\dfrac{1}{8}\right)^{-\frac{2}{3}}$ **b** $\left(\dfrac{4}{9}\right)^{-\frac{3}{2}}$ **c** $\left(\dfrac{125}{64}\right)^{\frac{2}{3}}$ **d** $\left(\dfrac{5}{9}\right)^{\frac{3}{2}} \times \sqrt{5}$

5 Simplify these expressions completely. Leave your answers as rational powers of prime numbers.

  a $64^{\frac{1}{3}} \times 64^{\frac{1}{12}}$ **b** $81^{\frac{1}{4}} \times 9^{\frac{1}{8}}$ **c** $\dfrac{16^{\frac{5}{12}}}{16^{\frac{1}{6}}}$ **d** $\dfrac{36^{\frac{4}{3}}}{6^{\frac{1}{3}}}$

6 Simplify:

  a $25^2 \times 5^{-2}$ **b** $16^{\frac{1}{2}} \times 4^{-\frac{3}{2}}$ **c** $7^{-\frac{1}{2}} \times 343^{\frac{1}{2}}$

7 Simplify these expressions completely. Leave your answers as simplified radicals.

  a $\sqrt[3]{16} \times \sqrt[3]{8}$ **b** $\sqrt[4]{12} \times \sqrt[4]{48}$ **c** $\dfrac{\sqrt[4]{64}}{\sqrt[4]{4}}$

  d $\dfrac{3\sqrt[3]{9}}{\sqrt[3]{81}}$ **e** $\sqrt[4]{4} \times \sqrt[8]{4} \times \sqrt[4]{2}$ **f** $\sqrt{8} \times \sqrt[3]{8} \times \sqrt[6]{8}$

  g $\dfrac{\sqrt[4]{12}}{\sqrt[3]{12}}$ **h** $\dfrac{\sqrt[3]{9}}{\sqrt[4]{27}}$

Problem solving

8 Write down an equivalent expression that contains fractional exponents:

  a 4 **b** 3 **c** $\dfrac{1}{4}$ **d** $\dfrac{3}{2}$

9 Write as simplified radicals with prime power radicands:

  a $2\sqrt[3]{16}$ **b** $\sqrt{24} \times \sqrt[4]{36}$ **c** $\dfrac{4^2}{\left(\sqrt{8}\right)^3}$ **d** $\dfrac{\sqrt[3]{5}}{2\sqrt[4]{10}}$

Problem solving

10 Solve these equations:

  a $8^{-x} = \dfrac{1}{2}$ **b** $32^{\frac{x}{5}} = 4$ **c** $\left(\dfrac{x}{64}\right)^{\frac{2}{3}} = \dfrac{9}{16}$

11 Simplify, leaving your answers as simplified radicals of prime numbers:

  a $25^{0.4} \times 5$ **b** $125^{0.3} \times 5^{0.1}$ **c** $9^{0.4} \times 81^{0.2} \times 3^{0.4}$

  d $\dfrac{5^{0.9}}{125^{0.3}}$ **e** $\dfrac{12^3 \cdot 9^{0.2}}{3^{0.4}}$

12 The quotation below has been encoded using simplified surds and fractional exponents.

Without using a calculator, **simplify** the following expressions completely. **Use** your results and the key to decode a quote by Stefan Banach.

> Key: $2\sqrt{3} = L$, $\frac{1}{2} = I$, $2 = A$, $5\sqrt{2} = O$,
> $3 = M$, $8 = D$, $\sqrt{3} = S$, $1 = N$

'Mathematics $\underline{}$

$$\left(\frac{1}{32}\right)^{\frac{1}{5}} \qquad \left(\frac{1}{27^{\frac{1}{3}}}\right)^{-\frac{1}{2}} \qquad \frac{15^{\frac{1}{2}} \times 20^{\frac{1}{2}}}{5\sqrt{3}} \qquad \frac{\sqrt{18}\,\sqrt{10}}{\sqrt{4}\,\sqrt{15}} \qquad \left(\frac{10^2}{2}\right)^{\frac{1}{2}}$$

$$12^{\frac{1}{2}} \qquad \frac{64^{\frac{2}{3}}}{\sqrt[3]{8}} \qquad \frac{3 \times \sqrt[3]{64}}{\sqrt{2}\,\sqrt{18}} \qquad \frac{3^{\frac{1}{4}} \times 6^{\frac{1}{4}}}{2^{\frac{1}{4}}} \qquad 81^{\frac{1}{4}} \qquad \frac{64^{\frac{1}{2}}}{\sqrt[4]{256}} \qquad \left(\frac{144^{\frac{1}{3}} \times 6^{\frac{1}{3}}}{6 \times 2^{\frac{2}{3}}}\right)^{-\frac{1}{2}} .\,'$$

- -

Reflect and discuss 7

How have you explored the statement of conceptual understanding? Give specific examples.

Statement of inquiry:

Representing numbers in different forms to simplify them can help understand human-made systems.

E1.2 Upper and lower bounds

Global context: Globalization and sustainability

Related concept: Approximation

Objectives

- Understand different aspects of approximations
- Give appropriate upper and lower bounds for data given to a specified accuracy
- Perform calculations with limits of accuracy

Inquiry questions

F
- How can you use upper and lower bounds?
- How accurate are approximated numbers?

C
- How do limits of accuracy affect your results when you perform mathematical operations?
- When does the choice of rounding up or rounding down depend on the situation?
- When does rounding give an impossible answer?

D
- Is it always acceptable to round?
- Are some approximations better than others?

FORM

ATL Critical-thinking

Recognize unstated assumptions and bias

Statement of inquiry:

Representing numbers in different forms to simplify them can help understand human-made systems.

📖 **Launch additional digital resources for this chapter.**

15

You should already know how to:

• round numbers to different levels of accuracy	**1** Round the following numbers to the given level of accuracy: **a** 5235 to the nearest hundred **b** 23.96067 to the nearest thousandth **c** 18.2352 to two decimal places
• understand inequality notation	**2** Draw the possible values of x on a number line: **a** $x \leq 4$ **b** $-2 \leq x < 3$ **c** $x > -5$
• convert numbers into standard form (scientific notation)	**3** Write down these numbers in standard form (without powers): **a** 4.243×10^2 **b** 1.125×10^{-3} **c** 9.8231×10^1 **d** 5.236×10^0

F Upper and lower bounds

- How can you use upper and lower bounds?
- How accurate are approximated numbers?

Every measurement made is approximated to a certain degree of accuracy.

The Empire State Building is 443 m high, measured to the nearest meter.

Its actual height is therefore closer to 443 m than 442 m or 444 m, meaning that it is anywhere between 442.5 m and 443.5 m.

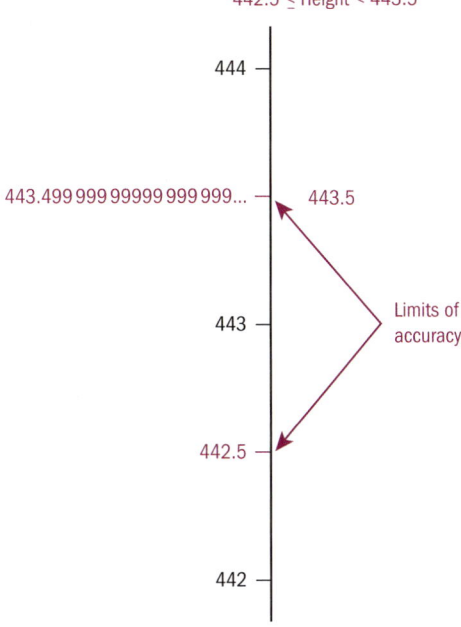

$442.5 \leq \text{Height} < 443.5$

444

443.499 999 99999 999 999... — 443.5

443

Limits of accuracy

442.5

442

The midpoint between 442 and 443 is the *lower bound* and the midpoint between 443 and 444 is the *upper bound*.

Reflect and discuss 1

The height of the Burj Khalifa in Dubai is 828 m measured to the nearest meter.

1 What is its smallest possible height?

2 What is its largest possible height?

3 What is the importance of knowing the degree of accuracy in order to determine the smallest or largest possible height?

From these questions you can see that there are limits of accuracy, meaning that at a certain degree of accuracy, the real value can be anywhere in between these limits.

Rounded to the nearest meter, the Burj Khalifa's exact height could be anywhere in the range $827.5 \leq h \,(m) < 828.5$.

In order to determine the range of values associated with rounding, you must calculate the upper and lower bounds. It helps to visualize these on a number line.

Most measurements are **continuous** because they can take on any value (usually within a range). They are not limited to discrete values, as are shoe sizes are for example. All continuous measurements are rounded to a certain degree of accuracy, which allows you to determine a range of values before the rounding has occurred.

Example 1

A suitcase weighs 16 kg to the nearest kilogram. Find the upper and lower bounds and display them on a number line.

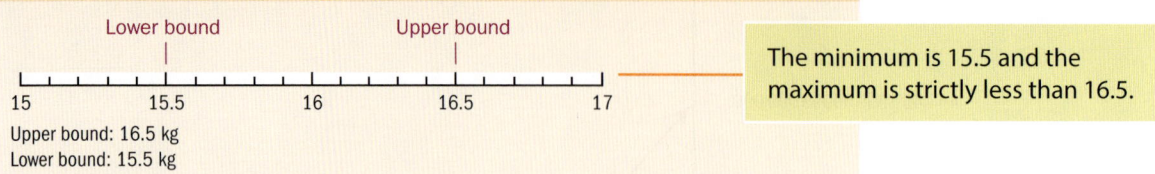

Lower bound   Upper bound

15   15.5   16   16.5   17

Upper bound: 16.5 kg
Lower bound: 15.5 kg

The minimum is 15.5 and the maximum is strictly less than 16.5.

Notice that the measurement given (16 kg) lies exactly halfway between the upper (16.5) and lower (15.5) bounds. Furthermore the range of the lower and upper bounds is equal to one unit of the specified accuracy (in this case, 1 kg).

To determine the upper and lower bounds:

1 *Add* half of the specified accuracy onto the value to find the upper bound.

2 *Subtract* half of the specified accuracy from the value to find the lower bound.

Example 2

Lucas is taking a field trip to the local zoo and the zookeeper states that the mass of the lion is 300 kg. His answer is correct to the nearest 100 kg. Determine the upper and lower bounds for the actual mass (m kg) of the lion.

to the nearest 100 kg ——————————————— Take the specified accuracy.

50 kg ————————————————————— Divide it by 2.

$300 + 50$ ——— To find the upper bound take the given mass and add half the specified accuracy.

$300 - 50$ ——— To find the lower bound take the given mass and subtract half the specified accuracy.

$250 \leq m < 350$ ——— Recall the convention that 5 rounds up to the next when determining which inequality signs to use.

The minimum mass of the lion could be 250 kg, and the maximum mass of the lion has to be strictly less than 350 kg (if the mass was equal to 350 kg, it would be rounded up to 400 kg).

Finding the limits of accuracy means finding the upper and lower bounds.

Practice 1

1 The length, in meters, of a piece of wood is 1.6 m to the nearest 0.1 m.
   Calculate the limits of accuracy of the actual length.

2 Crates of books are labelled 400 kg to the nearest 50 kg. Find the upper and
   lower bounds of the mass of a crate of books.

3 A piece of rope is 60 meters long, measured to the nearest meter.
   Calculate the limits of accuracy of the actual length.

4 The island of Mauritius is 60 km long to the nearest 10 kilometers.
   Find the upper and lower bounds of the island.

5 A ceramic artist makes models. A model is acceptable if its height is within
   3 mm of 7 cm.

   One model is 6.8 cm high. Determine whether it is acceptable. Let h be the
   height of a model in millimeters. Write down a suitable inequality to show
   the range of acceptable models.

6 A birthday card measuring 9.5 cm in length (given to the nearest 0.1 cm)
   is to be posted in an envelope measuring 10 cm, given to the nearest cm.
   Justify whether you can guarantee the card will fit in the envelope.

7 In science you are given the following measurements and the specified
   accuracy.

   Find the limits of accuracy for each measurement.

Mass	22 kg	2 s.f.
Length	12.6 cm	1 d.p.
Volume	2.04 cm^3	2 d.p.
Mass	0.7 tonnes	1 s.f.
Height	133 cm	cm
Area	52 000 m^2	thousand
Temperature	58.7 °C	1 d.p.

C Calculations with limits of accuracy

- How do limits of accuracy affect results when you perform
  mathematical operations?
- When does the choice of rounding up or rounding down depend
  on the situation?
- When does rounding give an impossible answer?

Exploration 1

At the market a bag of flour weighs 20 kg measured to the nearest kg. This is bought by the shopkeeper, who makes smaller bags of flour at 250 g measured to the nearest 10 g each, which he sells in his shop.

1 Find the maximum possible mass of the large bag of flour.

2 Find the minimum possible mass of the large bag of flour.

3 Find the maximum possible mass of the small bag of flour.

4 Find the minimum possible mass of the small bag of flour.

5 Find the number of small bags that can be filled from the large bag if the quantities above were exact.

6 Using your answers to questions **1–4**, find the maximum and minimum possible number of small bags that can be filled from the large bag.

7 Suggest how to find the maximum (or minimum) possible number of objects taken from situations involving upper and lower bounds.

For Exploration 1 you may have obtained the answer 83.673 47 for the maximum amount of bags of flour filled from the large bag. Rounding this number up to 84 bags would be correct if you were to follow the rules of rounding. However, the question implies complete bags of flour, and with 83.673 47 there are 83 complete bags. It would be incorrect to say that we could fill 84 bags, as the last bag would only be 67% full. Therefore, in this case, you must round down.

Reflect and discuss 2

- If the market seller was advertising the large bags of flour how many small bags would they say came from the large bag?

- Under which other circumstances do you not follow the conventional rounding rules?

- When would you round up and when would you round down?

In Exploration 1, in order to find the maximum or minimum number of small bags that could be filled from the large bag, calculations had to be made. Division was used to find the answer. When using operations to find the upper bounds or lower bounds of quantities that are calculated from measurements, it is important to think about which of the measurements' upper bound or lower bound to use in order to maximize (or minimize) the calculated quantity.

Apply the following rules to find the limits of accuracy for calculations.

To maximize the result of calculations:

Operation	Which limit to use for the measurements
×	upper bound × upper bound
+	upper bound + upper bound
÷	upper bound ÷ lower bound
−	upper bound − lower bound

To minimize the result of calculations:

Operation	Which limit to use for the measurements
×	lower bound × lower bound
+	lower bound + lower bound
÷	lower bound ÷ upper bound
−	lower bound − upper bound

Example 3

The length of a frame is 9.5 cm and the width is 7.6 cm, both measured to the nearest mm.

a Find the upper and lower bounds for the length (l) and width (w) of the frame.

b Find the upper and lower bound for the area of the frame.

9.45 cm ≤ l < 9.55 cm — Find the upper and lower bound for the length of the frame (to the nearest mm).

7.55 cm ≤ w < 7.65 cm — Find the upper and lower bound for the width of the frame (to the nearest mm).

9.55 cm × 7.65 cm = 73.0575 cm² — The maximum possible area arises from the product of the upper bounds for the length and width.

9.45 cm × 7.55 cm = 71.3475 cm² — The minimum possible area arises from the product of the lower bounds for the length and width.

71.35 cm² ≤ A < 73.06 cm² — These values are the upper and lower bounds for the area of the frame.

Reflect and discuss 3

- Which degree of accuracy is appropriate for the final answer, given the degree of accuracy of the original measurements?

Practice 2

1   A crane can lift 1600 kg, given to 2 significant figures. It is being used to load boxes that weigh 48 kg to the nearest kg. Find the maximum number of boxes the crane could possibly lift.

2   The length (l cm) of a photoframe is 9.5 cm and the width (w cm) is 7.6 cm, both measured to 1 decimal place. Write down an inequality for possible values for the perimeter of the photoframe.

3   Amanda's garden is rectangular and measures 9.5 m by 21 m both correct to 2 significant figures. Find the upper and lower bound for the area and perimeter of her garden.

4   Amelia leaves the house at 8.03am (to the nearest minute) and returns from her run at 8.27am. Calculate the maximum length of time of her run.

5   A bottle of soda contains 1 liter correct to the nearest deciliter. Tarryn wants to fill 90 ml glasses correct to the nearest 10 ml. Find the maximum number of full glasses she could possibly fill. Find the minimum number of full glasses she could possibly fill.

D Consequences of rounding

• Is it always acceptable to round?
• Are some approximations better than others?

Exploration 2

The price of gold is calculated based on its mass. On 6 Jan 2020, this was the price of gold:

• US$1566.45 per oz
• US$50362.54 per kg
• US$50.36 per g

The imperial ounce is used to measure the mass of gold, and 1 oz = 31.103 g.

1   Calculate the price of 10 oz of gold.

2   Convert 10 oz to g, then calculate the price of the resulting mass (using the price per g) of gold.

3   Convert 10 oz to kg, then calculate the price of the resulting mass (using the price per kg) of gold.

4   Discuss whether the variations in the previous three results are acceptable.

5   Determine whether 31.103 is close enough to 30 to round 1 oz to 30 g.

6   Convert 10 oz to g using the approximation 1 oz = 30 g, then calculate the price of the resulting mass (using the price per g) of gold.

7   Compare the previous answer to your answer in question 2, and then discuss your answer to question 5.

Sometimes it seems acceptable to round a quantity, but rounding after calculations are performed can have consequences that are less acceptable.

Exploration 3

The following measuring tools are used to measure length or distance:

- A rope that is 10 m long.
- A piece of string that is 1 m long.
- A classroom ruler of 1.5 m that has increments of 1 cm.
- A standard 30 cm ruler that has increments of 1 mm.

1 What other tools can you think of to measure length or distance?

2 Determine which measuring tool is best for measuring each of the following:

    a The length of a dining table.

    b The length of a living room.

    c The length of a living room on an architect's scale drawing.

    d The length of a football field.

3 How would you measure the following?

    a The distance between two cities that are approximately 10 km apart.

    b The distance between London, UK and Sao Paulo, Brazil.

    c The distance between the Earth and the Moon.

4 For each of the previous measurements, discuss the level of accuracy that is acceptable in different situations.

5 For each of the previous measurements, discuss an acceptable unit to round to depending on the situation.

6 How would you decide which unit of measurement is acceptable to round to based on the type and size of the measurement being made?

Different measuring tools have different levels of accuracy that help us determine how to round the measurements. When rounding amounts, it is accepted that the exact measurements can lie anywhere between the limits of accuracy. We must decide whether these limits of accuracy are good enough in a given situation.

Reflect and discuss 4

1 Which factors can limit the accuracy of a measurement?

2 Is it possible to make an exact measurement?

3 Is it necessary to make an exact measurement?

Summary

When quantities are rounded to a specified accuracy there is always an upper and lower bound, also known as the limit of accuracy.

To determine the upper and lower bounds:

    1 Add half of the specified accuracy onto the value to find the upper bound.

    2 Subtract half of the specified accuracy from the value to find the lower bound.

Calculations can be performed with both upper and lower bounds.

Apply the following rules to find the limits of accuracy for calculations.

To maximize the result of calculations:

Operation	Which limit to use
×	upper bound × upper bound
+	upper bound + upper bound
÷	upper bound ÷ lower bound
−	upper bound − lower bound

To minimize the result of calculations:

Operation	Which limit to use
×	lower bound × lower bound
+	lower bound + lower bound
÷	lower bound ÷ upper bound
−	lower bound − upper bound

Mixed practice

1 The numbers below have been rounded to the nearest 10, **write down** the largest and smallest values they could be:

    a 40   **b** 70   **c** 120

2 These numbers have been rounded to the nearest whole number, **calculate** the limits of accuracy.

    a 2   **b** 17   **c** −85

3 These lengths have been rounded to 3 s.f., **write down** the upper and lower bounds:

    a 12.5 cm   **b** 21.7 cm

    c 35.8 cm   **d** 52.1 cm

    e 80.4 cm

4 A field is 85 m wide and 145 m long, both lengths have been rounded to the nearest meter.

    a **Find** the largest and smallest possible perimeter.

    b **Find** the largest and smallest possible area.

5 When the area of a rectangle is rounded to the nearest whole number, it becomes 40 cm². One side of the rectangle is 10 cm (to the nearest cm). **Find** the maximum and minimum lengths the other side could have.

6 Tommo drove from Milan to Rome. The distance recorded in his car was 574 km, correct to the nearest km. He used 47.3 liters of petrol, to the nearest tenth of a liter. **Calculate** the upper bound for the petrol consumption in km per liter for Tommo's journey. Give your answer to 2 decimal places.

7 X and Y are continuous values, both measured to 2 significant figures.

    $X = 120$ and $Y = 350$

    Calculate the greatest possible value of $\frac{Y}{X^2}$.

8 $x = 6.4$ is correct to 1 decimal place and $y = 8.3$ is correct to 1 decimal place.

    Calculate the lower bound of:

    a $x + y$ **b** $y - x$

    c xy **d** $y \div x$

    Calculate the upper bound of:

    e $x + y$ **f** $y - x$

    g xy **h** $y \div x$

Review in context

Globalization and sustainability

Human-made technological enhancements such as satellites and space travel have helped us better understand the world in which we live. Sometimes, technology is used to perform very exact calculations on very big numbers. For example, sending a rocket out of the Earth's atmosphere and into space requires complex calculations and exact results. At the same time, measurements are approximated so that we can represent large amounts in our minds and easily compare them; this is the case when comparing distances between planets, for example.

These scientific advancements have ensured a better understanding of the environment we live in.

1 A satellite travels around the Earth in a circular orbit 500 km above the Earth's surface. The radius of the Earth is taken as 6375 km. Both quantities given to the nearest 25 km.

 a **Write down** the limits of accuracy for the radius of the satellite's orbit.

 b **Calculate** the maximum possible distance travelled by the satellite in one orbit of the Earth (use the value of π as 3.14).

 c **Write down** the difference between the maximum possible and minimum possible distances travelled by the satellite in one orbit of the Earth.

2 The distance from the Earth to the Moon is 384 400 km correct to the nearest 100 km. One fuel tank can last 36 000 km correct to the nearest 1000 km. Find the number of fuel tanks the rocket should take to ensure it could make a return journey.

SUN   MERCURY   EARTH

3 The distance between the Earth and Mars is constantly changing as the planets rotate about the Sun. When the Earth and Mars are at their closest, they are aligned to the Sun, as shown above. Such a 'Mars close approach', as it is called, happens about every two years, and is the ideal time to send an uncrewed mission to study the planet. In May 2018, the Insight Mission launched from California. Insight travelled at a speed of 10 000 km/h, correct to the nearest 1000 km/h towards Mars. At that time, the distance between Earth and Mars was 57.6 million km, correct to 3 significant figures.

 a **Calculate** the minimum number of days (to the nearest day) the spaceship could have taken to get to Mars in 2018.

 b **Calculate** the maximum number of days the spaceship would have taken to reach Mars in 2018.

With the invention of radar, scientists were able to measure the distance from Earth to Venus very precisely. By timing how long it took the radar beam to travel at the speed of light to Venus and back, the total distance to Venus could be determined from the equation:

$$\text{Distance} = \frac{\text{speed of light} \times \text{total time}}{2}$$

Reflect and discuss 5

How have you explored the statement of inquiry? Give specific examples.

Statement of inquiry:

Representing numbers in different forms to simplify them can help understand human-made systems.

Statement of inquiry:

Using logic to make and validate generalizations enhances the development of models.

Key concept:

Logic is a method of reasoning and a system of principles used to build arguments and reach conclusions.

F **Which logical skills enable you to model real-life situations effectively?**

A model is a depiction of real-life events using expressions, equations or graphs.

Lateral thinking

Three friends have lunch in a bistro and the bill is US$25. They each give the waiter US$10. The waiter doesn't know how to divide up the US$5 in change evenly between three people, so he gives each person US$1 back, and keeps US$2 for himself as a tip.

Now, each customer contributed US$10 and got US$1 back, so effectively they each paid US$9, which means they paid US$27 altogether. So, US$27 plus the US$2 that the waiter kept adds up to a total of US$29.

Where has the remaining US$1 gone from the original US$30 that they gave the waiter?

The mathematics here seems logical, but the outcome does not. Which do you think is in error?

We make generalizations all the time based on what we observe. How valid are those generalizations? To be valid, a generalization must be supported by facts that use logic and reasoning.

C How do you validate generalizations?

Science generally uses the method of inductive reasoning to validate generalizations, whereas mathematics generally uses deductive reasoning.

Inductive reasoning involves finding evidence that supports a statement. The more supporting evidence you find, the more you can be sure that the statement is true.

Statement: Every swan I have seen is white, so that means **all** swans are white.

Test: Would you be happy to wager a lot of money that all swans are white? If not, how could you test your hypothesis?

Deductive reasoning involves generating new facts by manipulating existing ones. The transport puzzle below uses deductive reasoning.

Transport puzzle

A farmer is travelling to market with a bag of grain, a chicken, and a wolf. While he is with them, he can prevent the chicken from eating the grain, and the wolf from eating the chicken.

Of course, sometimes even logicians overlook sensible questions: Why would the farmer be travelling with a wolf in the first place?

He needs to cross a river in a small boat that has room for him and only one other passenger or object at a time.

How can the farmer get himself, the grain, the chicken and the wolf safely to the other side of the river? Can you work it out using the fewest number of trips?

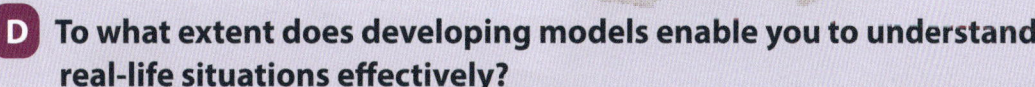

D To what extent does developing models enable you to understand real-life situations effectively?

A model is a depiction of real life events using expressions, equations or graphs.

Should you take an umbrella?

How reliable are weather forecasts? Data shows that on the whole they are around seven times more accurate now than they were 20 years ago, because computers are getting faster, and the mathematics more sophisticated. The mathematical models take account of the formation of the atmosphere, equations of motion and thermodynamics and the uncertainty of a chaotic system.

Global context: Scientific and technical innovation

Exploration: Explore the natural world by developing realistic models

📖 Launch additional digital resources for this unit.

Global context: Scientific and technical innovation

Related concept: Models

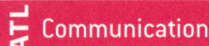

Objectives

- Solving systems of inequalities algebraically and graphically
- Modelling real-life problems with linear programming

Inquiry questions

F
- Can you use all the equivalence transformations to solve inequalities algebraically?
- How can you solve inequalities graphically?

C
- What does it mean to be linear?
- How do the gradients of different lines demonstrate the relationship between them?

D
- What are the advantages and limitations of linear programming?
- Can good decisions be calculated?

ATL Communication

Organize and depict information logically

📖 **Launch additional digital resources for this chapter.**

Statement of inquiry:

Using logic to make and validate generalizations enhances the development of models.

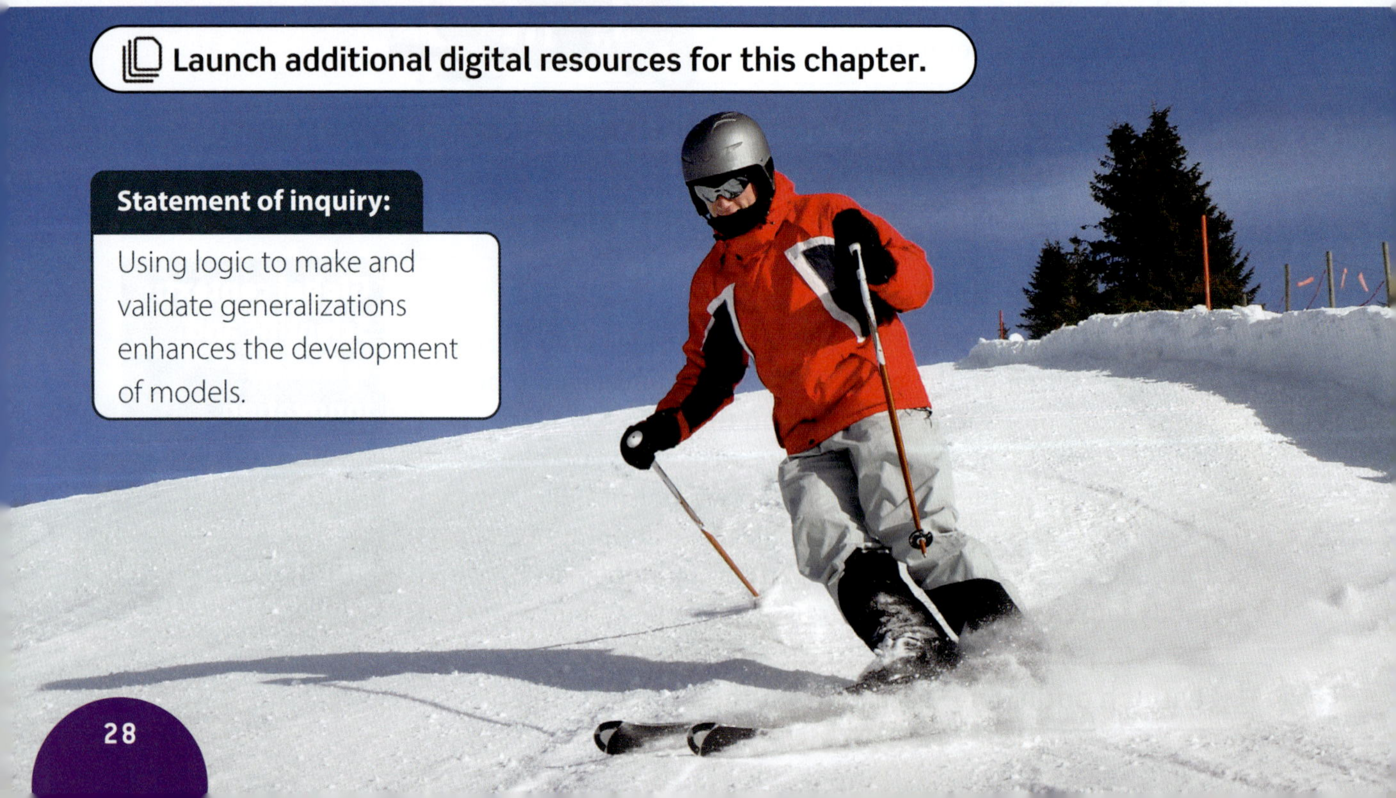

You should already know how to:

• work with inequalities	**1** Start with the inequality $4 < 6$. **a** Add 2 to each side. **b** Subtract 4 from each side. **c** Multiply each side by 3. **d** Divide each side by -2. Determine if you still have a valid inequality after each step.
• solve equations using equivalence transformations	**2** Solve these equations. Describe the equivalence transformations you use. **a** $3x + 7 = 13$ **b** $\frac{x}{4} + 5 = 8$
• solve linear inequalities algebraically	**3** Solve these inequalities. **a** $4x > 12$ **b** $2x - 1 < 3$ **c** $5x + 7 \geq 22$ **d** $-7 < 3x - 1 < 5$
• graph linear equations	**4** Draw the graph of: **a** $y = 3x - 2$ **b** $x + 2y = 6$

F Solving inequalities algebraically

- Can you use all the equivalence transformations to solve inequalities algebraically?
- How can you solve inequalities graphically?

In solving inequalities, you learned to use the equivalence transformations that are used in solving equalities. For example:

$3x - 2 > 1$ —————————————————————— Addition principle: add 2 to each side.

$3x > 3$ ——————————————— Multiplication principle: multiply each side by $\frac{1}{3}$

$x > 1$

Solution set is $\{x \mid x \in \mathbb{R}, x > 1\}$

In this section you will investigate why you can use these equivalence transformations for inequalities as well.

Exploration 1

1 Choose two numbers a and b, so that $a > b$.

Fill in the missing sign: $a - b \,\square\, 0$

Determine if this is true for all a and b, where $a > b$. Try with positive and negative values of a and b.

2 Choose two numbers a and b, so that $a < b$.

Fill in the missing sign: $a - b \,\square\, 0$

Determine if this is true for all a and b, where $a < b$. Try with positive and negative values of a and b.

Definitions of inequality:

$a > b$ if and only if $a - b > 0$

and

$a < b$ if and only if $a - b < 0$

You can use these definitions to prove some theorems about inequalities and equivalence transformations.

Theorem 1: Adding the same number to both sides of an inequality gives another valid inequality.

Using algebra:

i   if $a > b$ then $a + c > b + c$

ii if $a < b$ then $a + c < b + c$

Choose some numbers for a, b and c and check these statements. Make sure to include some negative numbers.

The theorem states that if you add the same number to both sides of an inequality, the inequality still holds. The proof shows that this is true for all real numbers.

Proof of Theorem 1i:

When $a > b$:

$a > b \Rightarrow a - b > 0$ —————— Using the definition of inequality.

$a - b + c - c > 0$ —————— $c - c = 0$, and adding 0 does not change the value.

$a + c - b - c > 0$ —————— Rearrange.
$a + c - (b + c) > 0$

So $a + c > b + c$ —————— Using the definition of inequality.

Reflect and discuss 1

- Prove Theorem 1ii for $a < b$, to show that when $a < b$, $a + c < b + c$.

- Does it matter whether c is a positive or negative number? Explain.

- When working with equations or inequalities, do we need a subtraction principle, or is the addition principle enough? Explain.

Theorem 2: Multiplying both sides of an inequality by the same *positive* real number c gives another valid inequality.

Using algebra:

i   if $a > b$ then $ac > bc$

ii if $a < b$ then $ac < bc$

Exploration 2

1 Prove Theorem 2i and ii, making sure that you justify all your steps.

2 Determine if the theorem holds when you divide both sides by a positive, non-zero real number.

3 Use Theorem 2 to prove that if $a < 1$ then $a^2 < a$.

4 Explain if it is possible that $-a > 0$.

<table>
<tr><td>

Theorem 3: If both sides of an inequality are multiplied by a negative real number, the direction of the inequality changes. This means that if $a, b \in \mathbb{R}$, and $c \in \mathbb{R}^-$ then:

i if $a > b$ then $ac < bc$ and

ii if $a < b$ then $ac > bc$

</td><td>

Try multiplying both sides of inequalities like $2 < 5$ or $4 > -1$ by negative numbers, to see what happens to the inequality sign.

</td></tr>
</table>

Proof of Theorem 3i:

$a > b$

$a > b \Rightarrow a - b > 0$ — Using the definition of inequality.

If $c < 0$, then $c(a - b) < 0$ — The product of numbers with different signs is a negative number.

$ca - cb < 0$ — Expand the brackets.

$ca < cb$ — Using the definition of inequality.

Exploration 3

1 Prove Theorem 3ii.

2 Determine if Theorem 3 holds when you divide both sides by a negative real number.

> The definition of inequality and Theorems 1, 2 and 3 all hold for $\geq$ and $\leq$.

When you multiply both sides of an inequality by a negative real number, the direction of the inequality changes. Theorem 3 shows this is true for **all** real numbers, and not just the ones you have used.

Solve the inequalities in Practice 1 using Theorems 1, 2 and 3, which you have just proved.

Practice 1

Solve:

1 $3x - 7 < 5$ **2** $\dfrac{x}{6} - 7 > 2$ **3** $3(4 - m) > 9$

4 $5x - 7 \geq 3x + 9$ **5** $1 - \dfrac{3}{2}x \leq x - 4$ **6** $-\dfrac{2x+1}{3} > 5x + 2$

7 $-2(a - 3) < 5(a - 2) - 12$ **8** $2(1 - b) + 5 \geq 3(2b - 1)$ **9** $4k - 11 \leq \dfrac{3k}{2} + 5$

ATL

Exploration 4

One way to solve the double inequality $-4 < 3x + 2 < 5$ is:

Add -2 to both sides: $-6 < 3x < 3$

Multiply both sides by $\frac{1}{3}$: $-2 < x < 1$

Another way is to rewrite the double inequality as two distinct inequalities:
$-4 < 3x + 2$ and $3x + 2 < 5$

Solve them separately:
$-6 < 3x$ and $3x < 3$
$-2 < x$ and $x < 1$

Combine the solution sets: $-2 < x < 1$

1 Solve the double inequality $-9 < 5 - 7x \leq 12$ in two ways algebraically.

2 Solve $-14 < -7(3x + 2) < 21$

    a by first using the equivalence transformation 'multiply by $-\frac{1}{7}$'

    b by expanding the brackets first.

    Explain which method you prefer.

3 Does the pair of inequalities $4x < 4$ and $3x - 5 \geq 1$ have a common solution set? Explain. ———————————

4 Given that $-1 < x < 4$, find two values m and n such that $m < 2x + 3 < n$.

> In step **3**, is there one set of values that satisfies both inequalities?

You can solve inequalities graphically in a similar way to solving equations graphically.

For the inequality $3x - 7 < 5$, draw the lines $f_1(x) = 3x - 7$ and $f_2(x) = 5$ and find where they intersect.

The inequality $3x - 7 < 5$ means that $3x - 7$ cannot take the value 5. Use a dashed line for $f_2(x) = 5$ to show that points on the line $f_2(x) = 5$ are not possible solutions.

The lines intersect at $x = 4$. This is the value of x that makes both sides equal.

For $3x - 7 < 5$ you need values of x such that $f_1(x) < f_2(x)$. From the graph, the line for $f_1(x)$ is below $f_2(x)$ when $x < 4$, showing that the values of $f_1(x)$ are less than the values of $f_2(x)$ when $x < 4$.

The solution is $x < 4$.

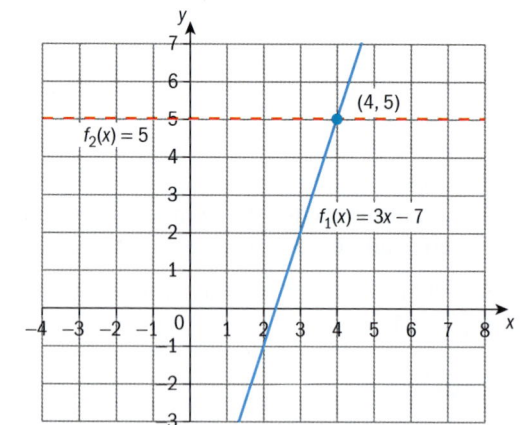

Check your solution by choosing a point with $x < 4$, for example: $(2, 3)$.

Substitute $x = 2$ into the inequality:
$3x - 7 = 6 - 7 = -1 < 5$ ✓

Now choose a point with $x > 4$, say: $(5, 7)$.

Substitute $x = 5$ into the inequality: $3x - 7 = 15 - 7 = 8$

So, 8 is not less than 5, so the point does not satisfy the inequality.

Example 1

Solve the inequality $5x - 7 \geq 3x + 9$ graphically.

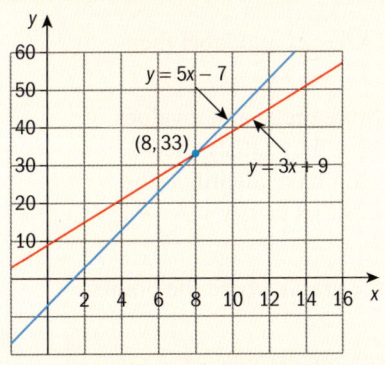

Plot the graphs of $y = 5x - 7$ and $y = 3x + 9$. The inequality sign is $\geq$, so use solid lines to show that the values on the lines are included.

The point of intersection is where the two functions are equal.

$x \geq 8$

When $x = 9$,

$5x - 7 = 45 - 7 = 38 \qquad 3x + 9 = 27 + 9 = 36$

$38 \geq 36$ ✓

The line $y = 5x - 7$ is above the line $y = 3x + 9$ when $x \geq 8$.

Check by substituting an x-value into the inequality.

Practice 2

1 Solve the inequalities in Practice 1 graphically. Check against your algebraic solutions.

Problem solving

2 Write down the two inequalities that could be represented by the non-shaded region of this graph.

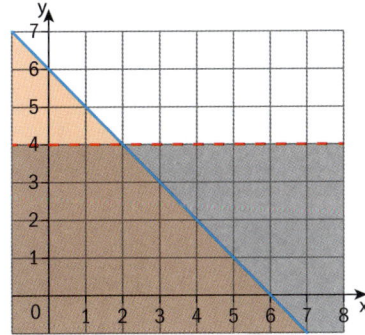

3 Verify that the inequality $3x + 2 < 9x + 6$ has an infinite number of solutions.

C Systems of linear inequalities

- What does it mean to be linear?
- How do the gradients of different lines demonstrate the relationship between them?

A system of equations has more than one variable and more than one equation that are all true simultaneously.

A system of inequalities has more than one variable and more than one inequality that are all true simultaneously.

Exploration 5

1 Graph the system of equations $y = x + 1$ and $y = 4 - 2x$ and label their point of intersection clearly.

2 Choose a point on your coordinate grid. Substitute the x- and y-values for this point into the two equations. Determine if they satisfy the inequality $y \leq x + 1$. Choose more points until you have identified the region of the graph that contains the set of points that satisfy $y \leq x + 1$. Shade this region of the graph.

3 Repeat step **2** to find and shade the region of the graph where the points satisfy the inequality $y \geq 4 - 2x$.

4 On your graph, find the region that satisfies both inequalities $y \leq x + 1$ and $y \geq 4 - 2x$. Test some points in the region.

5 Determine how you would modify your graph if you had $y < x + 1$ and $y > 4 - 2x$ instead of $y \leq x + 1$ and $y \geq 4 - 2x$. State whether or not the solution set would be the same.

Reflect and discuss 2

- Why do you think that you have learned how to find the solution set for a system of linear inequalities graphically rather than algebraically?

- Try to find the solution to the system of linear inequalities $y \leq x + 1$ and $y \geq 4 - 2x$ algebraically. What difficulties do you experience?

Example 2

Solve this system of inequalities graphically, showing clearly the region that satisfies both $y < x + 2$ and $y \geq 3 - 2x$.

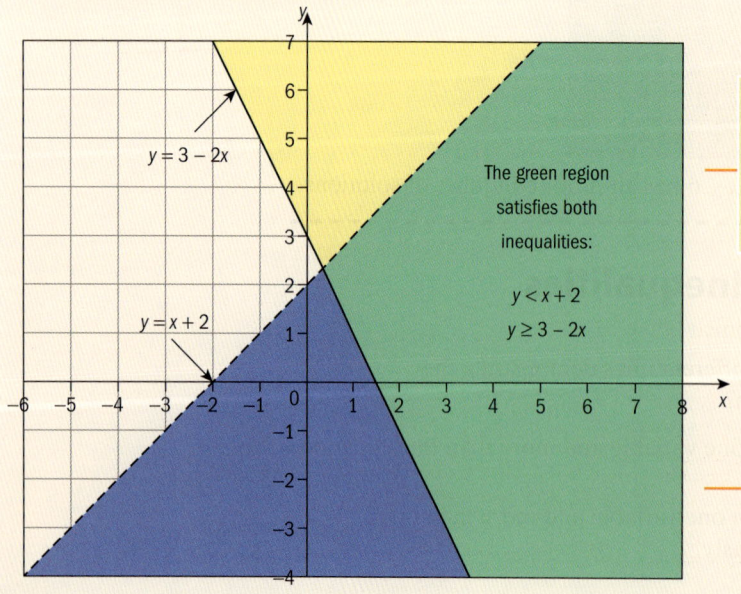

The green region satisfies both inequalities:

$y < x + 2$
$y \geq 3 - 2x$

Graph $y = x + 2$. Use a dashed line.

Test a point on one side of the line. Shade the region that satisfies $y < x + 2$.

Graph $y = 3 - 2x$. Use a solid line. Test points, then shade the region that satisfies $y \geq 3 - 2x$.

All points that satisfy the system of linear inequalities are in the overlap of the two shaded regions. Points on the dashed line are not in the solution set.

Practice 3

1 Graph these systems of inequalities. Shade the region of the solution set.

a $y < 4$; $y \leq 2x - 6$ **b** $x \geq 3$; $y > x$

c $y \leq -x - 2$; $y \geq 2 - 5x$ **d** $2y - x < 4$; $y + 2x < 3$

e $x \geq -3$; $3y > 5x + 6$ **f** $3x + 2y > -2$; $x + 2y < 2$

g $4x + 2y \leq 2$; $y > -2$ **h** $y > 23x + 3$; $y \geq -43x - 3$

Problem solving

2 Write the system of inequalities satisfied by the shaded region in the graph.

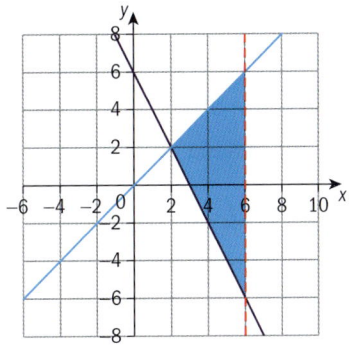

3 Graph these systems of inequalities. Shade the region of the solution set.

a $y < 5$; $x \geq -3$; $y < x$ **b** $y > x - 2$; $y > 0$; $x < 0$

4 Graph these systems of inequalities.

a $x \geq 0$; $x + y < 7$, $y < 6$ **b** $-2 \leq x < 7$; $y > 3x + 2$

c $x \geq -1$; $2x - y < 12$; $x > y$ **d** $y \leq 2x$; $3x + y > 2$; $x < 8$

- -

When a real-life problem is modelled by a system of linear inequalities, you can solve the system graphically. This process is called *linear programming*.

> Linear programming was developed during World War II to help optimize the allocation of labour and materials for the war effort. It is sometimes called linear optimization. Nowadays it is used as a tool in the decision-making process by a wide range of groups. For example, industries use it to allocate labour, transport, materials and other resources to maximize profit and minimize cost.

Exploration 6

1 Graph the inequalities $y \leq -\frac{1}{2}x + 7$, $y \leq 3x$ and $y \geq x - 2$.

2 Shade the region that contains the solution set.

3 The region is a triangle. Write down the coordinates of the vertices of this triangle.

4 If the vertices give the maximum and minimum values of $z = x + y$, explain why you think this happens.

In Exploration 6, you optimized (found the maximum/minimum) of a function z in x and y, where x and y satisfy a system of inequalities.

> The region of the graph that contains the solution set is called the **feasible region**. This region might be a polygon.
>
> A system of linear equalities is optimized on one of the vertices of the feasible region polygon.

Explaining why the system of linear inequalities is optimized on one of the vertices of the feasibility region polygon uses mathematics beyond the level of this course.

You can use this method to solve real-world problems, such as this one:

A furniture manufacturing company makes desks and chairs.

It takes 8 hours to make a desk, and 2 hours to varnish it.

It take 2 hours to make a chair, and 1 hour to varnish it.

One week there are 400 hours of worker time available for making desks and chairs, and 120 hours of worker time for varnishing them.

The company sells each desk for US$50 and each chair for US$20. Determine the number of desks and chairs the company should produce that week to maximize its revenue.

Revenue is the amount of money the company will be paid for the desks and chairs.

1 Identify the variables.

Let x be the number of desks made, and y be the number of chairs.

It takes $8x$ hours to make x desks, and $2y$ hours to make y chairs.

It takes $2x$ hours to varnish x desks, and y hours to varnish y chairs.

2 Identify the constraints.

There are 400 hours available for making desks and chairs, so one constraint is 'the total time for making desks and chairs is less than or equal to 400'.

This is expressed mathematically as $8x + 2y \le 400$.

There are 120 hours available for varnishing, so another constraint can be expressed as $2x + y \le 120$.

Also, both x and y are greater than or equal to 0, so $x \ge 0$ and $y \ge 0$.

This is a system of four inequalities.

3 Graph the system of inequalities.

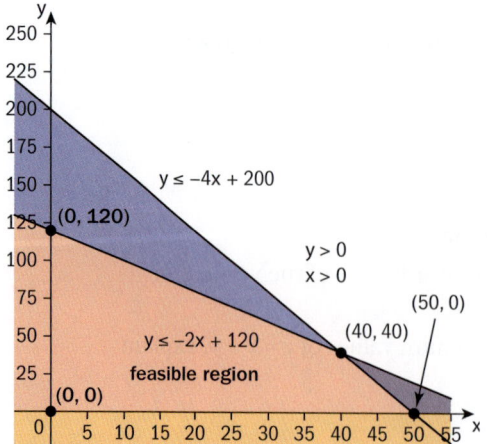

4 Shade the feasible region.
The numbers of desks and chairs that can be manufactured given the company's constraints all fall within this region. Write down the coordinates of its vertices: (0, 0), (0, 120), (50, 0) and (40, 40).

5 Determine the function to be maximized.
Desks sell for US$50 and chairs for US$20, so selling x desks and y chairs gives total revenue $R = 50x + 20y$.

$R = 50x + 20y$ is the **objective function** – the one to be optimized using values that satisfy the constraints.

6 Test the coordinates of the vertices with the constraints and objective function.

	x	y	$8x + 2y$	$2x + y$	$50x + 20y$
(0, 0)	0	0	0	0	US$0
(50, 0)	50	0	400	100	US$100
(0, 120)	0	120	240	120	US$2400
(40, 40)	40	40	400	120	US$2800

You can see from the table that the maximum revenue is US$2800 from making and selling 40 desks and 40 chairs.

Linear programming

Linear programming is a method of maximizing or minimizing a linear function subject to linear constraints within the problem.

The objective function is the linear function representing cost, profit, or some other quantity to be optimized (maximized or minimized) subject to the constraints.

The constraints form a system of linear inequalities that model the real-life problem.

The feasible region is the area of the graph that contains the solutions to the system of linear inequalities.

If there is an optimal solution to a linear programming problem, it will occur at one or more vertices of the feasibility region polygon.

Example 3 is a simplified version of a real-life problem at the end of World War II, where British and US planes were flying supplies into the Berlin airport.

Example 3

Up to 10 planes can fly into a particular airport each day. Each US plane can carry 30 tons of supplies and requires two crew members. Each British plane can carry 20 tons and requires one crew member. There are 14 crew members in total (they can fly on either US or British planes). Find the maximum mass of supplies that can be transported each day.

x = number of US planes

y = number of British planes

Identify the variables.

▶ Continued on next page

$0 \le x \le 10; 0 \le y \le 10$

$x + y \le 10$ ———————————— The maximum number of planes that can fly in is 10.

x US planes need $2x$ crew members,
y British planes need y crew members.

$2x + y \le 14$ ———————————— The total number of crew members is 14.

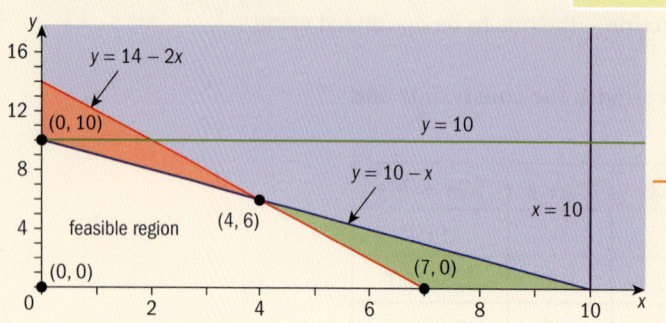

Another way of showing the solution is to shade the regions that *do not satisfy* the inequalities. The feasible region is left unshaded.

Vertices: (0, 0), (0, 10), (7, 0), (4, 6) ———————— Identify the vertices of the unshaded polygon that is the feasible region.

Objective function:

Total mass of supplies in x US planes and ———————— Determine the objective function.
y British planes is $W = 30x + 20y$.

	x	y	$x + y$	$2x + y$	$30x + 20y$
(0, 0)	0	0	0	0	0
(0, 10)	0	10	10	10	200
(7, 0)	7	0	7	14	210
(4, 6)	4	6	10	14	240

Test the coordinates of the vertices with the constraints and objective function.

Find the one that optimizes the objective function.

The maximum mass of supplies that could be transported each day is 240 tons.

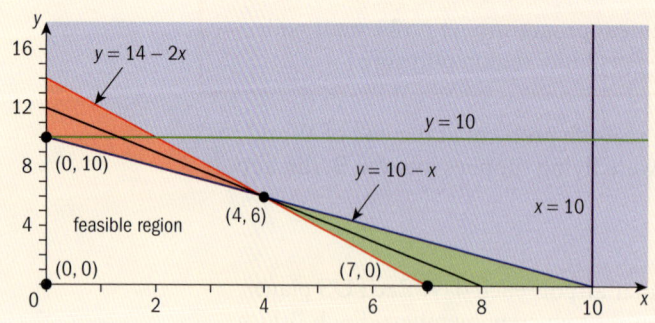

As a check, you can graph the objective function $30x + 20y = 240$ (here in black) to check that it intersects the other lines at (4, 6).

Practice 4

1 Maximize the objective function $P = 50x + 20y$, given the four constraints:

$$x + 4y \leq 21 \qquad -4x + 6y \leq 0$$

$$0 \leq x \leq 15 \qquad y \geq 0$$

2 Maximize the objective function $z = 0.4x + 3.2y$ given the four constraints:

$$x \geq 0, \, y \geq 0 \qquad x + y \leq 7$$

$$x + 2y \geq 4 \qquad y \leq x^2 + 5$$

3 Maximize the objective function $R = 5y - 2x$, given the three constraints:

$$99 \leq x < 201 \qquad 79 < y \leq 181 \qquad y + x \leq 300$$

> Graph the system of inequalities, and test the vertices of the feasible region polygon in the objective function.

4 A shoe manufacturer produces mid-top and high-top athletics shoes. Cutting machines cut the fabric for the shoes. Stitching machines stitch the fabric. The cutting machines run 4 hours per day, and the stitching machines run 5 hours per day.

A mid-top shoe takes 1 minute to cut, and 2 minutes to stitch.

A high-top shoe takes 3 minutes to cut, and 2 minutes to stitch.

The profit is US$13 on a mid-top shoe and US$16 on a high-top shoe.

Determine how many shoes of each kind should be made in order to maximize profits, and what the maximum possible profit is.

Problem solving

5 A school wants to buy small and large minibuses to transport students to sports activities. It has US$210 000 to buy the minibuses, and US$1200 to insure them.

The table gives some information about different sizes of minibuses.

Size	Maximum number of people	Cost	Insurance
Small	8	US$11 000	US$120
Large	15	US$24 000	US$80

Determine how many of each size minibus the school should buy to maximize the number of students they can transport.

6 An educational software company produces two software packages: an algebraic solver and a graphing program. It projects a demand for at least 100 algebraic solvers and 80 graphing programs each day. It can produce up to 200 algebraic solvers and 170 graphing programs per day. It needs to produce at least 200 software packages each day to satisfy existing orders. Each algebraic solver makes a loss of US$1.50. Each graphing program makes a profit of US$4.50.

Determine how many of each software package the company should produce each day to maximize its profits.

7 World Polar Products makes skis for the Alpine Skiing World Championship competitions.

To make one downhill ski takes an average of 2 hours to cut the material needed, 1 hour to shape the ski, and 3 hours for the finishing. To make one cross-country ski takes 2 hours to cut the material, 2 hours for shaping, and 1 hour for finishing. Each week the company has 140 staff and machine hours for cutting, 120 hours for shaping and 150 hours for finishing. It makes a profit of US$10 for each downhill ski and US$8 for each cross-country ski. Find the maximum profit it can make in one week.

8 Amelie received US$120 000 from a trust fund on her 25th birthday. She wants to invest it in different funds to maximize the interest she receives.

She can invest in three types of investment:

Type of investment	Interest per annum
Municipal bond	2%
Bank mutual fund	3.2%
Speculative money market fund	5%

To minimize her risk, she decides to invest only US$20 000 in the speculative money market fund. Her tax adviser says she has to invest at least three times as much in the municipal bond as in the bank's mutual fund. Determine the optimum investment amounts for each type of investment.

D Linear programming

- What are the advantages and limitations of linear programming?
- Can good decisions be calculated?

In Practice 4 you used linear programming to solve problems in different real-life situations.

Activity

Research the use of linear programming in industry. Which types of industry use it, and for what applications?

Reflect and discuss 3

- What type of problems can you solve using linear programming? What kinds of functions are used?
- All the examples and problems you have seen deal with only positive numbers. Why do you think this is?
- What kinds of real-world problems would not be suitable for linear programming?
- What are the advantages of using linear programming?
- What are the limitations of mathematical modelling using linear programming?

Summary

Definitions of inequality

$a > b$ if and only if $a - b > 0$

and

$a < b$ if and only if $a - b < 0$

Theorem 1: Adding the same number to both sides of an inequality gives another valid inequality.

Using algebra:

    i if $a > b$ then $a + c > b + c$

    ii if $a < b$ then $a + c < b + c$

Theorem 2: Multiplying both sides of an inequality by the same positive real number gives another valid inequality.

Using algebra:

    i if $a > b$ then $ac > bc$

    ii if $a < b$ then $ac < bc$

Theorem 3: If both sides of an inequality are multiplied by a negative real number, the direction of the inequality changes. This means that if $a, b \in \mathbb{R}$, and $c \in \mathbb{R}^-$ then:

    i if $a > b$ then $ac < bc$ and

    ii if $a < b$ then $ac > bc$

Linear programming

Linear programming is a method of maximizing or minimizing a linear function subject to linear constraints within the problem.

The **objective function** is the linear function representing cost, profit, or some other quantity to be optimized (maximized or minimized) subject to the constraints.

The constraints form a system of linear inequalities that model a real-life problem.

The feasible region is the area of the graph that contains the solutions to the system of linear inequalities.

If there is an optimal solution to a linear programming problem, it will occur at one or more vertices of the feasibility region polygon.

Using linear programming to solve real-life problems:

- Identify all variables and parameters.
- Identity all constraints. This is your system of inequalities.
- Graph your system of inequalities, and identify the polygon that makes up the feasibility region.
- Substitute the values of the vertices of the polygon into the system of inequalities and the objective function. Identify the ordered pair that optimizes the function.

Mixed practice

1 Solve these inequalities algebraically:

a $4 - 2x \leq 2$ **b** $\frac{x}{3} + 5 < 11$

c $2(x + 1) > x - 7$ **d** $3(x + 1) < 2(1 - x)$

e $3x + 1 \geq 2x + 5$ **f** $10 \leq 2x \leq x + 9$

g $x < 3x - 1 < 2x + 7$

2 Solve the inequalities in **1a–d** graphically.

3 Graph these inequalities. **Show** clearly the region that satisfies the system of inequalities.

a $0 < x < 4$; $y < 1$

b $x > 0$; $x + y < 10$; $y > x$

c $2y > x$; $y < 2x$; $x + y < 8$

d $y \geq 2x - 3$; $y \geq -3$; $y \leq -0.8x + 2.5$

Problem solving

4 A company hires out buses:

Bus	Hire cost
40-seater	UK£80
24-seater	UK£50

A school can spend up to UK£400 to hire buses to take 120 students on an outing.

Determine how many of each bus the school should hire to minimize the total cost of bus hire.

5 A factory manager has to decide which machines to install to manufacture a product.

Machine A

Output is 300 units per week. Needs 500 m² of space, and 10 operators.

Machine B

Output is 200 units per week. Needs 600 m² of space, and 6 operators.

The factory has 5050 m² of space available and 80 operators. Its production target is 2400 units per week. **Determine** if the factory can meet its production target. If it can, **determine** how many of each type of machine it should buy.

6 Your company has a maximum of US$2200 to spend on advertising. You plan to run at most 20 advertisements because each one needs to be different and creative. An advertisement in the weekday newspaper costs US$50, and in the weekend newspaper costs US$200. Each weekday advert results in an average of 100 new customers, and each weekend advert results in an average of 300 new customers. You want to maximize the number of new customers. **Find** the maximum number of weekday and weekend newspaper advertisements you can buy.

Objective D: Applying mathematics in real-life contexts
ii. select appropriate mathematical strategies when solving authentic real-life situations

Make sure you identify variables and constraints in each problem in order to solve the real-world problems.

Review in context

Scientific and technical innovation

1 Trees are planted in urban areas for beauty but also to remove air pollution. Trees with a large diameter, which cost UK£100 to plant, need $80\,m^2$ of space to grow and remove $1.5\,kg/year$ of pollutants. Smaller trees, costing UK£30, need $50\,m^2$ of space to grow but remove only $0.5\,kg/year$ of air pollutants. If your school has a budget of UK£1200 and $1500\,m^2$ of space, **determine** how many of each type of tree should be planted in order to maximize the amount of air pollutants removed.

2 A nutritionist prescribes this diet to a patient:

- a minimum of 400 units of carbohydrates
- a minimum of 500 units of fat
- a minimum of 300 units of protein

The nutritionist has combined these into two types of protein shake. Type A costs US$3 per pack and type B costs US$2.50 per pack. One pack of type A contains 10 units of carbohydrates, 20 units of fat and 15 units of protein. One pack of type B contains 25 units of carbohydrates, 10 units of fat and 20 units of protein. **Find** the minimum cost for a diet that consists of a mixture of these two shakes and meets the minimum requirements.

Reflect and discuss 4

How have you explored the statement of inquiry? Give specific examples.

Statement of inquiry:

Using logic to make and validate generalizations enhances the development of models.

3 Back to the beginning

Statement of inquiry:

Discovering relationships in patterns and studying equivalence between representations can lead to better models.

Key concept:

Relationships are the connections between quantities, properties or concepts; these connections may be expressed as models, rules or statements.

F What determines equivalence? What kind of patterns exist?

Patterns in language

Patterns play an important role in the learning and understanding of language. Simple sentences follow patterns – and those patterns often vary from language to language. In English, and in other Romance languages, the SVO structure is common: simple sentences are built using a Subject, a Verb and an Object, in that order.

Many languages use the SOV structure. In Turkish, for example, the sentence "İskender elmayı yedi" would translate in word order as "İskender the apple ate", but the English translation of the sentence would be "İskender ate the apple". The study of patterns in language structure is known as linguistics.

C How can relationships be represented effectively? How does equivalence affect representations?

Representation is the manner in which something is presented.

> The best representation may depend on what you want to show or to find out.

Which representation is best?

Here are four representations of a relationship between variables x and y.

1 Cartesian coordinate plane

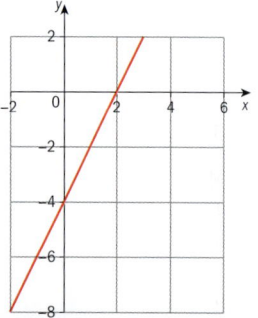

2 Mapping diagram

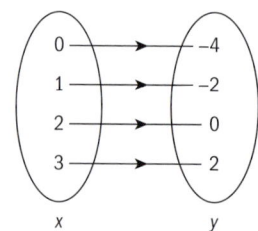

3 Table of values

x	0	1	2	3	4	5
y	−4	−2	0	2	4	6

4 Linear equation $y = 2x - 4$

Which representation best shows:

- that the function is linear?

- that $f(1) = -2$?

- that the y-coordinates increase by 2 for every increase in x?

D **To what extent does understanding patterns allow you to understand the natural world?**

Patterns in physics

Johannes Kepler (1571–1630) discovered physical laws that explain the motion of the planets around the Sun. His third law tells us that if T is the time it takes a planet to orbit the Sun, and r is the radius of its orbit, then $T \propto r^{\frac{3}{2}}$.

What does it mean to have an exponent of $\frac{3}{2}$? By looking for patterns when working with exponents, we can give fractional exponents a sensible definition.

Patterns in finance

When you invest money at a bank, the bank usually awards interest on your savings; many banks compound the interest annually.

What pattern is generated by the amount in the bank account at the end of each year?

Understanding the pattern at the end of each year can help you to work out what would be a fair value for an investment if you needed to withdraw money partway through the year.

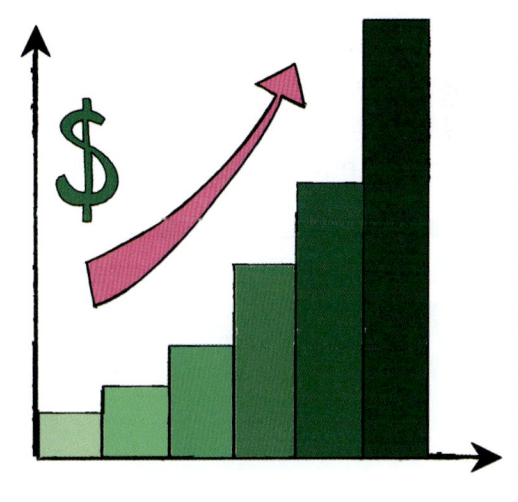

Global context: Scientific and technical innovation

Exploration: Explore systems and methods to create models

📑 **Launch additional digital resources for this unit.**

E3.1 Function transformations

Global context: Scientific and technical innovation

Related concept: Representation

RELATIONSHIPS

Objectives

- Understanding how various parameters affect the shape and position of a graph
- Applying translations, reflections and dilations to graphs
- Describing the transformation of a function algebraically and graphically
- Describing combinations of transformations of a function algebraically and graphically
- Writing the equation of a graph following one or more transformations

Inquiry questions

F
- How do transformations affect representations of lines and curves?
- What are the three transformations for linear and quadratic graphs?

C
- What is the relationship between a function and its transformation?
- How can transformations be represented in the equation of a graph?

D
- If the graph of a transformed function is the same as the graph of the original function, has the function been transformed?
- If two different transformations give the graph of the same transformed function, are the transformations really different?

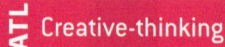

ATL Creative-thinking

Generating novel ideas and considering new perspectives

📖 **Launch additional digital resources for this chapter.**

Statement of inquiry:

Discovering relationships in patterns and studying equivalence between representations can lead to better models.

You should already know how to:

• sketch graphs of linear and quadratic functions	**1** Sketch a graph of: **a** $f(x) = 2x + 3$ **b** $f(x) = x^2$
• write quadratic functions in vertex form	**2 a** Write the quadratic function $y = x^2 + 6x + 8$ in vertex form. **b** Write down the coordinates of the vertex of the graph of $y = x^2 + 6x + 8$.

F Changing graphs

- How do transformations affect representations of lines and curves?
- What are the three transformations for linear and quadratic graphs?

Changing the parameters of a line or quadratic curve changes its position on the coordinate plane.

For a straight line $y = mx + c$, the parameters are gradient m and y-intercept c.

For a quadratic function, $y = (x - h)^2 + k$, the parameters are h and k.

Exploration 1

1 Use your graphing software to draw the following pairs of curves on the given axes. In each case, describe briefly in words how the first curve must be transformed to match the second curve.

a $y = x^4 - 2x^3$ and $y = x^4 + 2x^3 - 2x - 1$.
Use x-values of -3 to 3 and y-values of -3 to 5.

b $y = x^3 - 13x^2 + 54x - 72$ and $y = x^3 - 4x^2 + 3x + 2$.
Use x-values of -2 to 8 and y-values of -4 to 4.

c $y = x^2 + x - 6$ and $y = 3(x + 3)(x - 2)$.
Use x-values of -4 to 3 and y-values of -20 to 6.

d $y = \sqrt{x + 4}$ and $y = \sqrt{2x + 4}$.
Use x-values of -4 to 4 and y-values of -1 to 4.

e $y = x^2 - \sqrt{8x}$ and $y = 2\sqrt{2x} - x^2$.
Use x-values of 0 to 4 and y-values of -6 to 6.

f $y = 0.5(x + 5)\sqrt{4 - x}$ and $y = \frac{1}{2}\sqrt{x + 4}(5 - x)$.
Use x-values of -10 to 10 and y-values of -6 to 6.

2 When describing the transformations in step **1**, you might have used everyday words like 'shift' and 'stretch'. It is important to use the correct terminology to make sure your meaning is fully understood.

Research the meanings of the words *reflection*, *dilation* and *translation*. All three have non-mathematical meanings as well as specific mathematical meanings.

3 Describe each of the transformations from step **1** using one of the terms reflection, dilation or translation.

In this section, you will encounter only these three types of transformation. All the reflections will be reflections in either the *x*-axis or the *y*-axis. The dilations will be measured from the *x*- or *y*-axis.

> A **translation** occurs when every point on a graph moves by the same amount in the same direction.
>
> A **dilation** is a stretch or a compression. If a graph undergoes dilation parallel to the *x*-axis, all the *x*-values are increased by the same scale factor. Similarly, if it is dilated parallel to the *y*-axis, all the *y*-values are increased by the same scale factor.
>
> A **reflection** maps points on one side of a mirror line to points the same distance away but on the other side of the mirror line.

Practice 1

1 These diagrams show examples of graph transformations. In each case, describe the single transformation that has taken place to transform the red curve into the blue curve.

a
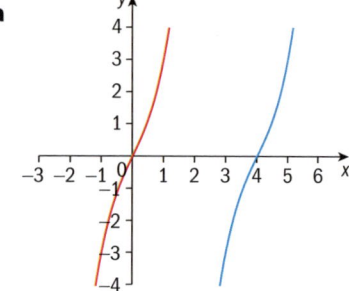

b
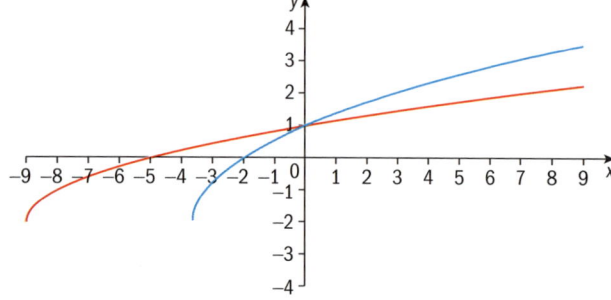

c
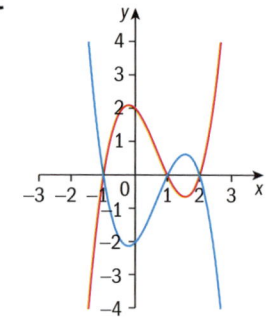

d
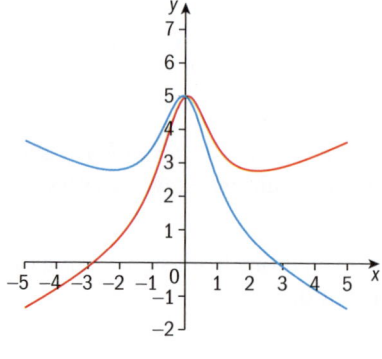

e

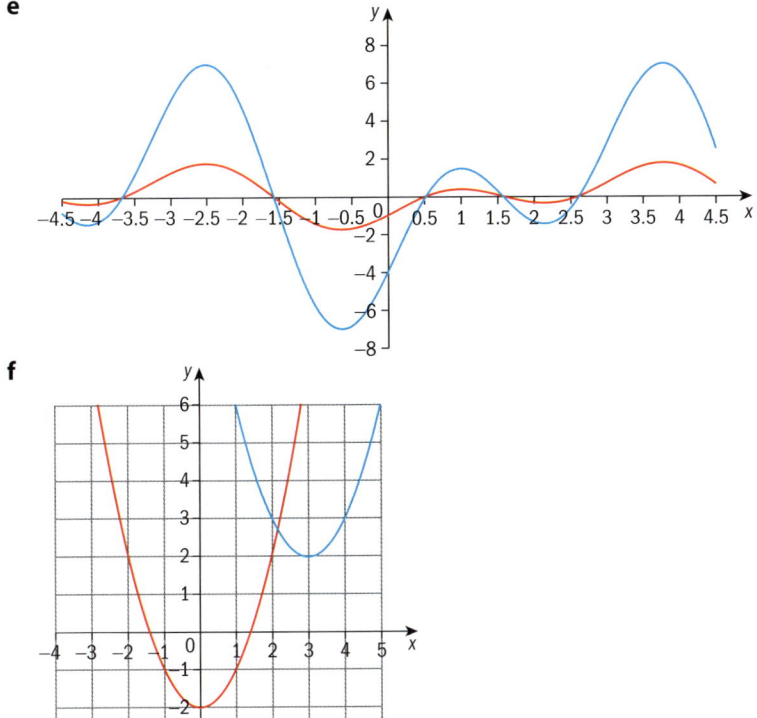

f

2 These diagrams show further examples of graph transformations. In each case, identify the two transformations that transform the red curve into the blue curve.

a

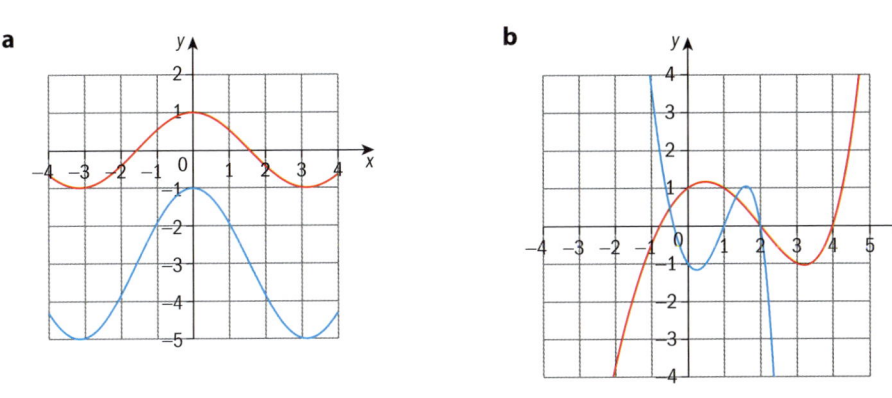

b

c

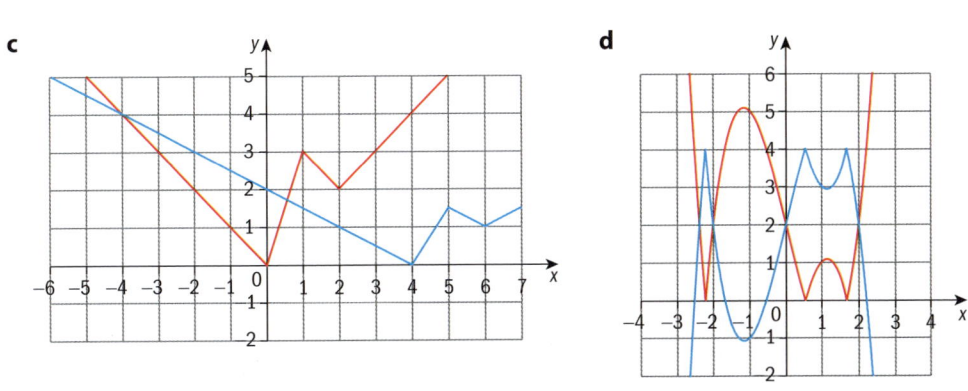

d

Problem solving

3 Use your graphical display calculator (GDC) to draw the graphs of $y = (x - 2)^2$ and $y = (x + 2)^2$.

Ronnie says that one graph is a translation of the other.
Reggie says that one graph is a reflection of the other.
Decide whether their claims are correct.
Explain what you notice.

Reflect and discuss 1

Draw the graph of $y = f(x)$ where $f(x) = 4x$.
Using your answers to Exploration 1, predict what the graph of $y = f(x) + 4$ will look like.
Predict also what the graph of $y = f(x + 1)$ will look like.

Check using your graphical calculator. What do you notice?
Do $y = f(x + 1)$ and $y = f(x) + 4$ represent the same transformation or different transformations?

C Linear and quadratic transformations

- What is the relationship between a function and its transformation?
- How can transformations be represented in the equation of a graph?

Objective B: Investigating patterns
ii. describe patterns as general rules consistent with findings

---

In this exploration, you are asked to make observations about how varying a parameter affects the graph. Once you have observed the pattern, you should try to describe it as precisely as possible. Then you should check your rule by testing a few more examples. Sometimes it is a good idea to ask a friend if they think your rule makes sense. If it does not, perhaps you need to try rephrasing it.

Exploration 2

1 Graph the linear functions $y = x$ and $y = x + k$ on your graphing software, and insert a slider to change the value of k between -10 and 10. Start with $k = 0$.

Try different values of k to explore how changing $y = x$ to $y = x + k$ changes the graph.

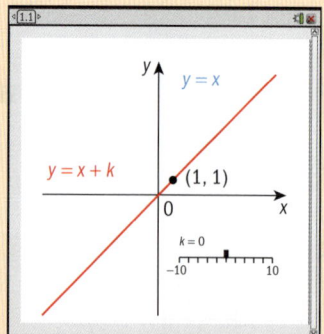

Try different values of k.

2 Repeat step **1** for three more linear functions: $y = 2x + k$, $y = -x + k$ and $y = 3x + k$.

Describe how changing $y = f(x)$ to $y = f(x) + k$ changes the graph.

▶ Continued on next page

3 Graph the linear functions $y = 4x$ and $y = 4(x - h)$. Insert a slider to change the value of h between -10 and 10. Start with $h = 0$.

Try different values of h to explore how changing $y = 4x$ to $y = 4(x - h)$ changes the graph.

4 Repeat step **3** for three more linear functions: $y = 2(x - h) + 3$, $y = (x - h) - 2$ and $y = 3(x - h)$

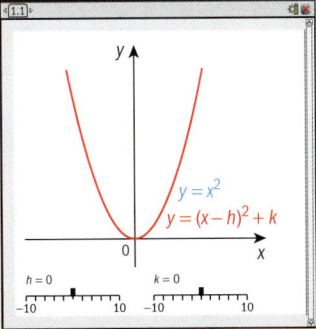

Describe how changing $y = f(x)$ to $y = f(x - h)$ changes the graph.

5 Graph the quadratic functions $y = x^2$ and $y = (x - h)^2 + k$ on your graphing software, and insert two sliders to change the values of h and k between -10 and 10. Start with $h = k = 0$, so $y = x^2$.

6 Find the values of h and k and write the equation of the parabola $y = (x - h)^2 + k$ that is:

a 4 units higher than $y = x^2$

b 4 units to the left of $y = x^2$

c both 4 units higher and 4 units to the left of $y = x^2$.

7 a Explain how changing the function $y = f(x)$ to $y = f(x - h)$ changes its graph.

b Explain how changing the function $y = f(x)$ to $y = f(x) + k$ changes its graph.

Vertical and horizontal shifts in the graph of a function are called **translations**.

- $y = f(x - h)$ translates $y = f(x)$ by h units in the x-direction.

  When $h > 0$, the graph moves in the positive x-direction, to the right.

  When $h < 0$, the graph moves in the negative x-direction, to the left.

- $y = f(x) + k$ translates $y = f(x)$ by k units in the y-direction.

  When $k > 0$, the graph moves in the positive y-direction, up.

  When $k < 0$, the graph moves in the negative y-direction, down.

- $y = f(x - h) + k$ translates $y = f(x)$ by h units in the x-direction and k units in the y-direction.

Reflect and discuss 2

When $h > 0$, why does $y = f(x - h)$ translate the function $y = f(x)$ by h units to the right and not to the left?

Example 1

The red, green and blue lines are parallel.
The red line has equation $y = f(x)$.
Find the equation of the other lines
in terms of $f(x)$.

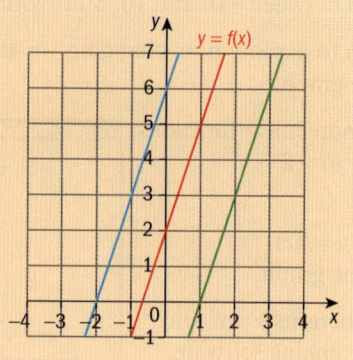

The blue line is a translation of the red line by 4 units
in the y-direction.

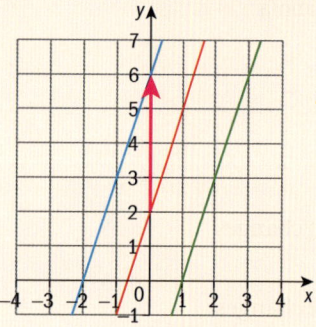

Find points on the two graphs
that correspond to each other.

Hence the blue line has equation $y = f(x) + 4$.

The green line is a translation of the blue line to the
right by 3 units.

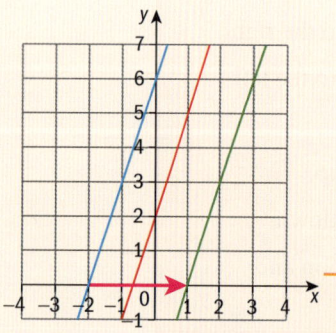

It is easiest to find corresponding points
between the blue and green lines.

Hence the green line has equation $y = f(x - 3) + 4$.

Horizontal translations
are of the form $f(x - h)$.

Example 2

The red curve is a translation of the blue curve, which has equation $y = f(x)$.

Find the equation of the red curve in terms of $f(x)$.

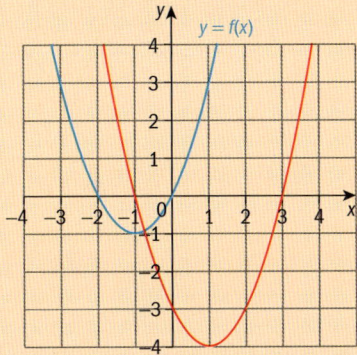

The vertex has moved from $(-1, -1)$ to $(1, -4)$. ——————————— Find corresponding points.

This is a translation of 2 units to the right and ——————————— Identify the translation.
3 units down.

The red curve has equation $y = f(x - 2) - 3$.

Practice 2

1 In each graph you are given the equation of one of the functions. The other
graphs are translations of that function. Find the equation of each function.

a

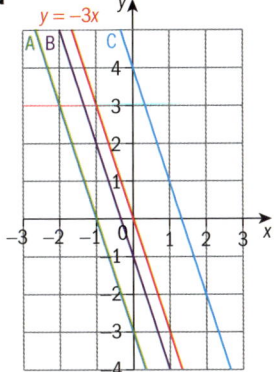

b

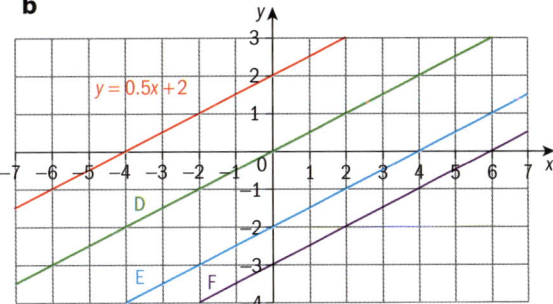

c

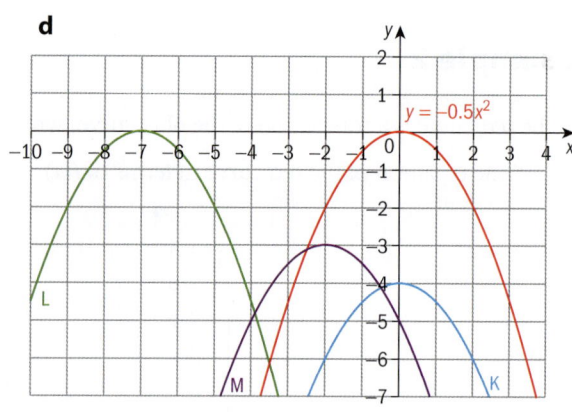

d

Problem solving

2 Without using graphing software or a calculator or finding any specific coordinates of points, sketch the graphs of these functions.

Label any intercepts with the axes.

a $y = x + 5$

b $y = 2x - 3$

c $y = -2x - 3$

d $y = x^2 + 5$

e $y = (x + 2)^2$

f $y = (x - 1)^2 - 1$

> Start with $y = x$ or $y = x^2$ and translate the graph.

Exploration 3

1 Use graphing software to graph the linear function $f_1(x) = mx + c$ and insert a slider to change the values of m and c between -10 and 10. Start with $f_1(x) = x$, with $m = 1$ and $c = 0$.

2 Add the graphs of $y = -f_1(x)$ and $y = f_1(-x)$.

3 Change the values of m and c using the slider. Describe the relationship between the graphs $y = f_1(x)$ and $y = -f_1(x)$. Identify the transformation that takes the graph of $y = f_1(x)$ to $y = -f_1(x)$.

4 Continue to vary the values of m and c using the slider. By examining your graphs, describe the transformation that takes the graph of $y = f_1(x)$ to the graph of $y = f_1(-x)$.

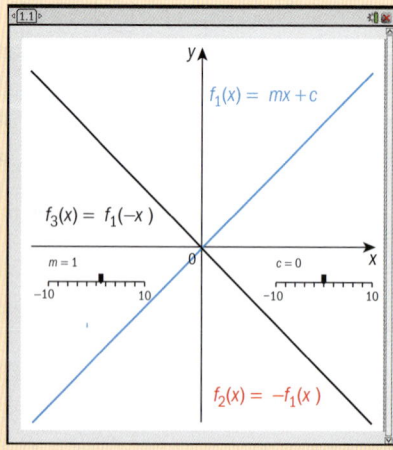

▶ Continued on next page

5 On a clear screen, graph the quadratic function $y = f_1(x) = (x - h)^2 + k$. Insert sliders to change the values of h and k between -10 and 10.

6 Add the graphs $y = -f_1(x)$ and $y = f_1(-x)$. By changing the sliders as you did in steps **3** and **4**, find the relationship between the graph of $y = f_1(x)$ and the graphs of $y = -f_1(x)$ and $y = f_1(-x)$.

7 Explain whether the generalizations you made in steps **3** and **4** hold true for quadratic functions.

> The graph of $y = -f(x)$ is a reflection of the graph of $y = f(x)$ in the x-axis.
>
> The graph of $y = f(-x)$ is a reflection of the graph of $y = f(x)$ in the y-axis.

Example 3

Here is the graph of $y = (x - 2)^2 + 3$.

Find the equations of graphs A and B.

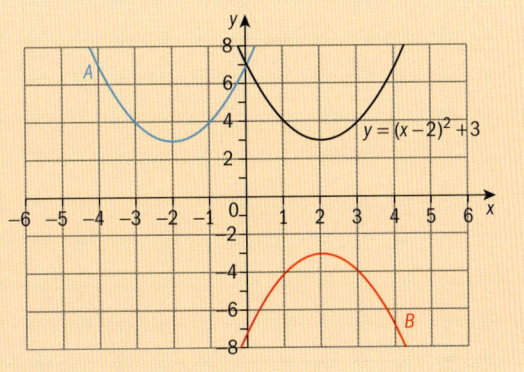

Graph A is a reflection of $y = (x - 2)^2 + 3$ in the y-axis.

Equation of $A = f(-x) = (-x - 2)^2 + 3$ ———— Reflection of $f(x)$ in the y-axis is $f(-x)$.

$\qquad = (-x - 2)(-x - 2) + 3$ ———— Substitute $-x$ into $f(x)$.

$\qquad = (x^2 + 4x + 4) + 3$

$\qquad = (x + 2)^2 + 3$ ———— Expand, then write in vertex form.

Graph B is a reflection of $y = (x - 2)^2 + 3$ in the x-axis. ———— Reflection of $f(x)$ in the x-axis is $-f(x)$.

Equation of $B = -f(x) = -(x - 2)^2 - 3$

Practice 3

1 Copy this sketch graph of $f(x) = 3x + 2$.

Sketch and label the graph of $f(-x)$ on the same axes.

Sketch and label the graph of $-f(x)$ on the same axes.

Label any intercepts with the y-axis.

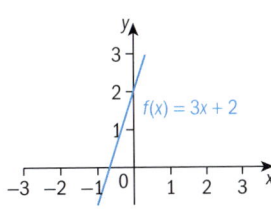

2 Copy this sketch graph of $f(x) = x^2 - 6x + 10$.

Sketch and label the graph of $f(-x)$ on the same axes.

Sketch and label the graph of $-f(x)$ on the same axes.

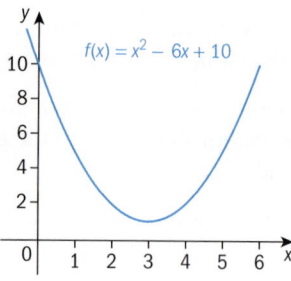

3 In each graph below you are given the equation of one of the functions. The other graphs are reflections of that function. Find the equation of each function.

a

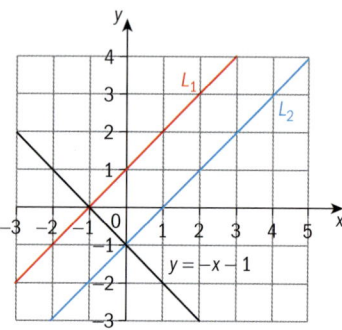

$y = -x - 1$

b

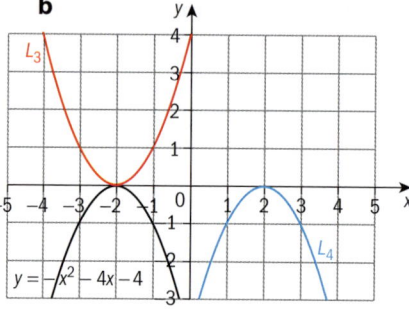

$y = -x^2 - 4x - 4$

c

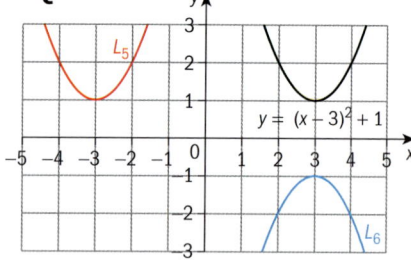

$y = (x - 3)^2 + 1$

d

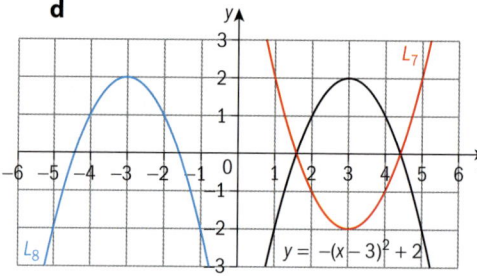

$y = -(x - 3)^2 + 2$

4 The graph of $y = x + 1$ is translated in the y-direction and then reflected in the y-axis to give line L.

Find the equation of line L.

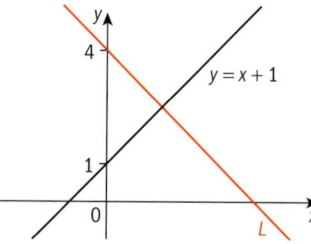

5 The graph of $y = x^2$ is translated in the x-direction and then reflected in the x-axis to give curve C. Find the equation of curve C.

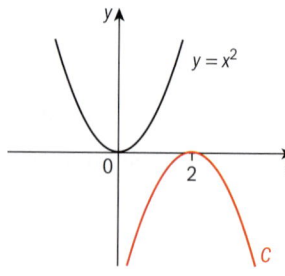

Exploration 4

1 Draw a coordinate plane with axes from -10 to 10.

   Plot these points: $(-4, -5)$, $(-3, -2)$, $(-2, 0)$, $(-1, 1)$, $(0, 0)$, $(1, -1)$, $(4, 1)$ and $(5, 3)$.

   This set of eight points defines the function $f(x)$. Join the points with a smooth curve.

2 A change is applied to $f(x)$ to give a new function $g_1(x)$. This change is defined as $g_1(x) = 2f(x)$.

   a Write down the coordinates of the eight points of $g_1(x)$.

   b Draw and label the graph of $g_1(x)$ on the same coordinate plane as $f(x)$.

   c Describe the change between $f(x)$ and $g_1(x)$.

3 Repeat step **2** for a new change $g_2(x) = \frac{1}{2}f(x)$.

4 Make a generalization for what happens when the function $f(x)$ changes to $g(x) = af(x)$:

   a when $0 < a < 1$ **b** when $a > 1$.

5 Draw the graph of $f(x)$ again on a new coordinate plane. A change is applied to $f(x)$ to give a new function $h_1(x)$. This change is defined as $h_1(x) = f(2x)$.

   a Write down the coordinates of the eight points of $h_1(x)$, for example the point $(-4, -5)$ will become $(-2, -5)$.

   b Draw and label the graph of $h_1(x)$ on the same coordinate plane as $f(x)$.

   c Describe the change between $f(x)$ and $h_1(x)$.

6 Repeat step **5** for a new change $h_2(x) = f\left(\frac{1}{2}x\right)$.

7 Make a generalization for what happens when the function $f(x)$ changes to $h(x) = f(ax)$:

   a when $0 < a < 1$ **b** when $a > 1$.

8 Use graphing software to see if your generalizations apply to linear and quadratic functions.

   a Graph the linear functions $f_1(x) = x$, $f_2(x) = a \times f_1(x)$ and $f_3(x) = f_1(a \times x)$ and insert a slider to change the value of a between 0 and 3. Start with $a = 1$ and then explore what happens when $0 < a < 1$ and when $a > 1$.

   b Repeat step **8a** for the quadratic function $f_1(x) = x^2$.

The mathematical term for stretch or compression is **dilation**.

$y = af(x)$ is a vertical dilation of $f(x)$, scale factor a, parallel to the y-axis.

$y = f(ax)$ is a horizontal dilation of $f(x)$, scale factor $\frac{1}{a}$, parallel to the x-axis.

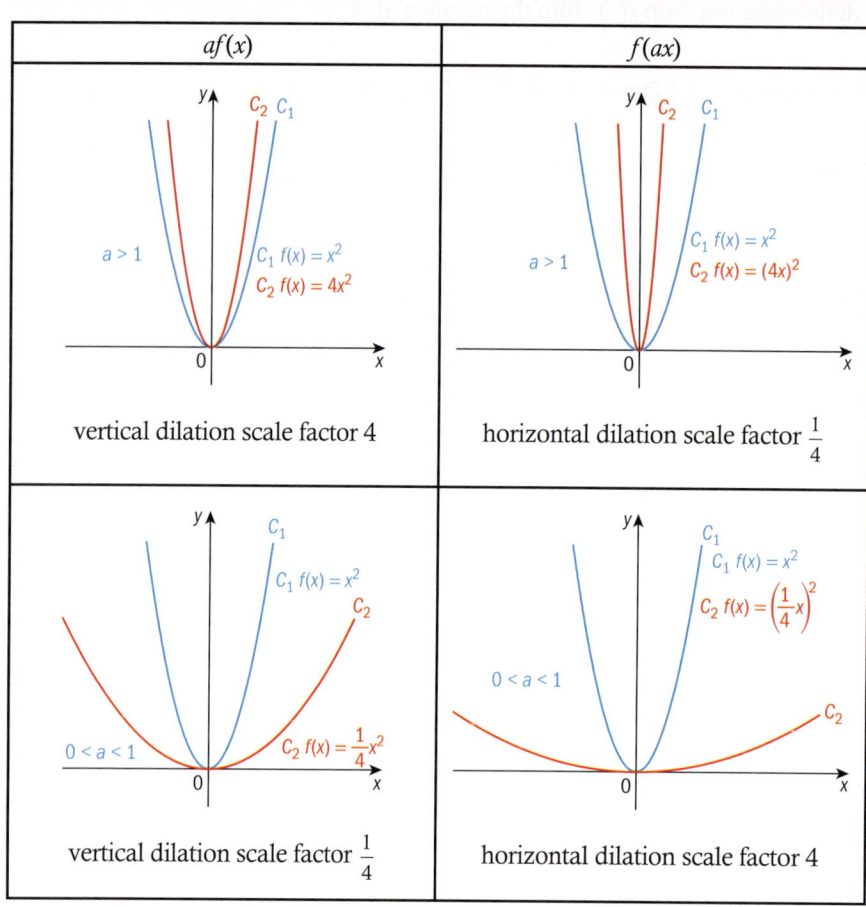

$af(x)$	$f(ax)$
vertical dilation scale factor 4	horizontal dilation scale factor $\frac{1}{4}$
vertical dilation scale factor $\frac{1}{4}$	horizontal dilation scale factor 4

Example 4

Here is the graph of $y = x^2$.

Describe the effect of the transformation, giving examples of how individual points are transformed, and sketch the graphs of:

a $2f(x)$

b $f(2x)$.

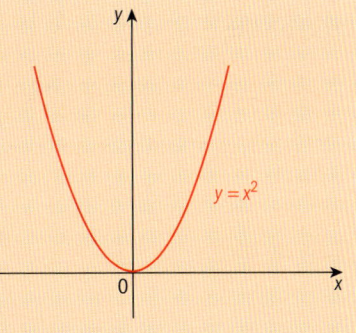

a The graph of $2f(x)$ is a dilation, scale factor 2, parallel to the y-axis.

$(0, 0) \rightarrow (0, 0)$

$(-2, 4) \rightarrow (-2, 8)$ ———————————— y-coordinates of points on the graph increase by scale factor 2.

$(1, 1) \rightarrow (1, 2)$

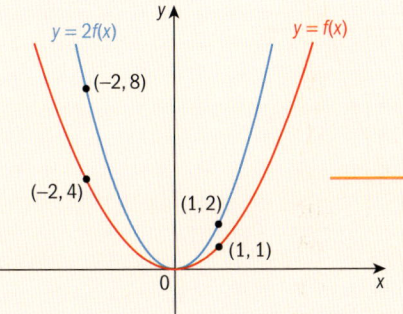

———————————— Sketch the graph. Label some points.

b Graph of $f(2x)$ is a dilation, scale factor $\frac{1}{2}$, parallel to the x-axis.

$(0, 0) \rightarrow (0, 0)$

$(2, 4) \rightarrow (1, 4)$ ———————————— x-coordinates of points on the graph increase by scale factor $\frac{1}{2}$.

$(-2.5, 6.25) \rightarrow (-1.25, 6.25)$

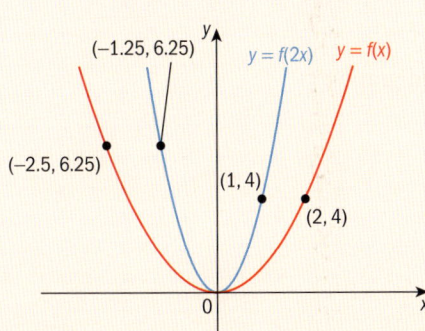

Practice 4

1 Copy this sketch of $f(x) = (x - 1)^2$.

Sketch the graph of $g(x) = 2f(x)$ on the same axes.

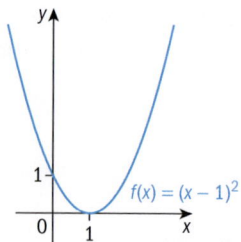

2 Copy this sketch of $f(x) = -x^2 + 4$.

Sketch the graph of $h(x) = f(2x)$ on the same axes.

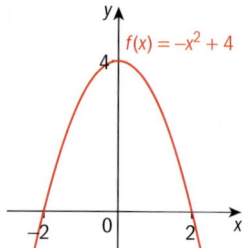

3 Copy this sketch of $f(x) = x^2 + 2x - 3$.

Sketch the graph of $g(x) = f(3x)$ on the same axes.

Sketch the graph of $h(x) = -f(3x)$ on the same axes.

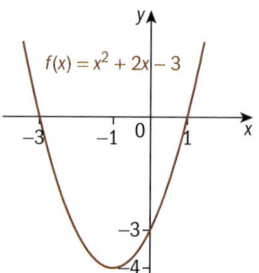

4 Draw the graph of $f(x) = x^2$.

Draw the graphs of $g(x) = f\left(\frac{1}{2}x\right)$ and $h(x) = f(2x)$ on the same axes.

5 Describe the transformation that maps the graph of $y = x^2$ to:

a $y = 3x^2$ **b** $y = \frac{1}{2}x^2$ **c** $y = (4x)^2$ **d** $y = \left(\frac{1}{3}x\right)^2$

6 Write down the equation of the graph that results when $y = x^2$ is transformed by a dilation:

a scale factor 5 parallel to the y-axis

b scale factor 4 parallel to the x-axis

c scale factor $\frac{1}{3}$ parallel to the y-axis.

7 Describe the transformation that takes the blue graph to the red graph:

a

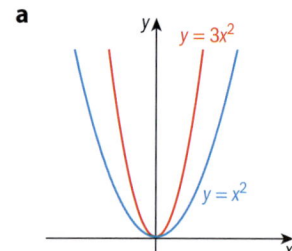

b

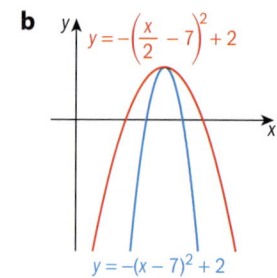

You need to be familiar with three types of transformation for linear and quadratic functions – translation, reflection and dilation.

Combinations of transformations:

- Any linear function can be defined by one or more transformations applied one after the other to the function $y = x$.

- Any quadratic function can be defined by one or more transformations applied one after the other to the function $y = x^2$.

ATL

Example 5

List the transformations applied to the function $y = x^2$ to give:

a $y = x^2 + 6x + 4$ **b** $y = -3x^2 - 12x - 11$

Sketch the transformed graphs.

a $x^2 + 6x + 4 = (x^2 + 6x) + 4$ — Write the function in vertex form.

$ = [(x + 3)^2 - 9] + 4$

$ = (x + 3)^2 - 5$

Start with $f(x) = x^2$. — Start with the original function $y = x^2$ and apply one transformation at a time.

$f(x + 3)$ is a horizontal translation of -3.

$f(x + 3) - 5$ is a vertical translation of -5 on $f(x + 3)$.

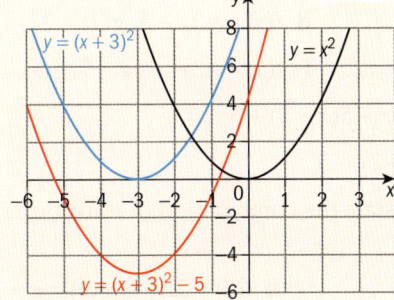

b $-3x^2 - 12x - 11 = -3(x^2 + 4x) - 11$

$ = -3[(x + 2)^2 - 4] - 11$

$ = -3(x + 2)^2 + 1$

Start with $f(x) = x^2$.

$y = 3x^2 = 3f(x)$ is a dilation parallel to the y-axis, scale factor 3.

$y = -3x^2 = -3f(x)$ is a reflection in the x-axis.

$y = -3(x + 2)^2 = -3f(x + 2)$ is a horizontal translation of -2.

$y = -3(x + 2)^2 + 1 = -3f(x + 2) + 1$ is a vertical translation of 1.

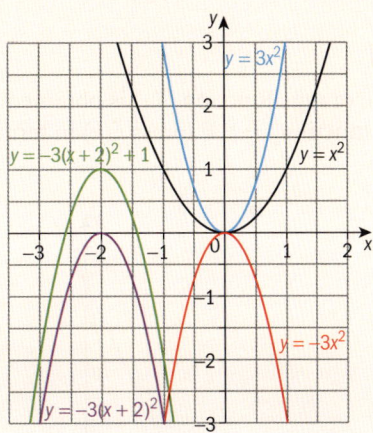

Reflect and discuss 3

- Why is the quadratic changed from standard form to vertex form in Example **5** in order to show the transformations that have been applied?

- In Example **5b**, does it matter in which order you apply the transformations?

- Why is it best to do the translations last?

Practice 5

ATL

1 List the transformations applied to the linear function $y = x$ to give:

   a $y = -4x$ **b** $y = 2x - 9$ **c** $y = 0.5x + 4$ **d** $y = -1.2x - 2.5$

2 List the transformations applied to the quadratic function $y = x^2$ to give each function. Sketch the graphs of the transformations.

   a $y = 25x^2$ **b** $y = 3(x - 9)^2$ **c** $y = -x^2 + 4$

   d $y = x^2 + 8x + 16$ **e** $y = 2x^2 - 12x + 9$ **f** $y = -0.5x^2 - 4x + 1$

3 Express $g(x)$ in terms of $f(x)$ and state the transformation applied to $f(x)$ to get $g(x)$:

   a $f(x) = x - 5$, $g(x) = 4x - 20$ **b** $f(x) = 2x + 5$, $g(x) = 6x + 5$

   c $f(x) = -2x - 5$, $g(x) = 2x + 5$ **d** $f(x) = -2x - 5$, $g(x) = 2x - 5$

   e $f(x) = 2x^2 + 3x$, $g(x) = 2x^2 + 3x - 12$ **f** $f(x) = -3x^2 + 6x - 7$, $g(x) = -3x^2 - 6x - 7$

   g $f(x) = x^2 - 5x + 6$, $g(x) = (x - 2)^2 - 5(x - 2) + 6$

   h $f(x) = 4x^2 - 8x + 12$, $g(x) = x^2 - 2x + 3$

4 Express $g(x)$ in terms of $f(x)$ and state the combination of transformations applied to $f(x)$ to get $g(x)$:

   a $f(x) = 3x - 8$, $g(x) = -3x + 3$ **b** $f(x) = 2x + 6$, $g(x) = x - 3$

   c $f(x) = x^2 + 4x$, $g(x) = x^2 - 4x + 4$ **d** $f(x) = 2x^2 - 2x - 3$, $g(x) = -x^2 + x + 1.5$

   e $f(x) = 4x^2 - 5x + 7$, $g(x) = -4x^2 + 5x + 2$ **f** $f(x) = x^2 + 4x + 4$, $g(x) = x^2 - 6x + 9$

   g $f(x) = x^2 - 2x - 3$, $g(x) = x^2 + 6x + 4$ **h** $f(x) = x^2 + x + 1$, $g(x) = 9x^2 - 3x + 1$

Problem solving

5 For each pair of graphs, the orange function $f_2(x)$ is obtained by applying one transformation to the blue function $f_1(x)$. Express $f_2(x)$ in terms of $f_1(x)$, and state the transformation.

a

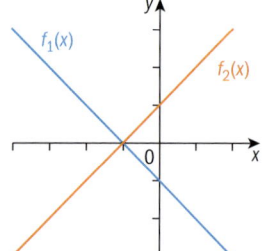

b

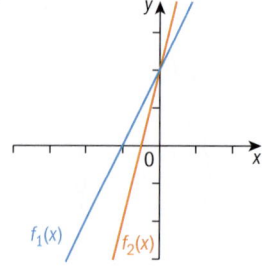

c

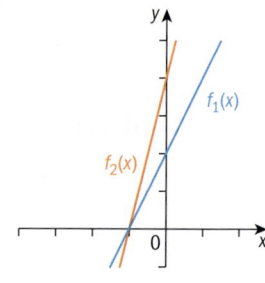

d

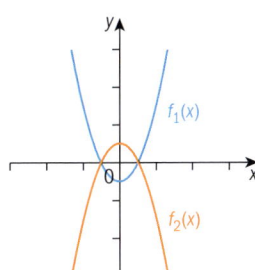

e

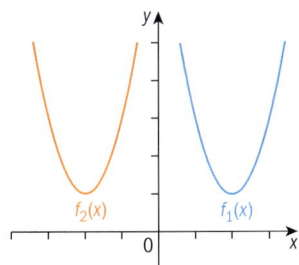

f

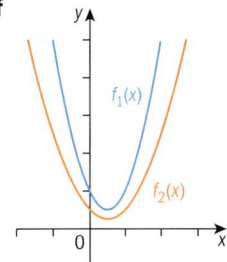

6 For each pair of graphs, the orange function $f_2(x)$ is obtained by applying two or more transformations to the blue function $f_1(x)$. Express $f_2(x)$ in terms of $f_1(x)$, and state the transformations.

a

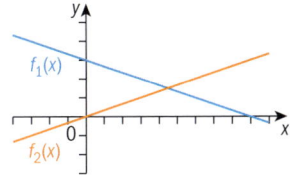

b

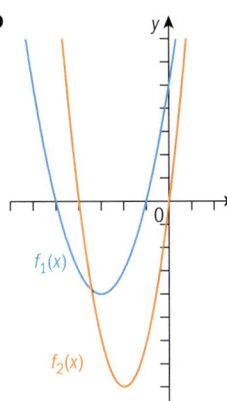

c

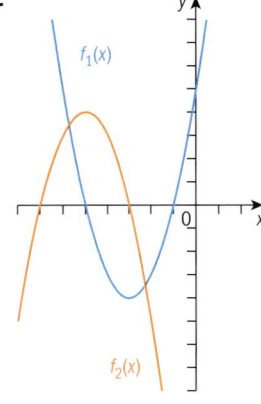

Translation, reflection and dilation transformations can be used on the graph of **any** function.

Example 6

Here is the graph of function $f_1(x)$ and the transformed function $f_2(x)$.

Identify the transformations that take $f_1(x)$ to $f_2(x)$.

Hence write the function $f_2(x)$ as a transformation of $f_1(x)$.

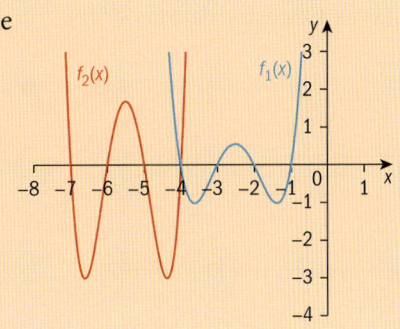

There has been a translation 3 units to the left.

There has been a dilation parallel to the y-axis scale factor 3. —— The minimum points at $y = -1$ have been transformed to minimum points at $y = -3$.

$f_1(x) \rightarrow f(x + 3)$ translation 3 units left

$\rightarrow 3f(x + 3)$ dilation scale factor 3 parallel to the y-axis

Therefore, $f_2(x) = 3f(x + 3)$

Example 7

Given the graph of $f_1(x)$, draw the graph of $f_2(x) = 5f_1(-x)$.

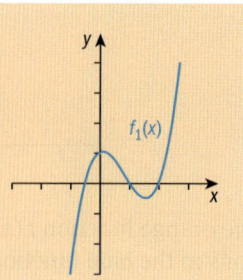

$f_1(-x)$: reflection in the y-axis. ———————————————— Identify the transformations.

$5f_1(-x)$: vertical dilation of scale factor 5 ———————— Multiply the y–value of all points by 5.

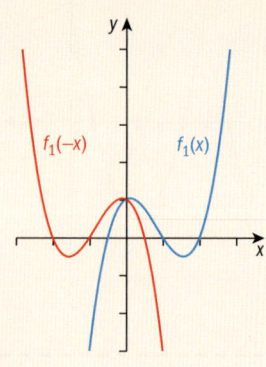
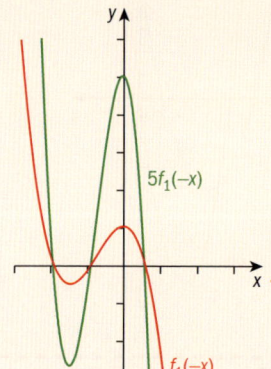

Draw the graph of each transformation.

Practice 6

1 For each pair of graphs, find the transformations applied to $f_1(x)$ to get $f_2(x)$.
Hence write the function $f_2(x)$ as a transformation of $f_1(x)$.

a

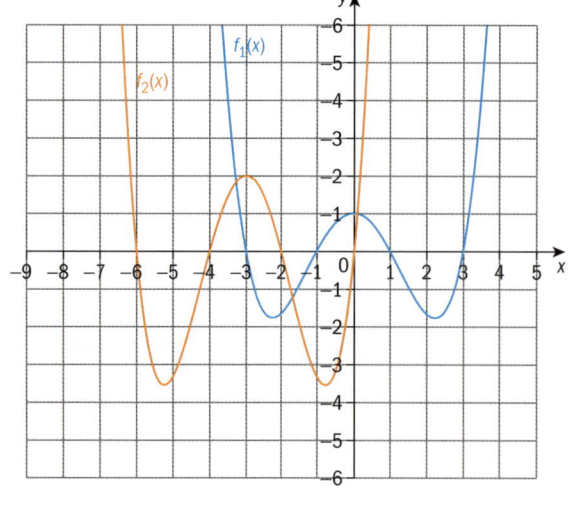

b

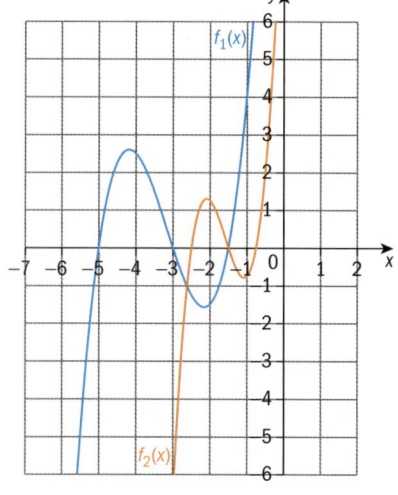

c

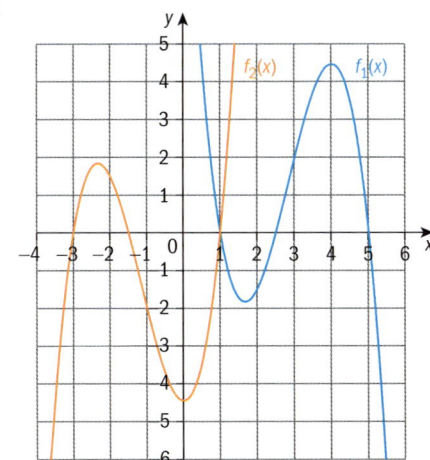

d

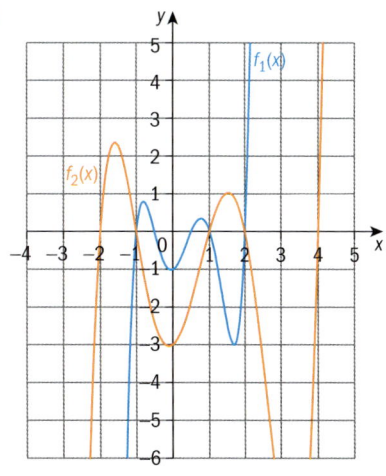

2 Given the graph of $f_1(x)$, draw the graph of $f_2(x)$.

a $f_2(x) = 2f_1(x - 3)$

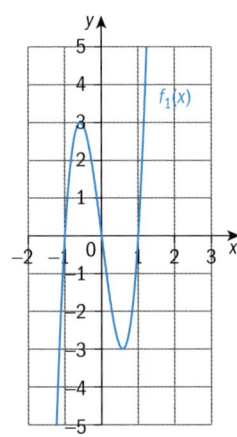

b $f_2(x) = f_1(-x + 5)$

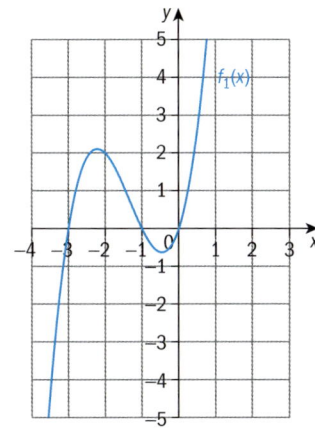

c $f_2(x) = 0.5f_1(-x)$

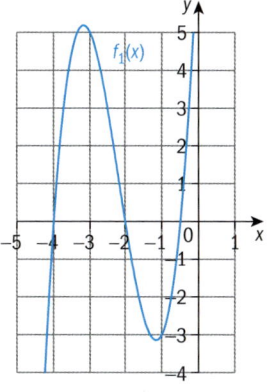

d $f_2(x) = 3f_1(x - 5)$

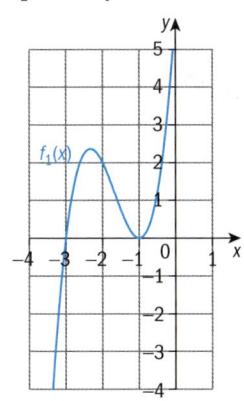

e $f_2(x) = -2f_1(x)$

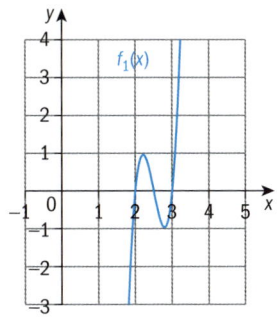

f $f_2(x) = f_1(-x) + 3$

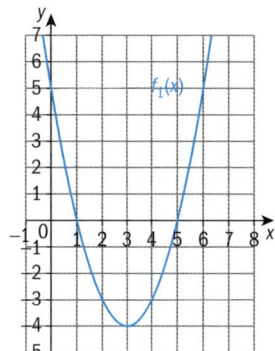

D Transformations or not?

- If the graph of a transformed function is the same as the graph of the original function, has the function been transformed?
- If two different transformations give the graph of the same transformed function, are the transformations really different?

Exploration 5

1 Use technology to graph different linear functions of the form $f(x) = mx + c$ and their reflections in the y-axis and the x-axis, $-f(-x)$.

2 Find functions where the graphs of $f(x)$ and $-f(-x)$ are the same. What is the value of c in these graphs?

In these graphs, are the original function and the transformed function identical?

3 For one of your graphs in step **2**, pick a point on the line. Apply the transformation $-f(-x)$ to that point by reflecting it in the x-axis and then the y-axis. Does the resulting point have the same coordinates as the original point? How does this affect your answer to step **2**?

4 What single transformation is equivalent to the two combined reflections?

Example 8

Consider the function $f(x) = 2x^2$. Show that the transformations $g(x) = 4f(x)$ and $h(x) = f(2x)$ both generate the same graph.

$g(x) = 4f(x)$ — Find the function generated by the first transformation.

$\qquad = 4(2x^2)$

$\qquad = 8x^2$

$h(x) = f(2x)$ — Find the function generated by the second transformation.

$\qquad = 2(2x)^2$

$\qquad = 8x^2$

$g(x) = h(x)$ — Both the functions generated by the two different transformations are equal.

The two transformations generate the same graph.

Reflect and discuss 4

- In Example 8 the function $g(x)$ is a vertical dilation by scale factor 4 of the function $f(x)$. The function $h(x)$ is a horizontal dilation by scale factor $\frac{1}{2}$. Do $g(x)$ and $h(x)$ represent the same transformation or different transformations of the function $f(x)$?

- Choose a point on the parabola $f(x) = 2x^2$. Apply each of the transformations to that point. Do the two new points have the same coordinates as each other? How does this affect your answer above?

Summary

Translations

- $y = f(x - h)$ translates $y = f(x)$ by h units in the x-direction.

- $y = f(x) + k$ translates $y = f(x)$ by k units in the y-direction.

- $y = f(x - h) + k$ translates $y = f(x)$ by h units in the x-direction and k units in the y-direction.

Dilations

- $y = af(x)$ is a vertical dilation of $f(x)$, scale factor a, parallel to the y-axis.

- $y = f(ax)$ is a horizontal dilation of $f(x)$, scale factor $\frac{1}{a}$, parallel to the x-axis.

Reflections

- The graph of $y = -f(x)$ is a reflection of the graph of $y = f(x)$ in the x-axis.

- The graph of $y = f(-x)$ is a reflection of the graph of $y = f(x)$ in the y-axis.

Combinations of transformations

- Any linear function can be defined by one or more transformations applied one after the other to the function $y = x$.

- Any quadratic function can be defined by one or more transformations applied one after the other to the function $y = x^2$.

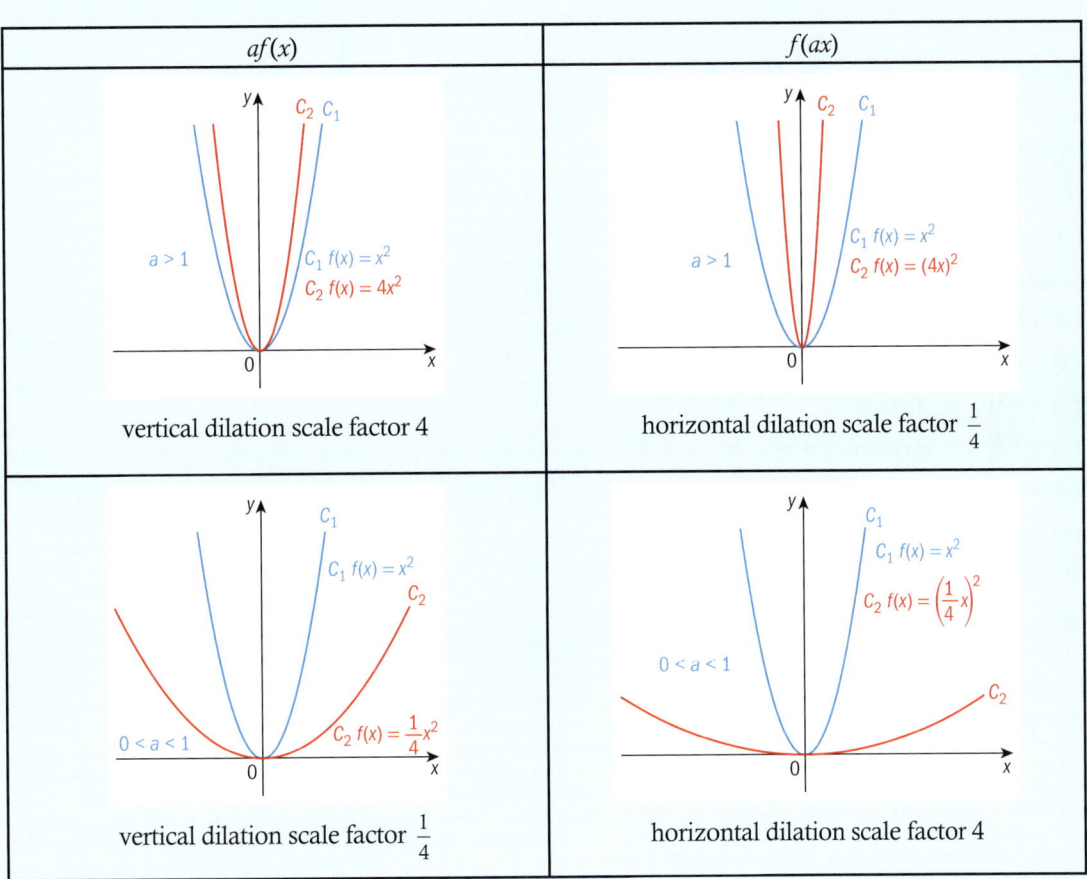

$af(x)$	$f(ax)$
vertical dilation scale factor 4	horizontal dilation scale factor $\frac{1}{4}$
vertical dilation scale factor $\frac{1}{4}$	horizontal dilation scale factor 4

Mixed practice

1 Here is the graph of $f(x) = x^2 - 2x - 1$.

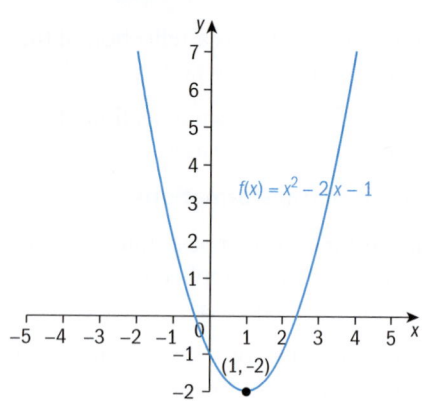

$f(x) = x^2 - 2x - 1$

$(1, -2)$

Use this graph to help you **sketch** the graph of each function and **write down** the coordinates of the new vertex.

a $f(x + 2)$ **b** $f(x) - 4$

c $-f(x)$ **d** $f(-x)$

e $2f(x)$ **f** $f(-3x)$

g $f(x + 1) - 3$ **h** $3 - f(x)$

i $-2f(x) - 1$ **j** $5f(-0.5x) + 4$

2 **State** which combination of transformations has been applied to $f(x)$ to get $g(x)$:

a $f(x) = x$, $g(x) = 2x - 8$

b $f(x) = -3x - 6$, $g(x) = x + 2$

c $f(x) = 12x + 5$, $g(x) = 6x + 6$

d $f(x) = x^2 + 4x + 4$, $g(x) = x^2 - 5$

e $f(x) = (x - 2)^2 + 1$, $g(x) = (x + 1)^2 - 2$

f $f(x) = 2x^2 + 8x + 4$, $g(x) = x^2 + 4x + 4$

3 For each pair of graphs, **find** the single transformation applied to $f_1(x)$ to get $f_2(x)$. **Write down** the function $f_2(x)$ as a transformation of $f_1(x)$.

a

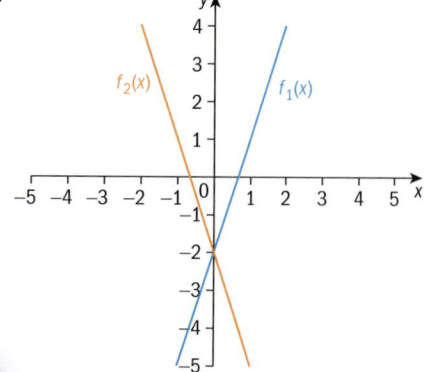

$f_2(x)$

$f_1(x)$

b

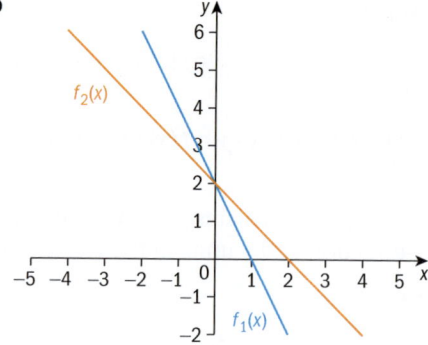

$f_2(x)$

$f_1(x)$

c

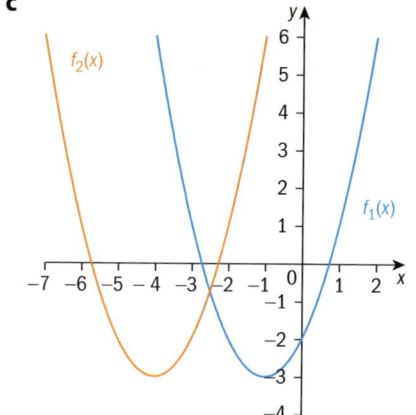

$f_2(x)$

$f_1(x)$

d

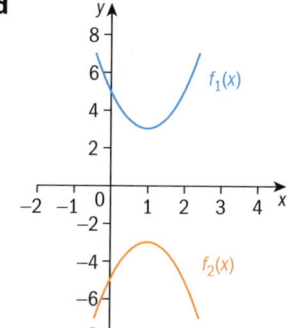

$f_1(x)$

$f_2(x)$

e

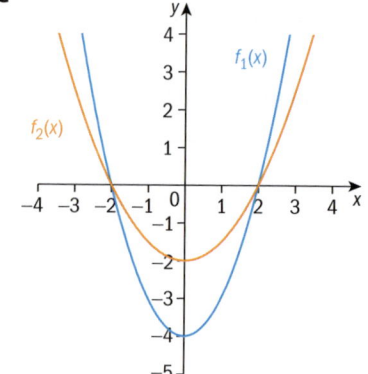

$f_1(x)$

$f_2(x)$

f

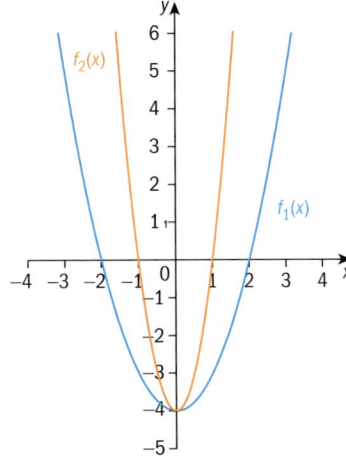

4 For each pair of graphs, **find** the transformations applied to $f_1(x)$ to get $f_2(x)$. **Write down** the function $f_2(x)$ as a transformation of $f_1(x)$.

a

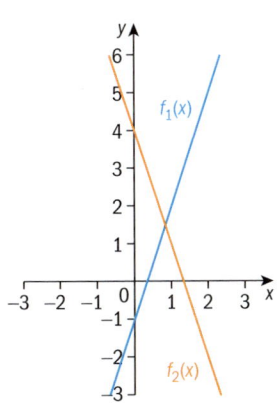

b

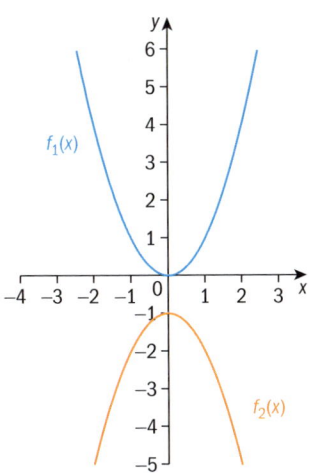

c

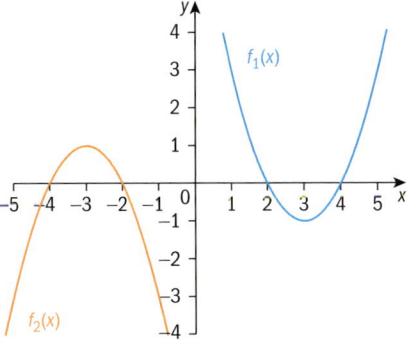

d

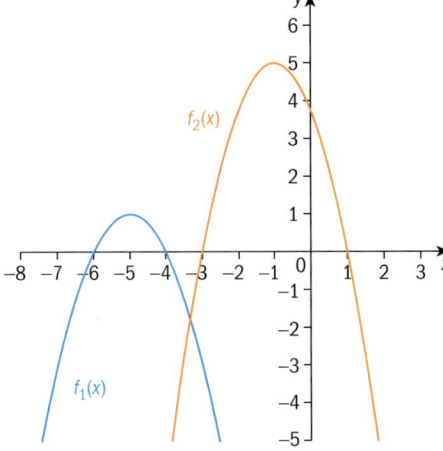

e

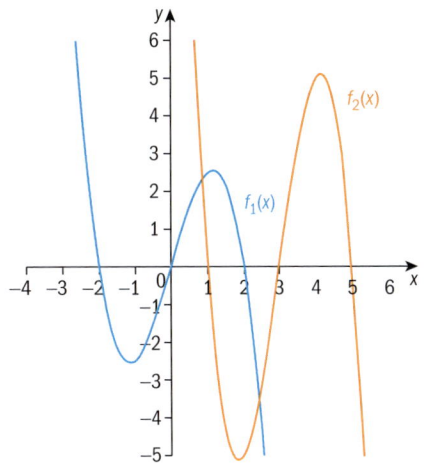

f

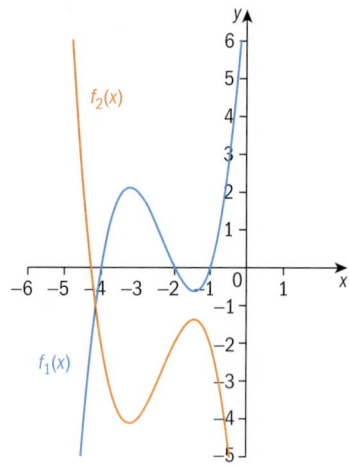

5 Given the graph of $f_1(x)$, **draw** the graph of $f_2(x)$.

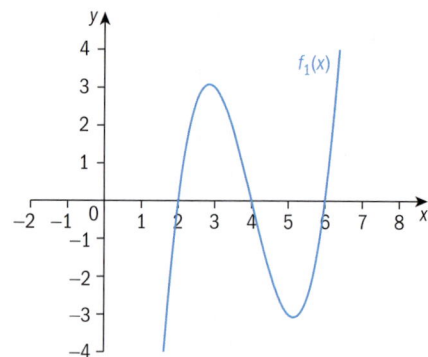

a $f_2(x) = 2f_1(x+4)$ **b** $f_2(x) = f_1(2x) + 4$

c $f_2(x) = -f_1(2x)$ **d** $f_2(x) = 2f_1(-x)$

Review in context

Scientific and technical innovation

Whenever an object such as a ball, arrow, or dart flies freely through the air, its motion is affected by gravity. Any object which isn't self-propelled (like a bird or a rocket would be) follows a path given by a parabola. This is because gravity always acts directly downward and exerts a constant force.

The path that an object takes in flight is known as its *trajectory*. The study of trajectories, motion of objects and rates of change is used in many areas of science and has contributed to great technological advances, such as auto-pilot functionalities and navigation in space.

1 A frog leaps from a lily pad. Viewed from the side, its initial position is given by (0, 0). The *x*-axis is horizontal and the *y*-axis is vertical; 1 unit represents 1 meter.

The trajectory of its flight is given by $y = f(x)$ where $f(x) = \frac{3}{4}x - \frac{1}{4}x^2$.

a **Draw** a graph of its trajectory.

b **Find** the horizontal distance it travels before returning to its starting height.

c The frog can change its jump by modifying the angle and speed with which it launches off. **Describe** clearly how its jump would vary if its new trajectory were given by

    i $y = f(2x)$ **ii** $y = 1.2f(0.7x)$ **iii** $y = f(-x)$

d **Explain** clearly why $y = -0.8f(x)$ does not model a trajectory for the frog's jump.

2 A student throws a ball from a window in a tall building.

Its trajectory is given by $y = h - 5\left(\dfrac{x}{u}\right)^2$, where (0, *h*) is the position from which it is thrown and *u* is its initial horizontal velocity in m/s.

a **Describe** the effect of increasing the value of *h* on the graph of the trajectory.

b **Describe** the effect of increasing the value of *u* on the graph of the trajectory.

3 A baseball player is practicing her batting on an indoor range. Let (0, 0) be the point at which she hits the ball. The ceiling of the indoor range is about 4 m higher than the point at which she hits the ball.

a Her first hit follows a trajectory given by $y = -\frac{1}{20}(x-10)^2 + 5$.

   i **Describe** the transformations that map a curve with equation $y = x^2$ onto a curve with equation $y = -\frac{1}{20}(x-10)^2 + 5$.

   ii **Show that** this curve passes through the point (0, 0) as described.

   iii Use the graph transformations to determine whether the maximum height of this curve is more than 4 meters above her hitting point and hence would hit the ceiling.

b Her second shot follows a trajectory given by $y=-\frac{1}{40}\left[(x-10)^2-100\right]$.

By considering graph transformations, find the coordinates of the maximum point of the curve. Hence **determine** whether or not the ball will hit the ceiling.

4 Car loans use simple interest so that, every month, the amount you owe on the loan (the loan balance) decreases by the same amount. (House loans or mortgages do not work this way.) Suppose you have US\$12 000 in car loans and you are making payments of US\$150 per month.

a **Write** an equation to represent the loan balance (b) as a function of the number of months that have gone by (t). Assume the function varies linearly.

b **Draw** a graph of this relationship, $y = b(t)$.

c **Find** $b(50)$. **State** what this amount represents.

d **Find** how long it will take you to pay off the loan.

e **Suggest** what change(s) to the scenario could produce a parallel graph with a higher y-intercept.

f **Suggest** what change(s) to the scenario could produce a graph with a lower y-intercept but the same t-intercept.

g **State** how the graph will be transformed if you increase your original payment to US\$250 per month. **Write down** an equation for this new scenario.

Reflect and discuss 5

How have you explored the statement of inquiry? Give specific examples.

Statement of inquiry:

Discovering relationships in patterns and studying equivalence between representations can lead to better models.

4 Mathematically speaking

Statement of inquiry:

Understanding health and validating lifestyle choices results from using logical representations and systems.

Key concept:

Logic is a method of reasoning and a system of principles used to build arguments and reach conclusions.

F **How can representing language with symbols facilitate mathematical operations?**

Is a picture worth a thousand words?

ABCD is a quadrilateral. *AB* is parallel to *CD* and perpendicular to *BC*.

Angle *ADC* = 70°. Find angle *DAB*.

- How does drawing a diagram help you solve this problem?
- Could you solve it without a diagram?

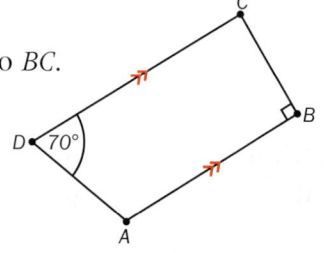

C **How do axioms enhance the understanding of logic?**

Axiomatic system for number

You have been working with the real number system since you first learned to count. The number system is based on a set of axioms, which are assumed to be true for real numbers.

Verify the axioms below for real numbers *x*, *y* and *z*.

Addition and multiplication are:

Commutative: $x + y = y + x$
$xy = yx$

Associative: $(x + y) + z = x + (y + z)$
$(xy)z = x(yz)$

Distributive: $x(y + z) = xy + xz$

These axioms form the basis for all of your number skills.

What factors validate our lifestyle decisions?

Systems are groups of interrelated elements.

Justification in medical research

Pharmaceutical companies are continually trying to produce new medicines to treat as-yet incurable conditions, or to treat curable conditions more effectively. Before a new drug can go on sale, the company needs to justify that the drug is safe and effective. To do this, they run clinical trials to test the drugs on humans and collect evidence on positive results as well as negative side effects.

All clinical trials have to be approved by a scientific and ethical committee. The researchers must justify that the volunteers in the trial will not be exposed to unnecessary risk, and that the new drug can reasonably be expected to improve patient care.

Ecosystems

When an ecosystem is in balance, all the living organisms within it are healthy and capable of reproducing themselves. If one part of the ecosystem is damaged – either by natural events or human activity – every other element of the ecosystem is affected.

Forest fires cause widespread destruction, but fire is a natural and vital element in some forest ecosystems. After a fire, more sunlight can reach the forest floor, which is free from dead wood and leaf litter and has increased nutrient levels from the ash. This creates perfect conditions for some trees and plants to thrive. Some species have evolved to withstand fire (or sometimes even rely on it) as part of their life cycle. For example, sand pine cones open to disperse their seeds only in intense heat.

Global context:
Identities and relationships

Exploration:
Explore personal and physical health and good lifestyle choices

📖 **Launch additional digital resources for this unit.**

E4.1 Independent events and conditional probability

Global context: Identities and relationships

Related concept: Systems

Objectives

- Drawing diagrams to represent and calculate independent and dependent events
- Determining whether two events are independent or dependent events

Inquiry questions

F
- What is the addition rule?
- What are independent events?
- What is conditional probability?

C
- How can an axiomatic system be developed?
- How does a system facilitate the solving of problems?

D
- What factors affect the decisions we make?

ATL Communication

Use and interpret a range of discipline-specific terms and symbols

📖 Launch additional digital resources for this chapter.

Statement of inquiry:

Understanding health and validating life-style choices results from using logical representations and systems.

You should already know how to:

• draw tree diagrams	**1** Caesar's new playlist contains ten songs from the 1980s and eight songs from the 1990s. He selects two songs at random, without choosing the same song twice. **a** Draw a tree diagram to represent this situation. **b** Find the probability that the two songs are both from the 1980s.
• use Theorem 1 (Addition rule) and Theorem 2 (Multiplication rule)	**2** You have a standard deck of 52 playing cards. **a** You take one card. What is the probability that you take either a red card or a face card? **b** You take one card, replace it, and then take another. What is the probability that you take a 5 followed by a face card? **c** You take one card and then take another, without replacement. What is the probability that you take a 5 followed by a face card?
• calculate probabilities of mutually exclusive events	**3** A box contains 12 soft-center chocolates and 15 hard-center chocolates. One chocolate is picked at random from the box. Let *A* be the event 'pick a hard center' and let *B* be the event 'pick a soft center'. **a** Find P(*A*). **b** Find P($A \cup B$).
• use Venn diagrams and set notation	**4** There are 33 students taking Art and 28 students taking Biology. There are 7 students taking both subjects. Represent this with a Venn diagram. **5** Make a copy of the Venn diagram below for each part of this question. Shade the part of the Venn diagram that represents: **a** *B* **b** *B'* **c** $A \cap B$ **d** $A \cup B'$ **e** $(A \cap B)'$

ATL

F Probabilities of combined events

- What is the addition rule?
- What are independent events?
- What is conditional probability?

Exploration 1

1 Construct a Venn diagram to illustrate this information:

- 30 students study one or more of three languages: French, German and Mandarin
- 5 study all three languages
- 6 study Mandarin only
- 2 study French and Mandarin but not German
- 15 students in total study Mandarin
- 2 study only French
- 3 study only German.

2 From your diagram, find $n(\text{French})$ and $n(U)$. Use these to find the probability that a student picked at random studies French.

3 Find $n(\text{French and Mandarin})$ and $P(\text{French and Mandarin})$ from your diagram. State what each of these numbers represent.

4 Explain how you can find $P(\text{French} \cap \text{German} \cap \text{Mandarin})$ from your Venn diagram.

5 Summarize your findings:

$P(F) =$ $\qquad\qquad$ $P(F \cap G) =$

$P(G) =$ $\qquad\qquad$ $P(G \cap M) =$

$P(M) =$ $\qquad\qquad$ $P(F \cap G \cap M) =$

$P(F \cap M) =$

6 Find $n(\text{French} \cup \text{Mandarin})$ and $P(\text{French} \cup \text{Mandarin})$ from your Venn diagram. Use the probabilities you found in step **5** to find and verify a formula for $P(\text{French} \cup \text{Mandarin})$. Do the same for $P(\text{French} \cup \text{German})$ and $P(\text{Mandarin} \cup \text{German})$.

Your results from Exploration 1 lead to the addition rule, used to determine the probability that event A **or** event B occurs, **or** both occur.

Theorem 1: Addition rule

$$P(A \cup B) = P(A) + P(B) - P(A \cap B)$$

A fair die is rolled once.

Let A be the event 'rolling a 1'.

Calculating $P(A) + P(B)$ adds the intersection $P(A \cap B)$ twice, so you need to subtract it once.

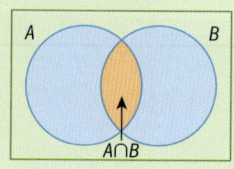

Let B be the event 'rolling a 2', and so on.

$$P(A) = \frac{1}{6} \quad P(B) = \frac{1}{6} \quad P(C) = \frac{1}{6} \quad P(D) = \frac{1}{6} \quad P(E) = \frac{1}{6} \quad P(F) = \frac{1}{6}$$

The events are mutually exclusive as it is impossible, for example, to roll a 1 and a 2 at the same time, so $P(A \cap B) = 0$.

$$P(A \cup B) = P(A) + P(B) - P(A \cap B)$$

$$= \frac{1}{6} + \frac{1}{6} - 0 = \frac{2}{6}$$

$$P(A \cup B \cup C) = P(A) + P(B) + P(C) - P(A \cap B \cap C)$$

$$= \frac{1}{6} + \frac{1}{6} + \frac{1}{6} - 0 = \frac{3}{6}$$

Italian mathematician Gerolamo Cardano (1501–76) analysed the likelihood of events with both cards and dice. His *Liber de Ludo Aleae* (Book on Games of Chance) discussed in detail many of the basic concepts of probability theory, but received little attention. Cardano often found himself short of money, so he would gamble as a means to make some. His *Ludo Aleae* even contains tips on how to cheat by using false dice and marked cards!

Independent events

If you roll a die twice, the outcome of the first roll does not affect the probabilities of the outcomes of the second roll. The results of the two rolls are independent of each other.

If the outcome of an event in one experiment does not affect the probability of the outcome of the event in the second experiment, then the events are **independent**.

Theorem 2: Multiplication rule

If A and B are independent events, then $P(A \cap B) = P(A) \times P(B)$.

ATL

Example 1

Tickets numbered 1, 2, 3, 4, 5, 6, 7, 8 and 9 are placed in a bag.

One ticket is then taken out of the bag at random.

Let A be the event 'the ticket's number is even', and let B be the event 'the ticket's number is a square number'.

a Represent the information on a Venn diagram.

b Calculate $P(A)$, $P(B)$ and $P(A \cap B)$.

c Explain whether or not the events are independent.

d Verify your answer to **c** using the multiplication rule.

e Verify that $P(A \cup B) = P(A) + P(B) - P(A \cap B)$. (The addition rule)

▶ Continued on next page

a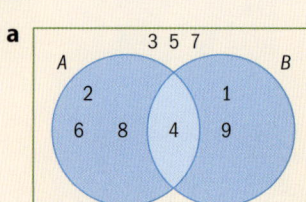

b $P(A) = \dfrac{n(A)}{n(U)} = \dfrac{4}{9}$

$P(B) = \dfrac{n(B)}{n(U)} = \dfrac{3}{9} = \dfrac{1}{3}$

$P(A \cap B) = \dfrac{n(A \cap B)}{n(U)} = \dfrac{1}{9}$

c The events are not independent because whether or not the ticket is an even number affects the probability of it being a square number.

d $\dfrac{1}{9} \neq \dfrac{4}{9} \times \dfrac{3}{9}$

$P(A \cap B) \neq P(A) \times P(B)$ —————————————

> If two events are independent then $P(A \cap B) = P(A) \times P(B)$.

e $P(A \cup B) = \dfrac{6}{9} = \dfrac{2}{3}$

$P(A) + P(B) - P(A \cap B) = \dfrac{4}{9} + \dfrac{3}{9} - \dfrac{1}{9} = \dfrac{6}{9} = \dfrac{2}{3}$ ——————

> Verify that $P(A \cup B) = P(A) + P(B) - P(A \cap B)$.

Practice 1

1 A fair six-sided die has the digits 1, 2, 3, 4, 5, 6 on its faces.

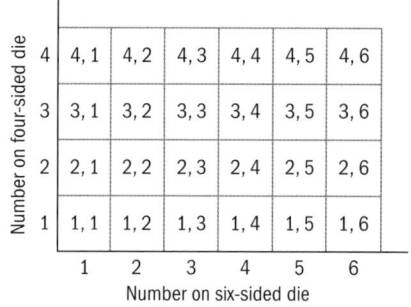

A fair four-sided die has the digits 1, 2, 3, 4 on its faces.

The two dice are rolled simultaneously.

The diagram represents the sample space of the possible outcomes.

a Let A be the event 'rolling a 1 on the four-sided die', and B be the event 'rolling a 1 on the six-sided die'.

Find $P(A \cap B)$, the probability that you roll a 1 on the four-sided die and a 1 on the six-sided die.

b Explain whether or not the events are independent.

c Verify your result using the multiplication rule.

2 A red die has faces numbered 1, 2, 3, 4, 5, 6 and a green die has faces numbered 0, 0, 1, 1, 2 and 2.

Let A be the event 'rolling a 2 on the red die'.

Let B be the event 'rolling a 2 on the green die'.

The two dice are rolled together.

a Calculate the probability of rolling a 2 on both the red die and the green die.

b Explain whether or not these events are independent.

c Verify your result using the multiplication rule.

3 Here is a standard set of dominos.

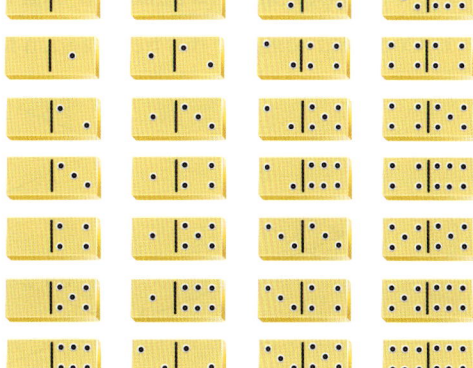

One domino is selected at random. It is then replaced and a second domino is drawn at random.

a If S is the set of outcomes of selecting 2 dominos, write down n(S).

b Let A be the event 'at least one of the values on the first domino is a six' and B be the event 'the second domino is a double' (both values are the same). Explain whether or not these events are independent.

c Verify your answer to **b** using the multiplication rule.

Problem solving

4 The Venn diagram shows the number of students in a class taking Mathematics (M) and Science (S). Use it to determine whether or not taking Mathematics and Science are independent events.

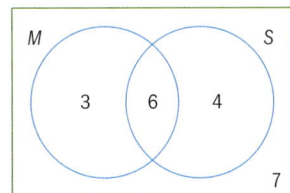

5 In a different class, four students take Mathematics only, two take both Mathematics and Science, six take Science only and 12 take neither subject.

Determine whether the choice of taking Mathematics and taking Science are independent events for this class.

6 Students in an after school activity programme register for either trampolining or table tennis. The table shows students' choices by gender:

	Trampolining	Table tennis	Total
Male	39	16	55
Female	21	14	35

A student is selected at random from the group. Find:

a P(male trampoliner)

b P(trampoliner)

c P(female)

d Determine whether or not the events trampolining and table tennis are independent events.

Exploration 2

The probability that it will rain tomorrow is 0.25. If it rains tomorrow, the probability that Amanda plays tennis is 0.1. If it doesn't rain tomorrow, the probability that she plays tennis is 0.9.

Let A be the event 'rains tomorrow' and B be the event 'plays tennis'.

1 Copy and complete this tree diagram for the events A and B.

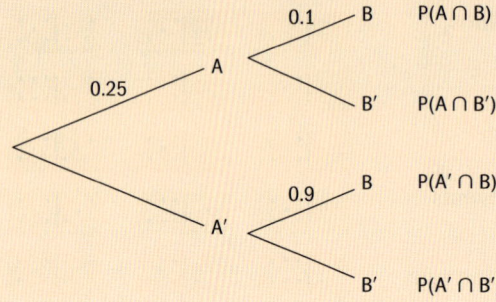

2 State whether A and B are independent events.

3 Find the probability that:

   a Amanda plays tennis tomorrow, given that it will be raining

   b Amanda does not play tennis tomorrow, given that it will be raining

   c Amanda plays tennis tomorrow, given that it will not be raining

   d Amanda does not play tennis tomorrow, given that it will not be raining.

In step **3** of Exploration 3 you should have found that the probability of Amanda playing tennis is conditional on whether or not it is raining.

In mathematical notation, $P(B|A)$ is 'the probability of B occurring **given that** the condition A has occurred', or 'the probability of B given A'.

Labelling the conditional probabilities on the tree diagram looks like this:

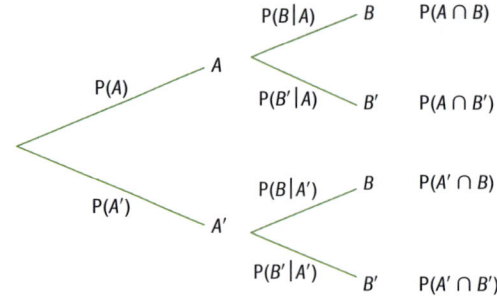

Multiplying along the branches for A and B gives: $P(A \cap B) = P(A) \times P(B|A)$.

This rearranges to: $P(B|A) = \dfrac{P(A \cap B)}{P(A)}$

The conditional probability rule:
$$P(B|A) = \frac{P(A \cap B)}{P(A)}$$

You can use this formula to calculate conditional probabilities.

Recall the following rules:

Theorem 1 The addition rule is:
For any events A and B, $P(A \cup B) = P(A) + P(B) - P(A \cap B)$.

Theorem 2 The multiplication rule is:
For independent events A and B, $P(A \cap B) = P(A) \times P(B)$.

You can use Theorem 2 as a test for independent events.

If A and B are independent events, then $P(A \cap B) = P(A) \times P(B)$.

A and B are independent events if the outcome of one does not affect the outcome of the other. Writing this using probability notation gives another theorem in the probability axiomatic system.

Theorem 3

If A and B are independent events then $P(B|A) = P(B|A') = P(B)$.

Example 2

The probability that a particular train is late is $\frac{1}{4}$. If the train is late, the probability that Minnie misses her dentist appointment is $\frac{3}{5}$. If the train is not late, the probability that she misses her dentist appointment is $\frac{1}{5}$.

Let A be the probability that the train is late and let B be the probability that Minnie misses her dentist appointment.

a Draw a tree diagram to represent this situation.

b Find $P(A \cap B)$.

c Find $P(B)$.

d Show that the train being late and Minnie missing her dentist appointment are not independent events using:
  i Theorem 2
  ii Theorem 3.

▶ Continued on next page

a

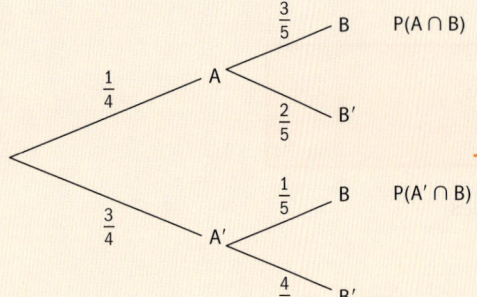

B (missing the appointment) is conditional on A (train being late).

b $P(A \cap B) = \frac{1}{4} \times \frac{3}{5} = \frac{3}{20}$

P (A and B) = P (A ∩ B).

c $P(A \cap B) = \frac{3}{20}$, $P(A' \cap B) = \frac{3}{4} \times \frac{1}{5} = \frac{3}{20}$

$P(B) = \frac{3}{20} + \frac{3}{20} = \frac{6}{20} = \frac{3}{10}$

B occurs either by P (A ∩ B) or P (A' ∩ B). These two events are mutually exclusive, so add the probabilities.

d i $P(A) \times P(B) = \frac{1}{4} \times \frac{6}{20}$

$= \frac{6}{80} = \frac{3}{40}$

$\frac{3}{40} \neq \frac{3}{20}$

So $P(A) \times P(B) \neq P(A \cap B)$ and events A and B are not independent.

Use Theorem 2.

d ii $P(B|A) = \frac{3}{5}$

$P(B|A') = \frac{1}{5}$

$P(B) = \frac{6}{20} = \frac{3}{10}$

$P(B|A) \neq P(B|A') \neq P(B)$ and therefore events A and B are not independent.

Use Theorem 3.

In Example 2 the probability of B differs depending on whether or not A has happened. So the outcome of A affects the outcome of B and thus the events A and B are not independent.

Reflect and discuss 1

- Describe another type of problem in probability where events are not independent. Explain how you know they are not independent.

- How is the tree diagram for the probability problem you thought of different from the one in Example 2?

Practice 2

For questions **1–4**, draw a tree diagram and determine whether or not events A and B are independent by using either Theorem 2 or Theorem 3.

1 One coin is flipped and two dice are thrown. Let A be the event 'coin lands tails side up' and let B be the event 'throwing two sixes'.

2 Jar X contains 3 brown shoelaces and 2 black shoelaces. Jar Y contains 5 brown shoelaces and 4 black shoelaces. Norina takes a shoelace from Jar X and a shoelace from Jar Y. Let A be the event 'taking a brown shoelace from Jar X' and let B be the event 'taking a brown shoelace from jar Y'.

3 There are 10 doughnuts in a bag: 5 toasted coconut and 5 Boston creme. Floris takes one doughnut and eats it, then he takes a second doughnut.

Let A be the event 'the first doughnut is toasted coconut' and let B be the event 'the second doughnut is toasted coconut'.

4 The probability that Mickey plays an online room escape game given that it is Saturday is 60%. On any other day of the week, the probability is 50%.

Let B be the event 'playing a room escape game' and let A be the event 'the day is Saturday'.

> As you ramble on through life, my friend,
> Whatever be your goal,
> Keep your eye upon the doughnut,
> And not upon the hole.
> – *The modified Optimist's Creed*

In questions **5–8**, determine whether or not the two events are independent. Justify your answer.

5 There are 10 students in your class: 6 girls and 4 boys. Your teacher selects two students at random after putting everyone's name in a hat. When the first person's name is selected, it is not put back in the hat. Let A be the event that the first person selected is a girl. Let B be the event that the second person selected is a girl.

6 Tokens numbered 1 to 12 are placed in a box and two are drawn at random. After the first token is drawn, it is not put back in the box, and a second token is selected. Let A be the event that the first token drawn is number 4. Let B be the event that the second number selected is an even number.

7 According to statistics, 60% of boys eat a healthy breakfast. If a boy eats a healthy breakfast, the likelihood that he will exercise that day is 90%. If he doesn't eat a healthy breakfast, the likelihood that he exercises falls to 65%. Let A be the event 'a boy eats a healthy breakfast'. Let B be the event 'exercises'.

Problem solving

8 Blood is classified in a variety of ways. It may or may not contain B antibodies.

Its rhesus status can be positive (Rh+) or negative (Rh−).

The likelihood of someone having B antibodies is 85%.

The likelihood of being Rh+ is 80%.

The likelihood of being B+ (having B antibodies and being Rh+) is 68%.

Let X be the event 'having B antibodies'. Let Y be the event 'being Rh+'.

The Venn diagram represents two events, A and B. Find the probability $P(B|A)$.

In this scenario, it is taken that A has already occurred. The sample space is reduced to the elements of A. This is represented in the Venn diagram at the right by the shading on event A.

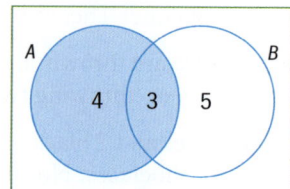

The region of B that is also in A, or $A \cap B$, represents 'B given A'. Here, the darker shading represents this region.

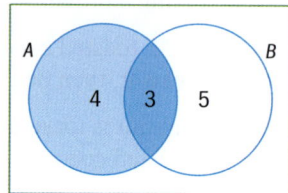

$$P(B|A) = \frac{\text{number of elements in } A \cap B}{\text{number of elements in } A} = \frac{n(A \cap B)}{n(A)} = \frac{3}{7}$$

In a Venn diagram you can calculate conditional probability by reducing the sample space to the **given** condition.

Example 3

In a group of 30 girls, 12 girls like milk chocolate, 15 like dark chocolate, 6 do not like chocolate. One girl is selected at random.

a Draw a Venn diagram to find the probability the girl likes chocolate.

b Given that she likes chocolate, find the probability she likes milk chocolate.

c Find the probability that she likes dark chocolate, given that she likes milk chocolate.

d Test whether liking milk and dark chocolate are independent events by using:
  i Theorem 2
  ii Theorem 3.

Let x be girls who like both milk and dark chocolate.

$$P(A \cup B) = P(A) + P(B) - P(A \cap B)$$

$$24 = 12 + 15 - x$$

$$24 = 27 - x$$

$$x = 3$$

Draw a Venn diagram.
Use Theorem 1 to find $n(A \cap B)$.

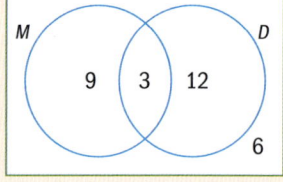

D is the event 'likes dark chocolate'.
M is the event 'likes milk chocolate'.

▶ Continued on next page

a P(likes chocolate) $= \dfrac{24}{30} = \dfrac{4}{5}$

b P(M | likes chocolate) $= \dfrac{12}{24} = \dfrac{1}{2}$ ———————— Reduce the sample space to only the **given** condition (likes chocolate). Ignore the 6 people who do not like chocolate.

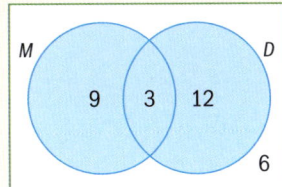

c P(D | M) $= \dfrac{3}{12} = \dfrac{1}{4}$ ———————————————————————— Reduce the sample space to M.

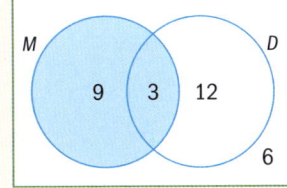

d i M and D are independent events if and only if: ———————— Using Theorem 2.

$$\text{P}(M) \times \text{P}(D) = \text{P}(M \cap D)$$

$$\text{P}(M) = \frac{12}{30} = \frac{2}{5}, \ \text{P}(D) = \frac{15}{30} = \frac{1}{2}, \ \text{P}(M \cap D) = \frac{3}{30} = \frac{1}{10}$$

$$\text{P}(M) \times \text{P}(D) = \frac{2}{5} \times \frac{1}{2} = \frac{1}{5}$$

$\text{P}(M) \times \text{P}(D) \neq \text{P}(M \cap D)$, therefore they are not independent events.

ii M and D are independent events if and only if: ———————— Using Theorem 3.

$$\text{P}(D|M) = \text{P}(D|M') = \text{P}(D)$$

$$\text{P}(D|M) = \frac{1}{4}, \ \text{P}(D|M') = \frac{2}{3}, \ \text{P}(D) = \frac{1}{2}$$

$\text{P}(D|M) \neq \text{P}(D|M') \neq \text{P}(D)$, therefore they are not independent events.

Practice 3

1 From the Venn diagram at the right, find:

   a P(B | A)   **b** P(A | B)

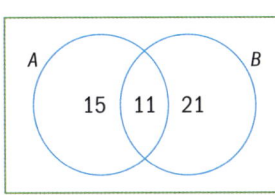

2 On a field trip, 50 students choose to do kayaking, caving, neither activity, or both.

32 students chose kayaking, 26 students chose caving, and 4 students chose neither activity.

   a Represent this information on a Venn diagram.

   b Find the probability that a student picked at random:

      i chose kayaking

      ii chose caving, given that they chose kayaking

      iii chose caving

      iv chose kayaking, given that they chose caving.

3 In a group of 30 students, 12 students study Art, 15 study Drama, and 8 study neither subject.

 a Represent this information on a Venn diagram.

 b Find the probability that a student picked at random:

  i studies Art

  ii studies Drama, given that the student studies Art

  iii studies at least one of Drama or Art

  iv studies **both** Drama and Art, given the student studies **at least one of** Drama or Art.

4 A group of 25 students are in a show. Of these, 10 of the students sing, 6 sing and dance, 5 students do not sing or dance. A student is selected at random. Determine the probability that, in the show, the student:

 a does not sing

 b does not dance

 c sings, given that the student does not dance.

Problem solving

5 The Venn diagram shows 35 students' homework subjects.

 a Find the probability that a student selected at random had:

  i Art homework

  ii Biology homework

  iii Chemistry homework.

 b Find:

  i $P(A|B)$ **ii** $P(B|C)$ **iii** $P(C|A')$

 c Determine the probability that a student picked at random had homework in all three subjects, given that the student had homework.

Art (A)   Biology (B)
5 2 4
7
3 6
1   7
Chemistry (C)

Exploration 3

In the first semi-final of a European Cup tournament, Italy play Spain. 42 students were asked to predict the winner.

- 10 males predicted Italy

- 6 males predicted Spain

- 15 females predicted Italy

- 11 females predicted Spain

1 Represent this information in a two-way table.

2 A student was selected at random. Find the probability that this student was male.

▶ Continued on next page

3 By altering the sample space as you did in the Venn diagrams, find the probability the student predicted Italy, given that the student was male.

4 Find the probability that the student was female given that the student predicted Spain.

5 Find:

   a $P(M)$ **b** $P(F)$ **c** $P(S)$

   d $P(I)$ **e** $P(F|S)$ **f** $P(S|F)$

   g $P(M|S)$ **h** $P(S|M)$ **i** $P(F|I)$

   j $P(I|F)$ **k** $P(M|I)$ **l** $P(I|M)$

M = Male
F = Female
I = Italy
S = Spain

6 In the other semi-final, England play Germany. The two-way table shows how 42 students predicted the winner.

	England (E)	Germany (G)	Total
Male (M)	6	8	14
Female (F)	12	16	28
Total	18	24	42

   a Find the probability that a student selected at random is male.

   b Find: **i** $P(M|E)$ **ii** $P(M|G)$

Reflect and discuss 2

Compare the probabilities for the two semi-finals in Exploration 3. Hence make a statement about which events, if any, are dependent and which are independent.

Practice 4

1 There are 28 participants in a golf competition. Of these, 5 are professional male players and 12 are professional female players. There are a total of 18 females playing.

   a Use this information to complete the two-way table.

	Male (M)	Female (F)	Total
Professional (P)			
Amateur (A)			
Total			

   b Use the table to calculate the following probabilities:

      i $P(M|P)$ **ii** $P(M|A)$ **iii** $P(M)$

   c Hence, using a theorem, determine whether being male and being a professional are independent events.

2 100 students were asked whether they were left- or right-handed, and whether or not they were on the school soccer team.

Use the results below to complete a two-way table and decide whether or not the events "being left-handed" and "being on the soccer team" are independent.

- P(left-handed) = $\frac{4}{10}$
- P(left-handed and not on the soccer team) = $\frac{3}{10}$
- P(right-handed and not on the soccer team) = $\frac{9}{20}$

Problem solving

3 From the table, determine if being a science teacher is independent of gender (male or female) in the school where this data came from. Justify your answer.

	Science teacher	Other teacher
Male	8	25
Female	16	50

C Developing an axiomatic system

- How can an axiomatic system be developed?
- How does a system facilitate the solving of problems?

Here are three important set definitions that have been previously defined.

1 The universal set U contains all sets under discussion.

For any subset $A \subset U$:

$A \cup U = U$ and $A \cap U = A$

2 There is an empty set $\varnothing$.

For any subset $A \subset U$:

$A \cup \varnothing = A$ and $A \cap \varnothing = \varnothing$

3 For any subset $A \subset U$ there exists a unique complementary set A' such that

$A \cup A' = U$ and $A \cap A' = \varnothing$

Reflect and discuss 3

- Use the set definitions to help you explain why these probability definitions are true.

$P(A \cup U) = P(U)$ $P(A \cup A') = P(U)$

$P(A \cap U) = P(A)$ $P(A \cap A') = P(\varnothing)$

$P(A \cup \varnothing) = P(A)$ $P(U) = 1$

$P(A \cap \varnothing) = P(\varnothing)$

- Explain what each definition means, in your own words.

Drawing a Venn diagram may help.

Starting from these rules and Axioms 1, 2 and 3, we can deduce new rules, which will hopefully agree with your intuition about probability.

Exploration 4

1 Suppose you roll a fair four-sided die with sides numbered 1-4. Find the probability of:

   a rolling a 3

   b not rolling a 3

   c rolling an even number

   d not rolling an even number

   e rolling a number less than 3

   f not rolling a number less than 3.

2 Suppose there are 5 choices on a multiple choice question, and a single correct answer.

   a What is the probability that you get the answer correct by guessing?

   b What is the probability of not getting the answer correct by guessing?

   c Repeat steps **a** and **b** for a multiple choice question with just 4 answer choices.

   d Repeat steps **a** and **b** for a True/False question.

3 How do your answers for P(A) and P(not A) relate to each other where A is any of the events mentioned in 1 or 2?

4 Generalize a rule for calculating the probability of an event's complement P(A') if you know P(A).

> A' means the same thing as not A.

> If A is an event then P(A') = 1 − P(A).

Proof of P(A') = 1 − P(A):

By Axiom 2, P(U) = 1. And by definition, P($A \cup A'$) = P(U). Therefore, P($A \cup A'$) = 1.

A and A' are mutually exclusive, so P($A \cup A'$) = P(A) + P(A'), by the addition rule. Hence P(A) + P(A') = 1.

This rearranges to P(A') = 1 − P(A).

Proof of P($\varnothing$) = 0:

$U' = \varnothing$	by definition
P(U) = 1	Axiom 2
P(A') = 1 − P(A)	complementary events
P(U') = 1 − P(U)	substituting U for A
P($\varnothing$) = 1 − P(U)	because $U' = \varnothing$
P($\varnothing$) = 1 − 1	because P(U) = 1
P($\varnothing$) = 0	

Exploration 5

1 Draw three Venn diagrams showing overlapping sets A and B and shade them to illustrate these three relationships:

$A = (A \cap B) \cup (A \cap B')$

$B = (B \cap A) \cup (B \cap A')$

$A \cup B = (A \cap B) \cup (A \cap B') \cup (A' \cap B)$

2 Hence complete these probability statements:

$P(A) = P((A \cap B) \cup (A \cap B'))$

$P(B) = P(\qquad)$

$P(A \cup B) = P(\qquad)$

3 From your Venn diagrams you can see that the events $A \cap B$ and $A \cap B'$ are mutually exclusive and hence you can apply Axiom 3. Hence, complete these statements.

$P(A) = P(A \cap B) + P(A \cap B')$

$P(B) =$

$P(A \cup B) =$

4 Add together the statements for $P(A)$ and $P(B)$.

5 Rearrange to produce the proof of the addition rule.

Definitions and axioms are the building blocks of any mathematical system. An axiom is a statement whose truth is assumed without proof.

Theorems are established and proven using axioms.

A corollary is a theorem that is a direct result of a given theorem. Usually, a theorem is a larger, more important statement, and a corollary is a statement that follows simply from a theorem.

A proposition is any statement whose truth can be ascertained.

Axioms, propositions, corollaries and theorems for Practice 5

Axiom 1: For any event A, $P(A) \geq 0$

Axiom 2: $P(U) = 1$

Axiom 3: If $\{A_1, A_2, A_3, ...\}$ is a set of mutually exclusive events then:

$P(A_1 \cup A_2 \cup ...) = P(A_1) + P(A_2) + ...$

Proposition 1 (complementary events): if A is an event then $P(A') = 1 - P(A)$

Corollary 1: $P(\varnothing) = 0$

Corollary 2: $P(A) \leq 1$

Theorem 1: For any events A and B, $P(A \cup B) = P(A) + P(B) - P(A \cap B)$

Theorem 2: For independent events A and B, $P(A \cap B) = P(A) \times P(B)$

Theorem 3: If A and B are independent events then $P(B \mid A) = P(B \mid A') = P(B)$.

Practice 5

1 A group of 50 students were asked if they liked canoeing and camping. There were 12 students who liked canoeing, 42 students who liked camping, and 8 students who liked both.

 a Draw a Venn diagram showing this information.

 b Determine how many students did not like either recreation.

 c Find the probability that a student chosen at random likes canoeing.

 d Determine if liking canoeing and liking camping are independent events.

 e State the axioms, propositions and corollaries you used in answering each of the questions **a** through **d**.

2 A group of 100 people were asked if they own a pair of sandals and if they own a pair of slippers. Of these, 48 people own slippers 14 people own both, 18 people own neither.

 a Draw a Venn diagram to show this information.

 b Determine how many people own sandals.

 c Find the probability that a person selected at random owns a pair of sandals, given that the person owns a pair of slippers.

 d Determine if the events are:
   i   mutually exclusive
   ii independent.

 e State the axioms, propositions and corollaries you used in answering each of the questions **a** through **d**.

3 A survey asked if people were right- or left-handed. There were 30 women and 70 men in the survey; 27 of the women were right-handed, 12 of the men were left-handed. Draw a two-way table showing this information.

 a Find the probability of being left-handed, given the person is female.

 b Determine whether being left- or right-handed are mutually exclusive events.

 c Determine whether being left- or right-handed are independent events.

 d State the axioms, propositions and corollaries you used in answering each of the questions **a** through **c**.

- -

You have discovered and used the axioms that lead to important probability theorems. How does this system make it easier to answer probability questions?

Example 4

Jenna and Dan are playing volleyball. The probability that Jenna serves the ball to the back of the court is $\frac{1}{5}$.

If Jenna's serve goes to the back of the court, the probability that Dan returns her serve is $\frac{1}{4}$.

If Jenna's serve does not go to the back of the court then the probability that Dan returns it is $\frac{5}{8}$.

The probability that Jenna's serve goes to the back of the court or that Dan returns it is $\frac{7}{10}$.

Let A be the event 'Jenna serves the ball to the back of the court'.

▶ Continued on next page

Let B be the event 'Dan returns Jenna's serve'.

a Find $P(A \cap B)$.

b Find $P(B)$.

c Show that A and B are **not** independent.

a

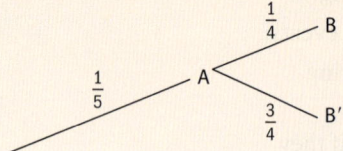

$$P(A \cap B) = \frac{1}{5} \times \frac{1}{4} = \frac{1}{20}$$

Draw just the part of the tree diagram you need to find $P(A \cap B)$.

b $P(A \cup B) = P(A) + P(B) - P(A \cap B)$ — Use Theorem 1.

$$\frac{7}{10} = \frac{1}{5} + P(B) - \frac{1}{20}$$

Use the information given in the question, plus $P(A \cap B)$ which you found from the tree diagram.

$$P(B) = \frac{7}{10} - \frac{1}{5} + \frac{1}{20} = \frac{11}{20}$$

c

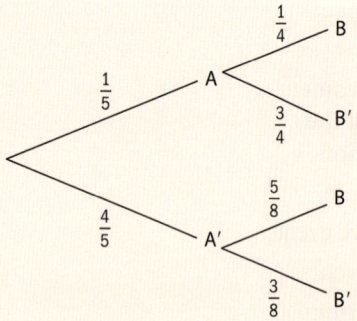

Draw a full tree diagram.

In the tree diagram, the probabilities are different for B depending on where the original serve was. Therefore events A and B are not independent.

Objective C: Communicating

v. organize information using a logical structure

In Practice 6, you will use the axioms of probability to put in place a structure to answer the problems.

Practice 6

1 In a class of 20 students, 12 of them study History, 15 study Geography and 2 students study neither History nor Geography.

Let A be the event 'number of students who study History'.

Let B be the event 'number of students who study Geography'.

a Write down:

    i $n(U)$

    ii $n(A)$

    iii $n(B)$

    iv $n(A \cup B)$

    v $P(A)$

    vi $P(B)$

    vii $P(A \cup B)$

b **i** Let $P(A \cap B) = x$. Use Theorem 1 to calculate x.

    ii Represent the information in a Venn diagram.

c Given that a student picked at random studies History, find the probability that this student:

    i also studies Geography

    ii does not study Geography.

d Given that a student picked at random does **not** study History, find the probability that this student:

    i studies Geography

    ii does not study Geography.

e Draw a tree diagram to represent this information.

2 Events A and B are such that $P(A) = 0.3$ and $P(B) = 0.4$.

    a **i** Use Axiom 3 to find $P(A \cup B)$ given that the events are mutually exclusive.

        ii Use Theorem 2 to find $P(A \cap B)$ given that A and B are independent.

    b Draw a tree diagram to represent the information in **b ii.**

> For **1 a iv**, look at the number of students who study neither History nor Geography and use Proposition 1.

- -

D   # Making decisions with probability

- What affects the decisions we make?

Objective D: Communication

iii. move between different forms of mathematical representation

---

You will need to use the table and also a tree diagram in order to solve the problem in Exploration 6.

Exploration 6

A new test can quickly detect kidney disease. Dr Julia Statham performs the test on 140 patients. She knows that 65 of them have kidney disease and 75 of them do not.

A positive test result indicates kidney disease.

A negative test result indicates no kidney disease.

▶ Continued on next page

Here are Dr Statham's results:

	Positive test result	Negative test result	Total
Has kidney disease	30	35	65
Does not have kidney disease	15	60	75
Total	45	95	140

Let T be the event 'patient test result is positive'.

Let D be the event 'patient has kidney disease'.

1 A patient is selected at random. Calculate:

   a $P(T)$ **b** $P(T')$ **c** $P(D)$ **d** $P(D')$

The test is successful if it gives a positive result for people with kidney disease and a negative result for people who do not have kidney disease. Dr Statham will use the test if it is 90% accurate.

2 Use the information in the table and your knowledge of conditional probability to decide whether or not the doctor should use the test.

3 Construct a tree diagram that represents the same information as the table.

4 Use the information in your tree diagram to confirm whether or not the doctor should use the test.

5 For this problem, which representation do you prefer: the table or the tree diagram? Explain.

Practice 7

1 After having an operation for an eye condition, a patient lost his sight and claimed that this was caused by the operation. The table shows the hospital's data on treatment for this eye condition.

	Lost sight	Did not lose sight
Patient had the eye operation	25	225
Patient did not have the eye operation	75	675

   a Using the information in the table, determine whether the patient's claim is valid. Justify your answer.

   b Represent this information in a tree diagram and use it to determine if the patient's claim is justified.

   c Determine which representation (the table or the tree diagram) best illustrates the validity of the patient's claim. Give evidence for your decision.

2 The Venn diagram represents 65 members of a sports club.

T is the event 'plays tennis' and G is the event 'plays golf'.

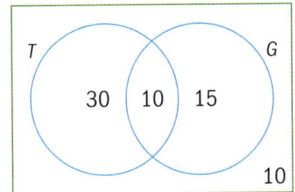

a Represent this information in a two-way table.

b Use both representations to determine if playing tennis and playing golf are independent events.

c Explain, with reasons, which representation was the easiest to work with.

Problem solving

3 The tree diagram shows information about 100 students at a university.

L is the event 'studies Law' and E is the event 'studies Economics'.

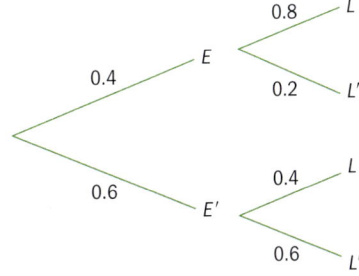

a Use the tree diagram to help you find the following probabilities.

i $P(E)$ **ii** $P(L|E)$ **iii** $P(L|E')$ **iv** $P(E \cap L)$

v $P(E \cap L')$ **vi** $P(E' \cap L)$ **vii** $P(E' \cap L')$ **viii** $P(L)$

b Determine whether studying Law and studying Economics are independent events.

Reflect and discuss 4

- Can you use any probability diagram to represent any situation?
- How do you decide which diagram is most useful for a given situation?

Practice 8

1 The cafeteria sells apples and waffles at morning break. There were 51 students in the cafeteria one morning. Of these, 33 students had apples (A), 18 had waffles (W), and 10 students had neither.

a From the information, and using Theorem 1, draw a Venn diagram.

b Hence, calculate:

    i $P(A)$ **ii** $P(W)$ **iii** $P(A|W)$ **iv** $P(W|A)$ **v** $P(W|A')$

c Make a two-way table to represent the information.

d Verify that the results are the same for each form of representation.

e Using Theorem 2 and Theorem 3, test whether having waffles and having apples are independent events.

In questions **2–4**, use the most appropriate representation to solve the problem.

2 70 students who worked in the holidays, 30 of whom are boys, were surveyed about their work. 12 boys and 28 girls worked full-time. The rest worked part-time.

a Given that a student worked part-time, find the probability the student is female.

b Find the probability that a person chosen at random is male and worked full-time.

c Using a theorem as a justification, determine whether 'being male' and 'working part-time' are independent events.

3 The probability of Gregoire arriving at school on time is 60% if there is fog, and 95% if it is clear. The probability of fog is 20%.

a Calculate the probability of Gregoire arriving at school on time.

b Calculate the probability that it is clear, given that Gregoire arrives late.

c Determine whether the events 'getting to school on time' and 'a clear morning' are independent. Justify your answer.

4 Out of 150 students, 30 are left-handed (L) and 80 are male (M). There are 14 left-handed students who are female (F).

a Find $P(F|L)$.

b Find $P(L|F)$.

c Determine whether the events 'being male' and 'being left-handed' are independent. Justify your answer.

- -

Summary

Theorem 1

For any events A and B,
$P(A \cup B) = P(A) + P(B) - P(A \cap B)$

In mathematical notation, $P(B|A)$ is 'the probability of B occurring **given that** the condition A has occurred', or 'the probability of B given A'.

The conditional probability rule:

$$P(B|A) = \frac{P(A \cap B)}{P(A)}$$

You can use **Theorem 2** as a test for independent events. If A and B are independent events, then
$P(A \cap B) = P(A) \times P(B)$.

Theorem 3

If A and B are independent events then
$P(B|A) = P(B|A') = P(B)$.

If A is an event then $P(A') = 1 - P(A)$.

Mixed practice

1 A lab has 100 blood samples that need to be tested. Of these, 45 are type O, 40 are type A and 15 are type B. Two samples are to be drawn at random without replacement to check for contamination.

   a **Draw** a tree diagram to represent this.

   b **Find** the probability that the first two samples have the same blood group.

   c **Find** the probability that the second sample is type A, given that the first one was type B.

   d **Find** the probability that the second sample is not type O, given that the first one was.

2 From the Venn diagram below, **find**:

   a $P(A)$ **b** $P(A \cap B)$

   c $P(A|B)$ **d** $P(B|A)$

   e $P(B)$ **f** $P(A|B')$

   g $P(B|A')$

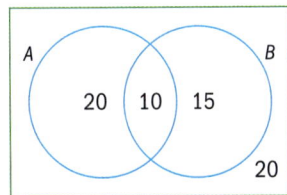

3 The probability that it will be sunny tomorrow is $\frac{4}{5}$. If it is sunny, the probability that the cafeteria will sell ice creams is $\frac{2}{3}$. If it is not sunny, the probability that the cafeteria will sell ice creams is $\frac{1}{3}$.

   a Represent this information in a tree diagram.

   b **Find** the probability that it will be sunny and the cafeteria will sell ice creams.

   c **Determine** if the sun shining and the selling of ice creams are independent events.

4 S is the event 'Tim is wearing shorts' and R is the event 'it is raining'.

   It is known that $P(R) = 0.5$, $P(S|R) = 0.2$, and $P(S|R') = 0.8$.

   a Represent this situation in a tree diagram.

   b **Use** both Theorem 2 and Theorem 3 to **verify** that events S and T are not independent.

5 Sahar is trying to determine if being tall (here defined as being 180 cm or more) is somehow related to liking basketball. She surveyed 70 students, 30 of which were over 180 cm. 48 students surveyed like basketball, 29 of which were under 180 cm.

   a **Draw** a two-way table to represent this.

   b **Find** P(tall).

   c **Find** P(not tall | likes basketball).

   d Are the events 'being tall' and 'liking basketball' independent? **Justify** your answer.

6 In a netball match there are 14 players on the court: 8 have brown hair and 6 have blue eyes. There are 4 students who have neither brown hair nor blue eyes. Let H be the event 'has brown hair' and B be the event 'has blue eyes'.

   a **Draw** a Venn diagram to represent this.

   b **Determine** these probabilities:

      i $P(H)$ **ii** $P(B)$

      iii $P(H \cup B)$ **iv** $P(H \cap B)$

      v $P(H')$ **vi** $P(B')$

     vii $P(H \cup B')$ **viii** $P(H \cap B')$

      ix $P(H \cup B)'$

   c **Find**:

      i $P(H|B)$ **ii** $P(H|B')$

     iii $P(B|H)$ **iv** $P(B|H')$

7 A survey was carried out regarding the school dress code. The two-way table shows the results:

	Should have dress code	Should not have dress code	Total
Middle school		30	45
High school	40		
Total	55	110	

   a Copy and complete the table.

   b **Use** Theorems 2 and 3 to **determine** whether type of school and wanting a dress code are independent events.

Review in context

Identities and relationships

1 The table shows the occurrence of diabetes in 200 people.

	Diabetes	No diabetes
Not overweight	10	90
Overweight	35	65

Let D be the event 'has diabetes'.

Let N be the event 'not overweight'.

a From the table **find**:

  i $P(D)$ **ii** $P(N)$

  iii $P(D|N)$ **iv** $P(D|N')$

b **Determine** whether having diabetes and not being overweight are independent events.

2 The probability that a randomly selected person has a bone disorder is 0.01. The probability that a test for this condition is positive is 0.98 if the condition is there, and 0.05 if the condition is not there (a false positive).

Let B be the event 'has the bone disorder' and T be the event 'test is positive'.

a **Draw** a tree diagram to represent these probabilities.

b **Calculate** the probability of success for the test. Note the test is successful if it tests positive for people with the disorder and negative for people without the disorder.

3 Michele is making drinks to sell at the school play. She makes a 'Super green smoothie' with baby spinach, cucumber, apple, kiwi and grapes, with a calorific content of 140 kcal per cup, and a 'Triple chocolate milk shake' with chocolate milk, chocolate syrup and chocolate ice-cream, with a calorific content of 370 kcal per cup.

She records the number of MYP and DP students buying each product. MYP students purchase 26 Super green smoothies and 48 Triple chocolate milk shakes. DP students purchase 13 Super green smoothies and 24 Triple chocolate milk shakes.

Determine, using both Theorem 2 and Theorem 3, whether the age of the student (MYP or DP) is independent of their choice of drink. Use a two-way table to answer this question.

4 A survey of 200 000 people looked at the relationship between cigarette smoking and cancer. Of the 125 000 non-smokers in the survey, 981 had cancer at some point in their lifetime. Of the smokers in the survey, there were 1763 people who had cancer.

a **Find** the probability that an individual selected from the study was a smoker who had battled cancer.

b **Find** the probability that someone who had never smoked had cancer.

c Let B be the event 'having cancer' and A be the event 'being a smoker' (includes being a former smoker). **Demonstrate** whether or not these two events are independent. **Justify** your answer mathematically.

d Does your answer in **c** encourage or discourage people from choosing to smoke? **Explain**.

5 The following information was extracted from a skin cancer website.

Statement 1: About 69% of skin cancers are associated with exposure to indoor tanning machines.

Statement 2: In the United States, 3.3 million people a year are treated for skin cancer out of a total population of 330 million.

Statement 3: 10 million US adults use indoor tanning machines.

Let A be the event 'developing skin cancer'.

Let B be the event 'exposure to indoor tanning'.

a **Write down** statements 1, 2 and 3 in probability notation.

b **Determine** whether developing skin cancer and exposure to indoor tanning are independent events.

Reflect and discuss 5

How have you explored the statement of inquiry? Give specific examples.

Statement of inquiry:

Understanding health and validating life-style choices results from using logical representations and systems.

5 Spacious interiors

Statement of inquiry:

Representing transformed objects and studying their form helps us enjoy their creativity in space.

Key concept:

Form is the understanding that the underlying structure and shape of an entity is distinguished by its properties.

F   What is space?

Space is the frame of geometrical dimensions describing an entity.

Dimensions

We live in a three-dimensional world, meaning that everything in our world can be located using three aspects: latitude, longitude and altitude. Letting time be the fourth dimension, people and objects can be located at a particular place and moment in time.

We can imagine what a two-dimensional universe would be like, if we simply look into a mirror, or observe shadows on the ground. These images possess no thickness. You are familiar with using the 2D coordinate plane to create graphs. This representation of 2D space is called the Cartesian plane, named after the French philosopher, scientist and mathematician René Descartes.

In order to locate three-dimensional objects, we need to add a third axis to the Cartesian plane. A point in 3D would therefore have three coordinates instead of two.

There is a wonderful book written over a hundred years ago by Edwin Abbott called *Flatland, a Romance of Many Dimensions*, about a two-dimensional world where one of its inhabitants encounters a mysterious visitor from the third dimension and struggles to comprehend how such a being could exist and what it might look like.

C How can you create different representations of space?

As big as a whale

Media reports use comparisons such as "an area the size of two football pitches" or "an area twice the size of Belgium."

A blue whale can be up to 30 m long and weigh as much as 200 tonnes.

- Which of these two comparisons gives you the best idea of the size of a blue whale?

A blue whale can be as long as 7 family cars and weigh as much as 33 elephants.

D To what extent does expressing shapes in different forms allow creativity?

Form and function

In design, form is the shape and appearance of an object. Function is the purpose of the object; does it do the job it was designed for? One definition of a good design is one that balances form and function—it does the job it was designed to do and is also attractive.

- Which do you think is the best chair design?

- Which do you think is the best logo design?

Global context: Personal and cultural expression

Exploration: Explore the ways in which we reflect on, extend and enjoy our creativity

📖 Launch additional digital resources for this unit.

E5.1 More geometric transformations

Global context: Personal and cultural expression
Related concept: Space

FORM

Objectives

- To dilate figures around a given point
- To dilate figures by rational and negative scale factors
- To find the equation of perpendicular lines

Inquiry questions

 F
- What are dilations?
- What are similar shapes?

 C
- Does position in space matter when transforming shapes?
- How do you rotate a line by 90°?
- How do geometric transformations compare to function transformations?

D
- How can shapes change size if the center of dilation is not in the same plane as the object?

ATL Creative-thinking

Practise visible thinking strategies and techniques

Statement of inquiry:

Representing transformed objects and studying their form helps us enjoy their creativity in space.

📑 Launch additional digital resources for this chapter.

You should already know how to:

• perform isometric transformations on geometric shapes	**1** Consider the following triangle: 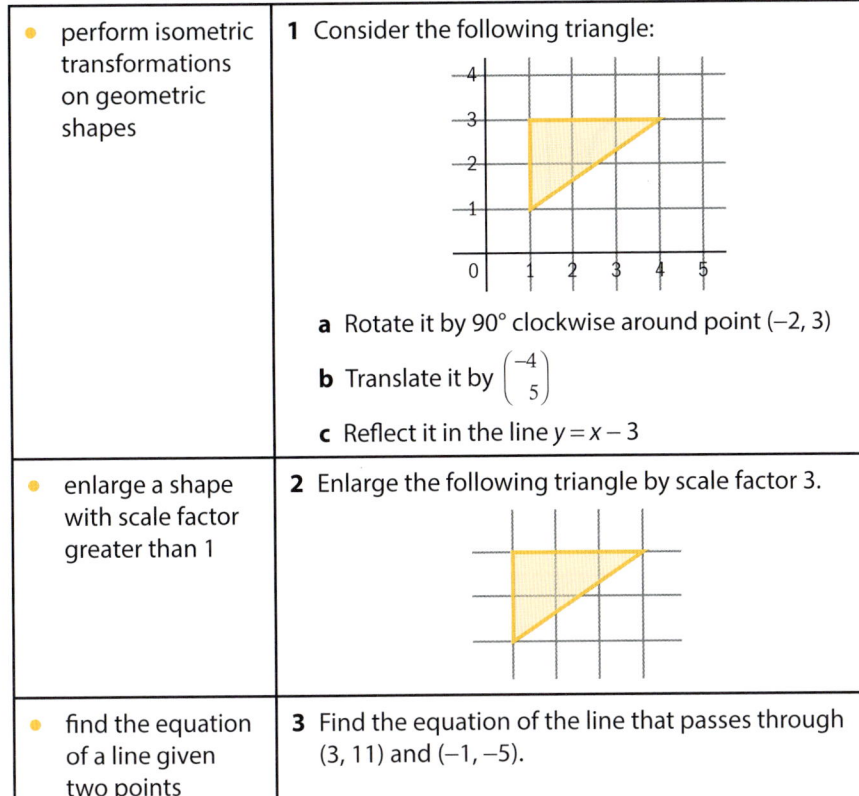 **a** Rotate it by 90° clockwise around point (−2, 3) **b** Translate it by $\begin{pmatrix} -4 \\ 5 \end{pmatrix}$ **c** Reflect it in the line $y = x - 3$
• enlarge a shape with scale factor greater than 1	**2** Enlarge the following triangle by scale factor 3.
• find the equation of a line given two points	**3** Find the equation of the line that passes through (3, 11) and (−1, −5).

> Geometry graphing software would be very useful throughout this question cycle.

F Dilations and similar shapes

- What are dilations?
- What are similar shapes?

Recall the following geometric transformations:

- **Isometric transformations** are the geometric transformations that change the position, the direction and the orientation of a figure, but not its size. These transformations include **translations**, **rotations** and **reflections**.

- A **dilation** is not an isometric transformation, because it changes the size of a figure, but not its shape. Dilations include **enlargements** and **reductions** in size.

- Two objects are **congruent** when they are the same shape and size. They are **similar** when they are the same shape but have a different size.

Exploration 1

1 Draw the following figures on a squared sheet of paper.

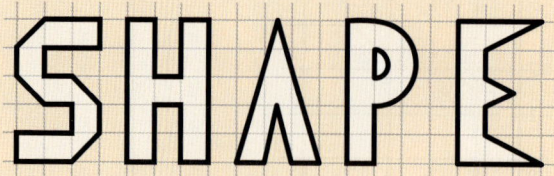

2 Draw each letter enlarged by a scale factor of 1.5, 2, 2.5, 3, and 4 (choose a different scale factor for each one).

3 Compare the lengths of the edges of each figure with the corresponding edges in the enlarged figure.

4 Compare the angles in each figure with the corresponding angles in the enlarged figure.

Two figures are **similar** when:

- the corresponding angles are equal in both figures, **and**
- all the lengths of one figure are multiplied by the same scale factor to obtain the corresponding lengths in the second figure.

A dilation is determined by a **scale factor**, that is the ratio of the corresponding sides of the original figure and its image. If the scale factor is larger than 1, the image is an **enlargement**; if the scale factor is smaller than 1 (but greater than 0), the image is a **reduction**.

Example 1

Draw the following shape when it is reduced by scale factor $\frac{2}{3}$.

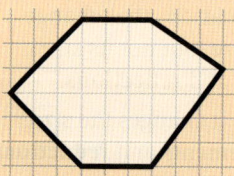

Since the scale factor is positive and smaller than 1, the transformation is a reduction (the transformed figure is smaller than the original figure).

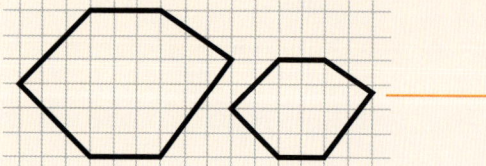

The length of each side of the original figure is multiplied by $\frac{2}{3}$ to obtain the reduced image.

Example 2

Justify whether the following pairs of shapes are similar. If they are, determine the scale factor of the dilation.

a

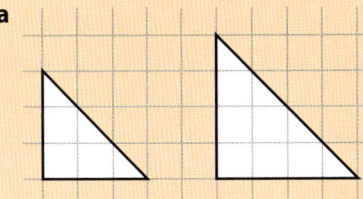

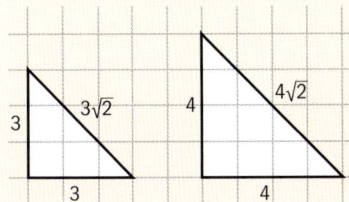

> Use the squares on the paper to help determine the lengths of each side. You might find the Pythagorean theorem useful for the diagonal lines.

The triangle on the right is an enlargement by a scale factor of $\frac{4}{3}$ of the triangle on the left.

> Each side of the triangle is multiplied by the same ratio of $\frac{4}{3}$. We know that it is an enlargement (and not a reduction) because the scale factor is larger than 1.

b

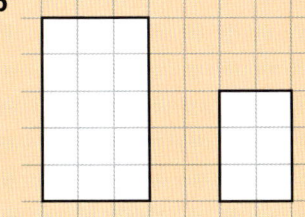

> The ratio of the heights of the rectangles is $\frac{3}{5}$, but the ratio of their widths is $\frac{2}{3}$.

Since the scale factors for different lengths are not the same for corresponding sides of the two figures, the shapes are not similar.

Practice 1

1 A rectangle has side lengths 2 cm and 8 cm. It is enlarged with scale factor 1.25. Draw the original rectangle and the enlarged rectangle.

2 Consider the following five triangles A, B, C, D and E:

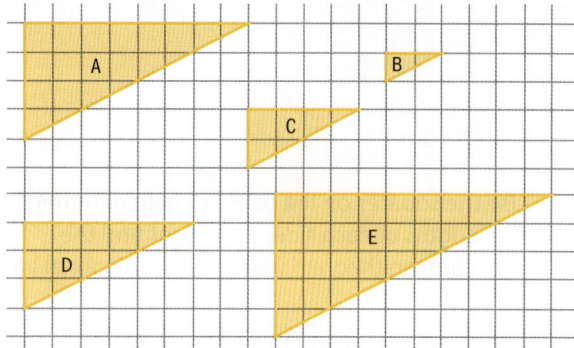

Determine the scale factor for each of the following dilations:

a Triangle B is dilated to triangle E

b Triangle C is dilated to triangle A

c Triangle A is dilated to triangle C

d Triangle A is dilated to triangle B

e Triangle C is dilated to triangle D

f Triangle D is dilated to triangle C

g Triangle D is dilated to triangle E

h Triangle E is dilated to triangle A

i Triangle A is dilated to triangle E

j Triangle E is dilated to triangle C

3 Consider the following quadrilaterals.

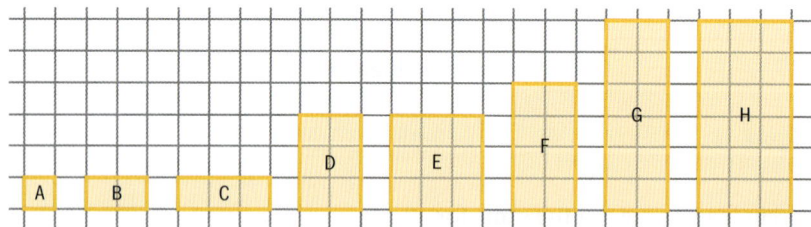

a Group them by similarity.

b For each group of similar figures, find the scale factor of each dilation.

Problem solving

4 Draw the following shape A on squared paper.

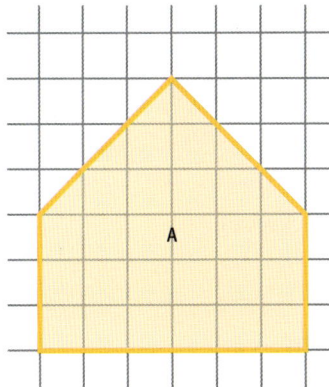

a Draw and label the following shapes on the same page:

  i Shape B is a dilation of A by scale factor 2

  ii Shape C is a dilation of A by scale factor $\frac{1}{2}$

  iii Shape D is a dilation of A by scale factor $\frac{2}{3}$

  iv Shape E is a dilation of A by scale factor $\frac{4}{3}$

b Determine the scale factor when shape C is dilated to shape D.

c Determine the scale factor when shape E is dilated to shape C.

C   More on geometric transformations

- Does position in space matter when transforming shapes?
- How do you rotate a line by 90°?
- How do geometric transformations compare to function transformations?

Exploration 2

1 Discuss how the position of a transformed figure is determined by each of the following transformations. Explain how the parameters of each transformation affect the position of the image.

   a A translation by $\begin{pmatrix} x \\ y \end{pmatrix}$.

   b A rotation of $d°$ in either direction (clockwise or counterclockwise) about a center of rotation $C(a, b)$.

   c A reflection in the mirror line $y = mx + c$.

2 Discuss why, until now, for a dilation by a scale factor r when $0 < r < 1$ and when $r > 1$, the positions of the original shape and the dilated shape are arbitrary.

3 Copy the following figure F1 on a coordinate plane on squared paper.

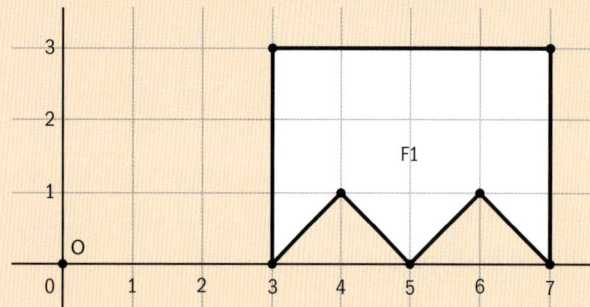

   a Draw the point $O(0, 0)$ at the origin.

      i For each point on the figure, measure its distance from O, and draw a point that is 3 times that distance from O in the same direction. All three points must be aligned each time.

      ii Connect the points you have just plotted and compare the new figure with the original figure. Label the new figure F2.

      iii Fully describe the transformation that was applied to the original figure to obtain the new figure.

   b Repeat steps a i–iii using the point $A(1, 3)$ instead of the origin, and label the new figure F3 (you may want to use a different colour).

   c Repeat the same steps again using the point $B(10, 4)$, and label the new figure F4.

   d Determine whether figures F2, F3 and F4 are enlargements of F1 and what the scale factor is.

   e Discuss how the position of points O, A and B determine the position of each enlargement.

> Geometry graphing software would be really helpful for this exploration.

> If you are using geometry software, draw the figure F1 and the point $O(0, 0)$, and then use the 'dilate from a point' tool (or equivalent) to create figure F2.

> On the geometry software, simply move the point from O to $A(1, 3)$ and then to $B(10, 4)$ and see what happens to the figure F2.

▶ Continued on next page

4 Copy the following triangle T1 on a coordinate plane on squared paper.

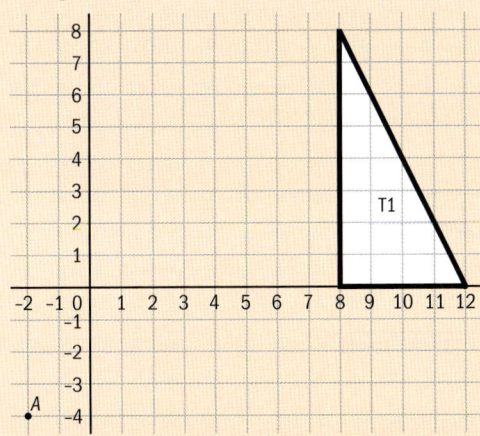

a Draw the point $A(-2, -4)$.

i Draw the triangle that is a reduction of scale factor $\frac{1}{4}$ from A in the same way as you drew the enlargements in the previous question. Label the new triangle T2. ─────────────

ii Draw the triangle that is a reduction of scale factor 0.5 from A. Label the new triangle T3.

iii Draw the triangle that is a reduction of scale factor $\frac{3}{4}$ from A. Label the new triangle T4.

b Discuss how the position of point A determines the position of each reduction.

> On the geometry software, draw triangle T1 and, without moving the point A, use the 'dilate from a point' tool (or equivalent) to create each of the triangles T2, T3 and T4.

There are two types of dilation:

- A dilation with only a scale factor r: each length in the original figure is multiplied by r to obtain the dilated figure.
- A dilation with a scale factor r and a **center of dilation** $C(x, y)$ (also called a **center of enlargement**): the distance from C to each point in the original figure is multiplied by r to obtain the dilated figure.

When there is a center of dilation C, the position of the figure is determined by C and r. If there is no center of dilation given, then the position is arbitrary.

Reflect and discuss 1

Until now, you have looked at scale factors that are either between 0 and 1, or greater than 1. Can the scale factor also be negative? What would this mean?

ATL

Exploration 3

Consider the following triangle and the point $C(3, 3)$ as the center of dilation.

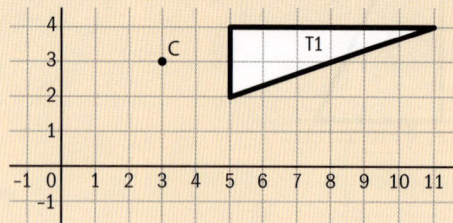

1 Explain why a dilation of triangle T1 by scale factor $r = 1$ around the point C generates exactly the same triangle.

2 Triangle T2 is obtained by a dilation of triangle T1 by scale factor $r = -1$ around the point C.

   a Draw triangle T2.

   b Fully describe a different transformation that also transforms T1 to T2.

3 Triangle T3 is obtained by a dilation of triangle T1 by scale factor $r = -2$ around the point C. Draw triangle T3.

4 Triangle T4 is obtained by a dilation of triangle T1 by scale factor $r = -\frac{1}{2}$ around the point C. Draw triangle T4.

5 Determine whether it is possible to transform T1 to obtain triangles T3 and T4 by using different transformations than the dilations previously used. Is it possible with a single transformation? Or with a combination of transformations?

6 Explain why it is necessary to have a center of dilation to dilate a figure by a negative scale factor.

> On the geometry software, draw triangle T1 and, without moving the point C, use the 'dilate from a point' tool (or equivalent) to create each of the triangles T2, T3 and T4.

Reflect and discuss 2

- When is position important for a dilation?
- When is the center of dilation necessary? When is it not necessary?
- How does the center of rotation compare to the center of dilation?

When the scale factor of a dilation is negative, the image is on the *opposite* side of the center of dilation. For this reason, a negative scale factor requires a center of dilation, otherwise the dilation is not possible.

A dilation with scale factor r, where $r < 0$, is an enlargement if $|r| > 1$ or a reduction if $0 < |r| < 1$. Here, $|r|$ indicates the size of the dilated figure, whereas the sign of r determines whether the dilated figure is on the same side or opposite side of the center of dilation.

Example 3

Dilate the following shape around point $C(6, 4)$ and by a scale factor of -2.

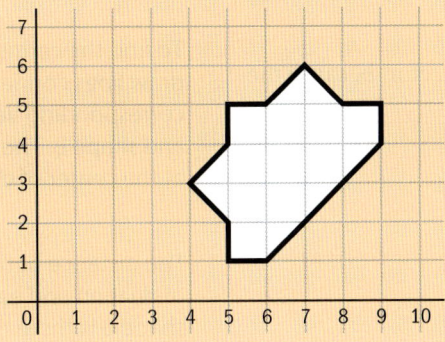

Draw the point $C(6, 4)$.

For each vertex in the shape:

- Measure its distance to C.
- Draw a point on the opposite side of C that is double this distance from C.
- Make sure the corresponding vertices and point C are all colinear.

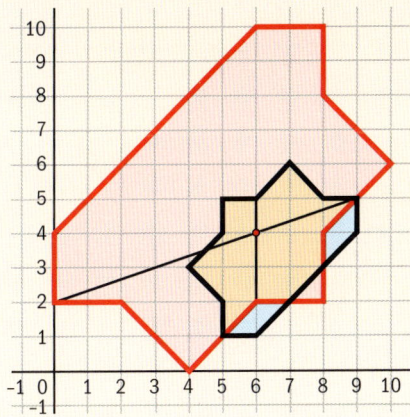

Example 4

In the following diagrams, show how shape A has been dilated to create shape B. Determine the center of dilation and the scale factor for each one.

a

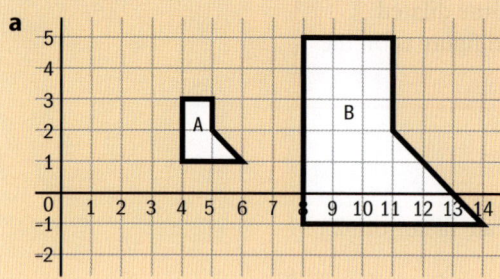

The dilation from A to B has a positive scale factor, because the shapes have the same orientation.

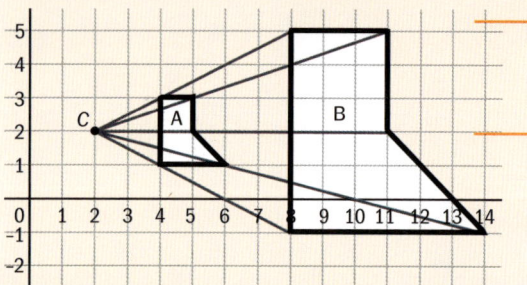

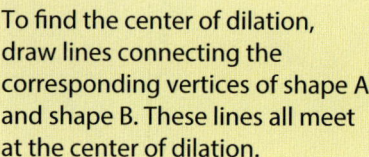

To find the center of dilation, draw lines connecting the corresponding vertices of shape A and shape B. These lines all meet at the center of dilation.

The distance between the center of dilation and each vertex of shape B is three times the distance between the center of dilation and each corresponding vertex of shape A.

The center of dilation is (2, 2) and the scale factor is 3.

b

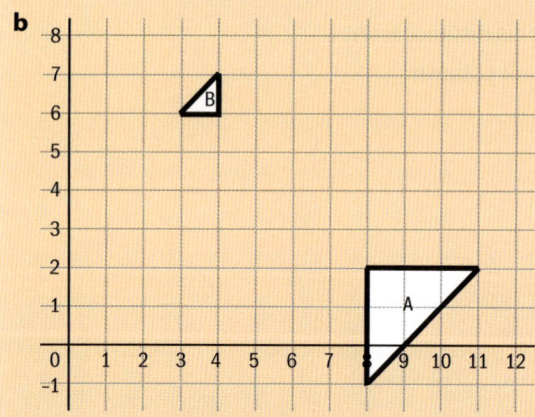

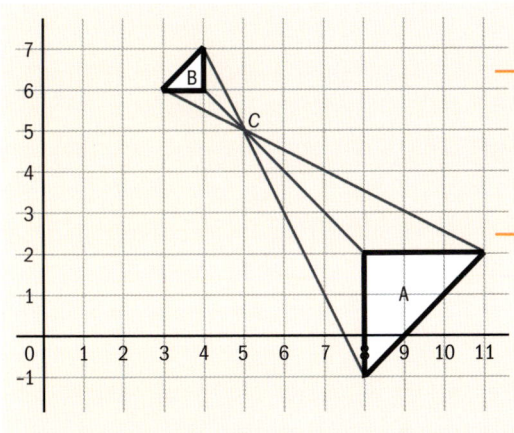

The dilation from A to B has a negative scale factor, because the shapes do not have the same orientation.

The distance between C and each point on shape B is $\frac{1}{3}$ the distance between C and the corresponding points on shape A.

The center of dilation is (5, 5) and the scale factor is $-\frac{1}{3}$.

Practice 2

1 Draw the following shape on squared paper.

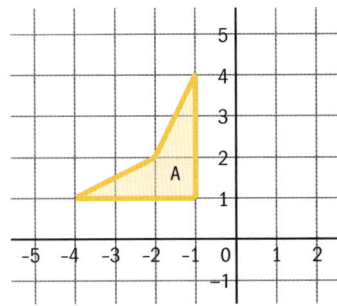

Then draw the following dilated shapes on the same diagram:

a B: Dilation of scale factor 2 from $P(1, 2)$

b C: Dilation of scale factor 3 from $P(1, 2)$

c D: Dilation of scale factor 4 from $P(1, 2)$

2 Draw the following shape on squared paper.

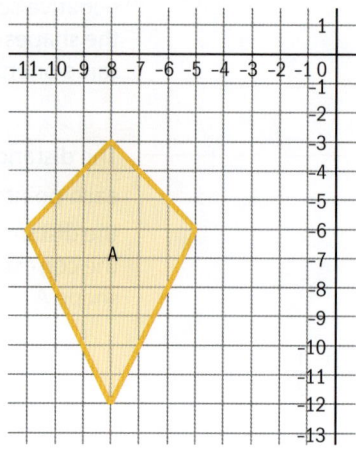

Then draw the following dilated shapes on the same diagram:

a B: Dilation of scale factor $\frac{1}{2}$ from $P(13, 0)$

b C: Dilation of scale factor $\frac{1}{4}$ from $P(13, 0)$

c D: Dilation of scale factor $\frac{1}{3}$ from $P(13, 0)$

d E: Dilation of scale factor $\frac{2}{3}$ from $P(13, 0)$

3 Draw the following shape on squared paper.

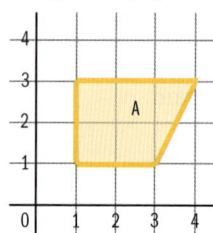

Then draw the following dilated shapes on the same diagram:

a B: Dilation of scale factor -1 from $P(-2, 2)$

b C: Dilation of scale factor -2 from $P(-2, 2)$

c D: Dilation of scale factor -3 from $P(-2, 2)$

d E: Dilation of scale factor $-\frac{1}{2}$ from $P(-2, 2)$

Problem solving

4 In the following diagram, shape A has been dilated four times to create shapes B, C, D and E. For each dilation, determine the center of dilation and the scale factor.

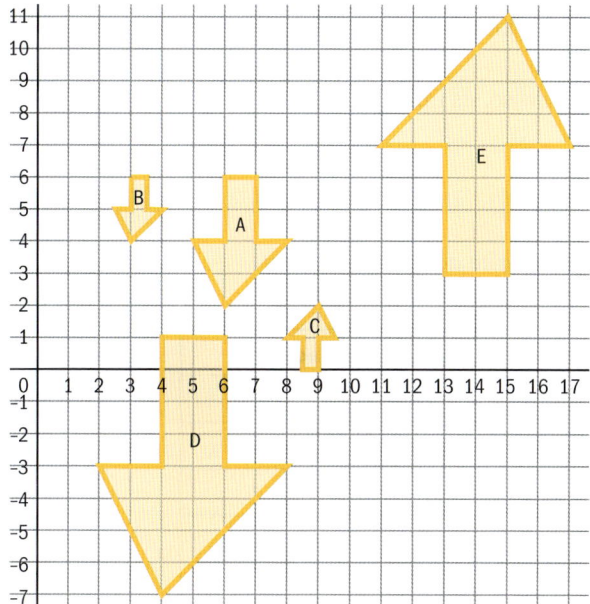

You may find a protractor useful.

Exploration 4

1 For each of the five points in the table below, find the coordinates of its image after each rotation about the origin.

Original point	Point rotated 90° clockwise around (0, 0)	Point rotated 90° counterclockwise around (0, 0)	Point rotated 180° around (0, 0)
A(5, 3)	A'(_ , _)	A"(_ , _)	A'''(_ , _)
B(2, 4)	B'(_ , _)	B"(_ , _)	B'''(_ , _)
C(−1, 6)	C'(_ , _)	C"(_ , _)	C'''(_ , _)
D(−5, −1)	D'(_ , _)	D"(_ , _)	D'''(_ , _)
E(2, −3)	E'(_ , _)	E"(_ , _)	E'''(_ , _)

2 Compare the coordinates of each point with the coordinates of its image after each rotation around the origin.

3 Generalize your findings in the last row of the table with original point $P(a, b)$ where $a, b \in \mathbb{R}$.

For $a, b \in \mathbb{R}$:

- When a point $P(a, b)$ is rotated 90° clockwise around the origin, its image is the point $P'(b, -a)$.
- When a point $P(a, b)$ is rotated 90° counterclockwise around the origin, its image is the point $P'(-b, a)$.
- When a point $P(a, b)$ is rotated 180° clockwise, its image is the point $P'(-b, -a)$.

ATL

Exploration 5

1 For each pair of points in the table below, write down the gradient between the two points in the second column.

Use squared paper to plot the points on a graph.

Two points	Gradient	Perpendicular gradient
$A(0, 0) - B(1, 4)$		
$C(2, 3) - D(8, 6)$		
$E(-1, -4) - F(3, 8)$		
$G(2, -6) - H(-1, 0)$		
$I(3, 3) - J(0, 4)$		

2 For each pair of points, find the perpendicular gradient and complete the third column.

Draw the perpendicular lines on the same graph.

3 Compare each gradient with its perpendicular gradient.

4 Multiply each gradient by the perpendicular gradient. What do you notice?

For $m \in \mathbb{R}, m \neq 0$:

- The product of perpendicular gradients is -1.
- If the gradient of one line is m, then the gradient of its perpendicular is $-\dfrac{1}{m}$.

Reflect and discuss 3

- Does the relationship between perpendicular gradients hold true for horizontal and vertical lines?

Example 5

Find the equation of the line l_1 that passes through the point $S(3, 7)$ and is perpendicular to the line $l_2: 3x + 2y + 2 = 0$. Give your answer in the form $ax + by + c = 0$, $a, b, c \in \mathbb{Z}$, $a > 0$

$l_2 : y = -\dfrac{3}{2}x - 1$	Write the line in slope–intercept form to find the gradient of the line.
$m_1 = \dfrac{2}{3}$	The gradient m_1 is the negative reciprocal of the perpendicular gradient m_2.
$l_1 : y - 7 = \dfrac{2}{3}(x - 3)$	The point–gradient form for a straight line is $y - y_1 = m(x - x_1)$.
$l_1 : y = \dfrac{2}{3}x + 5$	
$l_1 : 2x - 3y + 15 = 0$	Give your answer in the required form.

Practice 3

1 Justify whether each of the following lines is perpendicular to the line $y = 6x - 3$.

 a $y = -6x + 2$

 b $y = \dfrac{1}{6}x - 3$

 c $x + 6y = 12$

 d $y = 4 - \dfrac{1}{6}x$

 e $3x + 18y = 7$

 f $12y = 2x + 15$

2 Find the equation of the line that passes through the point $(-3, 3)$ and is perpendicular to the line $y = 3x + 2$.

3 Find the equation of the line that passes through the point $(3, 5)$ and is perpendicular to the line $x + y = 6$. Write the equation of the line in the form $ax + by + c = 0$, $a, b, c \in \mathbb{Z}$, $a > 0$.

4 Find the equation of the line that passes through the point $(1, 1)$ and is perpendicular to the line $\dfrac{9}{16}x + \dfrac{3}{4}y = 1$. Write the equation of the line in the form $ax + by + c = 0$, $a, b, c \in \mathbb{Z}$, $a > 0$.

Problem solving

5 Line l_1 passes through the point (4, 7) and has y-intercept (0, −5). Line l_2 is perpendicular to l_1 and has y-intercept (0, 5). Find the point of intersection of l_1 and l_2.

6 The coordinates of points A, B and C are (8, −1), (2, 2) and (x, 6) respectively. Find the value of x when AB is perpendicular to BC.

7 Quadrilateral $DEFG$ has vertices D(7, 6), E(13, 2), F(11, −1) and G(5, 3). Determine whether it is a rectangle. Justify your answer.

Reflect and discuss 4

How do graph transformations of functions compare to geometric transformations of shapes? How are they similar? How are they different?

You studied transformations of functions in section E3.1.

D   Dilations across different planes

- How can shapes change size if the center of dilation is not in the same plane as the object?

Until now, the center of dilation was always in the same plane as the dilated figures. What happens when the center of dilation is not in the same plane as the figure?

Exploration 6

1 Consider the following rectangle and the center of dilation C(5, 3) in the middle of the rectangle. Enlarge the rectangle by scale factor 2 from the center of enlargement C.

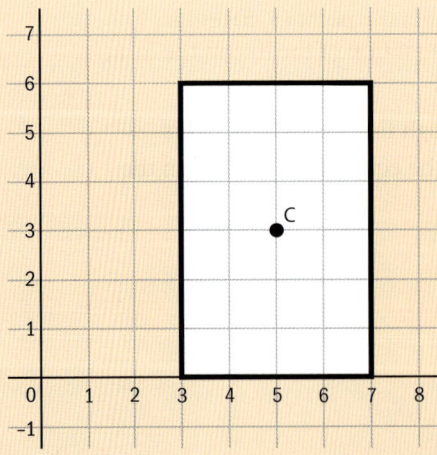

2 Now suppose that the image in question **1** is only a top view, that the rectangle is on the *XY*-plane but point *C* is actually 4 units above the *XY*-plane in the *z*-direction (the third dimension).

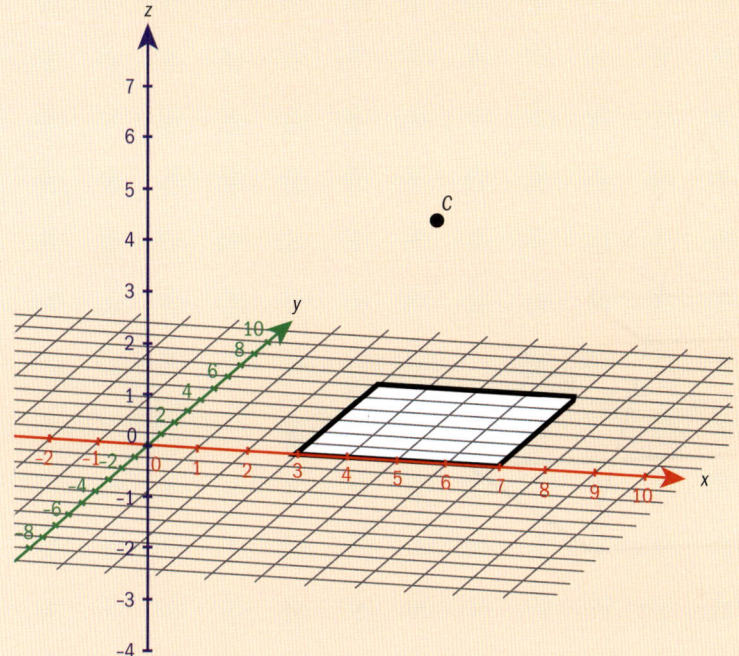

a The 3D coordinates of point *C* are (5, 3, 4). The 3D coordinates of one of the vertices of the rectangle is (3, 0, 0). Write down the 3D coordinates of the other vertices of the rectangle.

The coordinates of a point in 2D are *P*(*x*, *y*). The coordinates of a point in 3D are *P*(*x*, *y*, *z*).

b Determine where the dilated rectangle is if the original rectangle is enlarged by scale factor 2 from the center of enlargement *C*. Write down the 3D coordinates of the four vertices of the transformed rectangle.

For scale factor 2, you can double the distances separately in each dimension.

c Compare coordinates of the four vertices of the transformed rectangle to the corresponding coordinates of the transformed rectangle in question **1**. Determine what the top-view of the enlargement in question **2** looks like.

The top-view is what you see from directly above the *XY*-plane.

d Determine which 3D shape is made up of the transformed rectangle and the line segments that join the center of dilation *C* and each vertex of this rectangle.

▶ Continued on next page

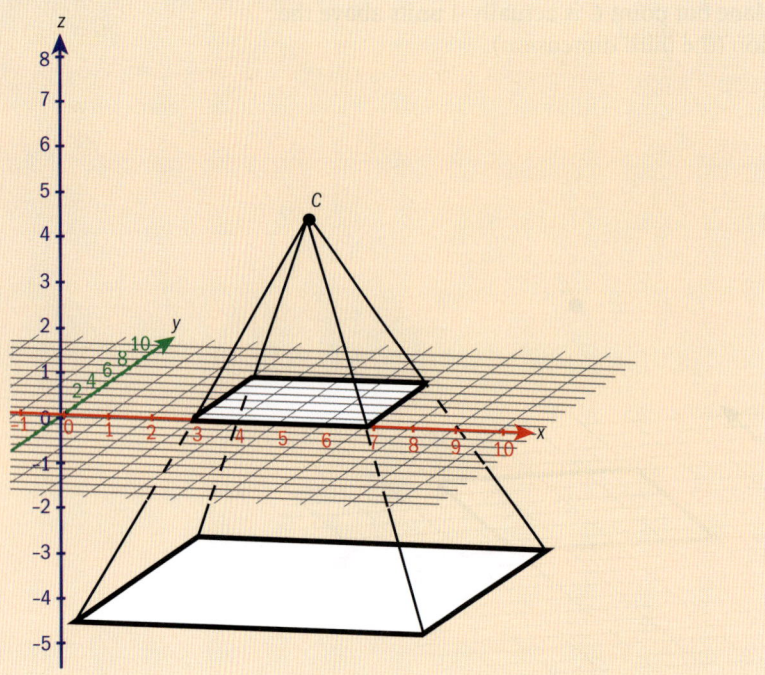

e Suggest why the original rectangle is a cross-section of this 3D shape.

Reflect and discuss 5

- If the lengths of the edges of a shape are multiplied by a scale factor r, by how much is the area of a shape enlarged? By how much is its volume enlarged?

Example 6

1 Consider the following cone. Its vertex is at $C(3, 0, 5)$, its base is the circle C_A with center $A(3, 0, -5)$ and radius 4, and its cross-section in the XY-plane is the circle C_B with center $B(3, 0, 0)$.

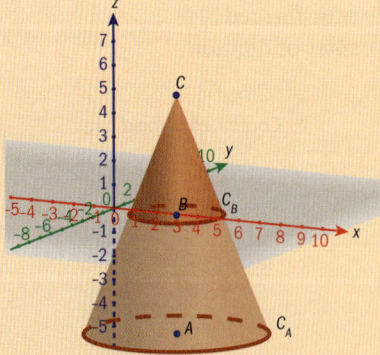

a Determine the center of dilation and scale factor of the reduction of circle C_A to circle C_B.

The center of dilation is the point C. ——————————————— C_A is an enlargement of C_B, or C_B is a reduction of C_A.

The scale factor of the reduction of circle C_A to circle C_B is $\frac{1}{2}$. ——

The distance between C and B is half the distance between C and A.

b Determine the radius of the circle with center B that is the cross-section of the cone on the XY-plane.

Since the radius of C_A is 4, and since C_B is a reduction by scale factor $\frac{1}{2}$ of C_A, then the radius of C_A must be $\frac{1}{2}$ of 4, which is 2.

This is the top-view of the same cone.

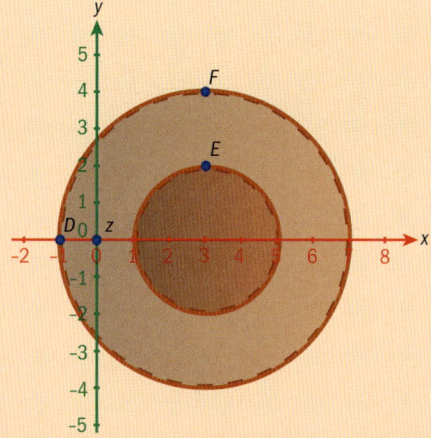

c Find the coordinates of points D, E and F if D and F are on circle C_A and E is on circle C_B.

Circle C_A is on the plane $z = -5$, so the z-coordinate of all the points on C_A is -5. Since C_A has radius 4 and center $A(3, 0, -5)$, we can deduce that the coordinates of D are $D(-1, 0, -5)$.

Point F is also on circle C_A so its z-coordinate is also -5. Since it is also a distance of 4 from center $A(3, 0, -5)$, we can deduce that the coordinates of F are $F(3, 4, -5)$.

Point E is on circle C_B so its z-coordinate is 0. Since C_B is a reduction by $\frac{1}{2}$ of C_A, the radius of circle C_B must be half of the radius of circle C_A. The radius of C_B is 2, so we can deduce that the coordinates of E are $E(3, 2, 0)$.

e Find the image G of point D when it is reduced by scale factor $\frac{1}{2}$ from point C.

Each coordinate of point G is half the distance away from C than D. $C(3, 0, 5)$ and $D(-1, 0, -5)$. This means that G is in the middle between C and D.

The middle between x_C and x_D is 1, so $x_G = 1$.

The middle between x_C and y_D is 0, so $y_G = 0$.

The middle between x_C and z_D is 0, so $z_G = 0$.

Thus, the coordinates of G are $G(1, 0, 0)$.

f C_I is the image of circle C_A after it is dilated by scale factor $-\frac{1}{2}$ around the same point $C(3, 0, 5)$. Find the coordinates of the center I of C_I and sketch C_I along with circle C_A, circle C_B and point C.

Since the scale factor is negative, the image C_I is $\frac{1}{2}$ the distance of C_A from point C, but in the opposite direction. Since the distance between C and A is 10, the distance between C and I must be 5 (which is $\frac{1}{2}$ of 10) but on the other side of C. So the coordinates of I are $I(3, 0, 10)$.

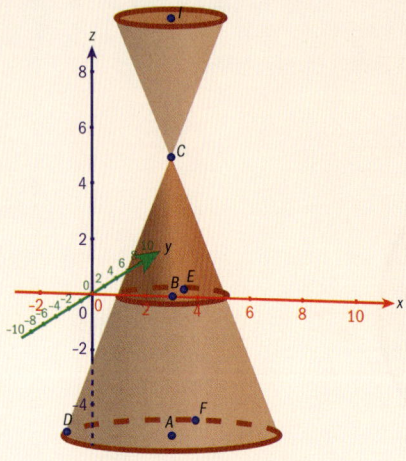

Practice 4

1   A pinhole camera is one way to observe the Sun without looking directly at it. It consists of a box with a small hole in the middle of one of its faces. The light from an object goes through the hole and the image of the object is projected on the opposite face inside the box.

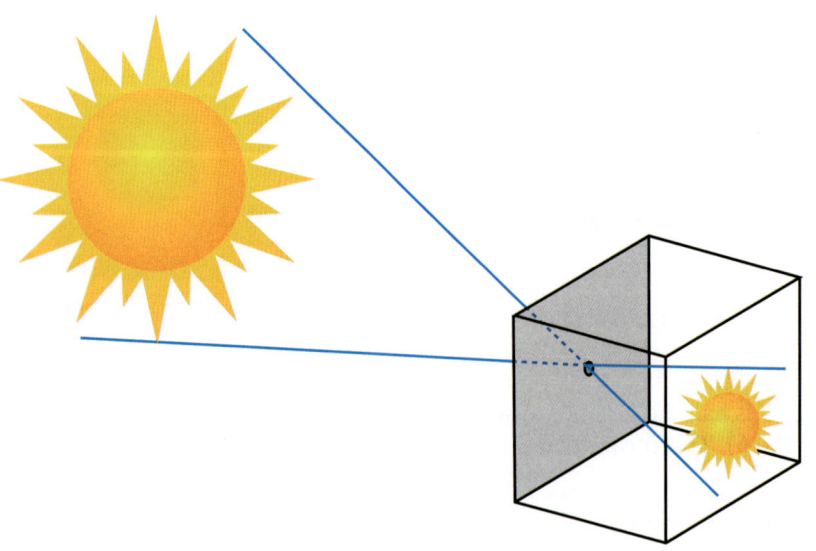

a Explain how this situation is like a dilation.

b State where the center of dilation is in a pinhole camera.

c Justify why the scale factor of the dilation is negative.

The radius of the Sun is 696 340 km and the distance between the Sun and the face of the Earth is 151.82 million km. The pinhole camera is a cubic box that has edges of length 1 m.

d Determine the scale factor of the dilation of the Sun to its image in the pinhole camera.

e Determine the radius of the image of the Sun on the inside of the box.

f Justify why the image of the Sun would be upside down compared to the original image (although it would be difficult to tell it was upside down!).

> The negative is upside down, so that when multiplied by a negative scale factor it becomes right-side up.

2 Before the era of digital photography, film cameras were used. Such a camera 'prints' the image on a transparent film (called a *negative*). Once the negative image is ready, it is placed in a machine called an *enlarger* (below). A light source above the negative film sends light through the film and through a lens, and an enlarged image is then projected onto the table below. A light-sensitive paper is placed on the table, and it is exposed to the light coming from the other side of the negative for a short amount of time (usually seconds). This paper (which will still look blank at this point) is then dipped into different chemical baths to reveal the image and fix it, becoming what we know as a *photograph*.

> The reason it is called a *negative* film is because the light colours appear as dark colours on the film, and vice versa. Thus, when light passes through the film, less light passes through the darker areas, leaving the corresponding areas lighter on the photograph. When light passes through a lighter area on the negative, it 'burns' the light-sensitive paper, creating a corresponding darker area on the photograph.

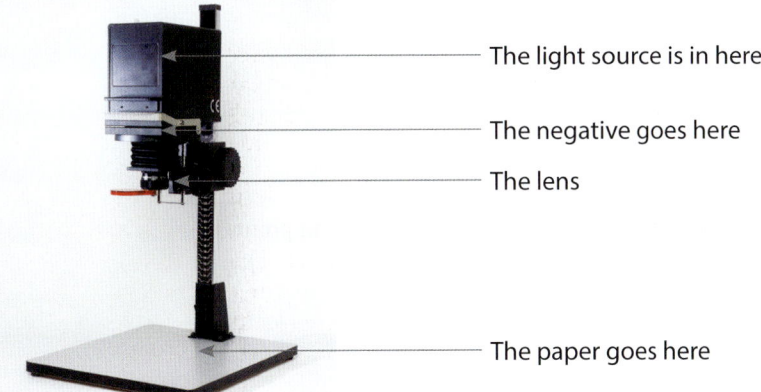

The light source is in here

The negative goes here

The lens

The paper goes here

On the right is a model of an enlarger used to print photos before current digital printing techniques. The light rays travel from the negative image to the enlarged image (the photograph) on the table.

The vertical distance between the negative and the lens is 10 cm, and the distance between the lens and the table is 50 cm.

a State where the center of dilation is in such an enlarger.

b Determine the scale factor when the negative image is enlarged to the photograph using this enlarger.

c The format of the negative used is 24 mm × 36 mm. Determine the maximum size of the printed image using this enlarger (assuming that photo paper of any size is available).

d Suggest why the machine is called an *enlarger*, and what this says about the scale factor.

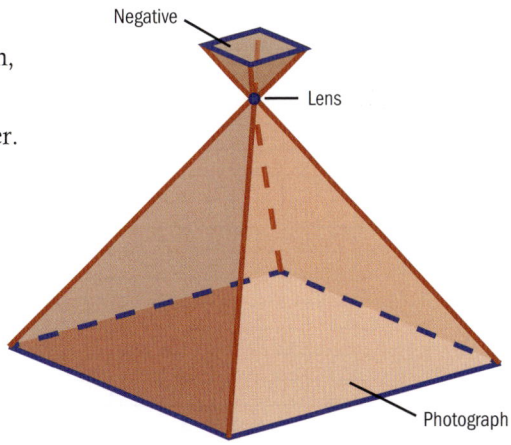

Negative

Lens

Photograph

Reflect and discuss 6

- How is the idea of enlarging a 3D object different to the idea of enlarging a 2D object about a point not within the plane?

Summary

Two figures are **similar** when:

- the corresponding angles are equal in both figures, and
- all the lengths of one figure are multiplied by the same scale factor to obtain the corresponding lengths in the second figure.

A **dilation** is determined by a **scale factor** r, that is the ratio of the corresponding sides of the original figure and its image.

- If $|r| > 1$, the image is an **enlargement**.
- If $0 < |r| < 1$, the image is a **reduction**.

Two types of dilations are possible:

- In a dilation with only a scale factor r, each length in the original figure is multiplied by r to obtain the dilated figure. In this case $r > 0$.

- In a dilation with a scale factor r and a **center of dilation** (or **center of enlargement**) $C(x, y)$, the distance from C to each point in the original figure is multiplied by r to obtain the dilated figure. In this case, $r \in \mathbb{R}$, $r \neq 0$.

A dilation with a negative scale factor requires a center of dilation (unlike a positive scale factor).

- $|r|$ indicates the size of the dilated figure.
- The sign or r determines whether the dilated figure is on the same side or opposite side of the center of dilation.

Mixed practice

1 The following star shape (A) is created by connecting the following points in the order given : (1, 1), (2, 2), (1, 2), (2, 0.5), (1.5, 2.5) and back to (1, 1):

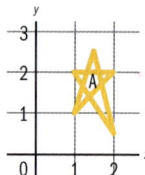

Fully **describe** each transformation of star A.

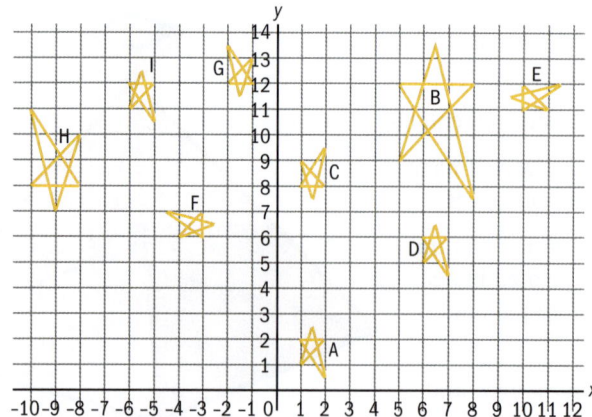

2 Quadrilateral *HIJK* has vertices *H*(−1, 6), *I*(2, 4), *J*(1, 1) and *K*(−2, 3). Determine whether it is a rectangle or not. **Justify** your answer.

3 Determine whether the diagonals of quadrilateral *ABCD* are perpendicular if it has vertices *A*(−1, 5), *B*(1, 4), *C*(1, −1) and *D*(−2, 3). **Justify** your answer.

4 A person is standing in a dark room. A powerful flashlight is 7 m away and projecting her shadow on a wall that is 14 m from her on the other side. The person's height is 176 cm, and the flashlight is 88 cm above the floor.

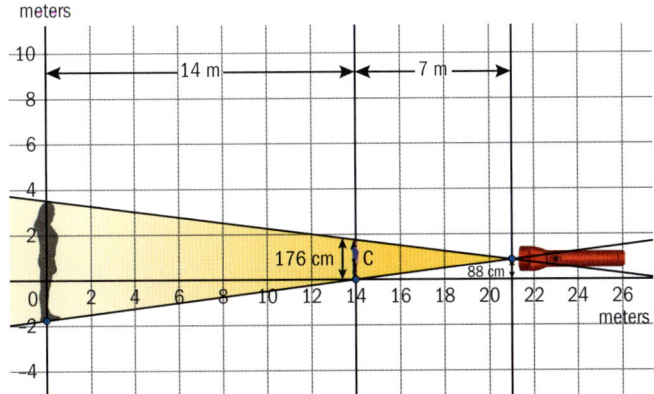

a **Explain** how the situation represents an enlargement.

b Ignoring the floor, if the shadow is floating on a wall with no floor, **find** the height of the shadow (as it would be in the diagram above).

In reality, there is a floor, so the shadow that is seen on the wall will actually be a part of the full shadow. The portion of the shadow that is cut off by the floor is represented in blue in the diagram below.

c **Explain** how the portion in blue is a new situation of dilation, where the center of dilation is the point on the floor where the person is standing.

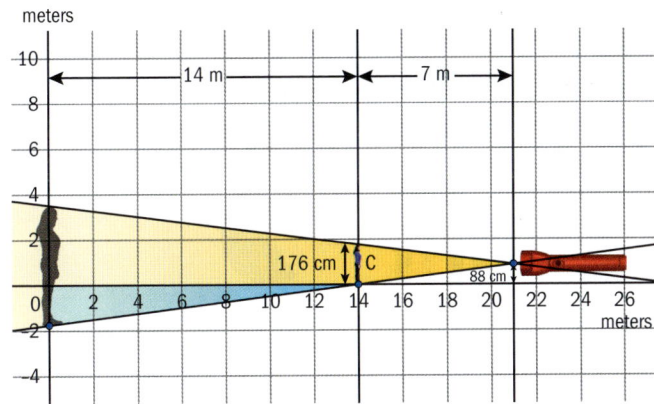

d **Determine** the length of the shadow that is visible above the floor on the wall.

Statement of inquiry:

Representing transformed objects and studying their form helps us enjoy their creativity in space.

Reflect and discuss 7

How have you explored the statement of inquiry? Give specific examples.

Statement of inquiry:

How quantities are represented can help to establish underlying relationships and trends in a population.

Key concept:

Relationships are the connections and associations between properties, objects, people and ideas.
Related concepts: representation, quantity, generalization.

F What makes a good representation?

Representation is the manner in which something is presented.

Representation is a visual presentation of information and can take many forms. It should be eye-catching and meaningful, relevant and purposeful. Its main aim is to present clarity and rigour to the viewer.

- What styles of representation of data can you think of?

- What do you think makes a graph useful?

- What can make a graph misleading?

C How does understanding quantities enable you to make generalizations about trends?

How many fish?

Suppose you want to know the quantity of fish in a lake. How would you go about this investigation? You could drain the lake and count all the dead fish; that would give you an accurate count, but it's not very practical, and not too considerate of the fish either!

One way to estimate the quantity is called the capture–recapture method:

Capture 100 fish, tag them, and then release them back into the lake. Assume that all these fish distribute themselves evenly and randomly throughout the lake.

Later, you capture 100 fish again and find that, of these, 5 are ones that you tagged previously. You know that there are 100 tagged fish in the lake. So how many batches of 100 fish would you need to capture all 100 tagged fish? If you assume you'd catch 5 tagged fish for every 100, then you would have to catch 100/5 = 20 batches. At 100 fish per batch that would mean there are an estimated 20 × 100 = 2000 fish in the lake.

- How many fish would you estimate are in the lake if you recaptured 11 tagged fish?

- What assumptions are being made in this method?

- What conclusion(s) could you draw if none of the fish you caught later on were tagged?

D To what extent does understanding trends and relationships make decision-making more effective?

Global context:
Globalization and sustainability

Exploration:
Analyze trends and the impact of decision-making on the environment

📖 Launch additional digital resources for this unit.

E6.1 Standard deviation

Global context: Globalization and sustainability

Related concept: Representation

Objectives

- Making inferences about data, given the mean and standard deviation
- Using different forms of the standard deviation formula
- Understanding the normal distribution
- Making inferences about normal distributions
- Using the standard deviation and the mean
- Making estimates for a population from a sample

Inquiry questions

F
- How do you calculate the standard deviation of a data set?
- What is the normal distribution?

C
- How is the meaning of 'standard deviation' represented in its different formulae?

D
- Can samples give reliable results?
- Do we want to be like everybody else?

ATL Communication

Make inferences and draw conclusions

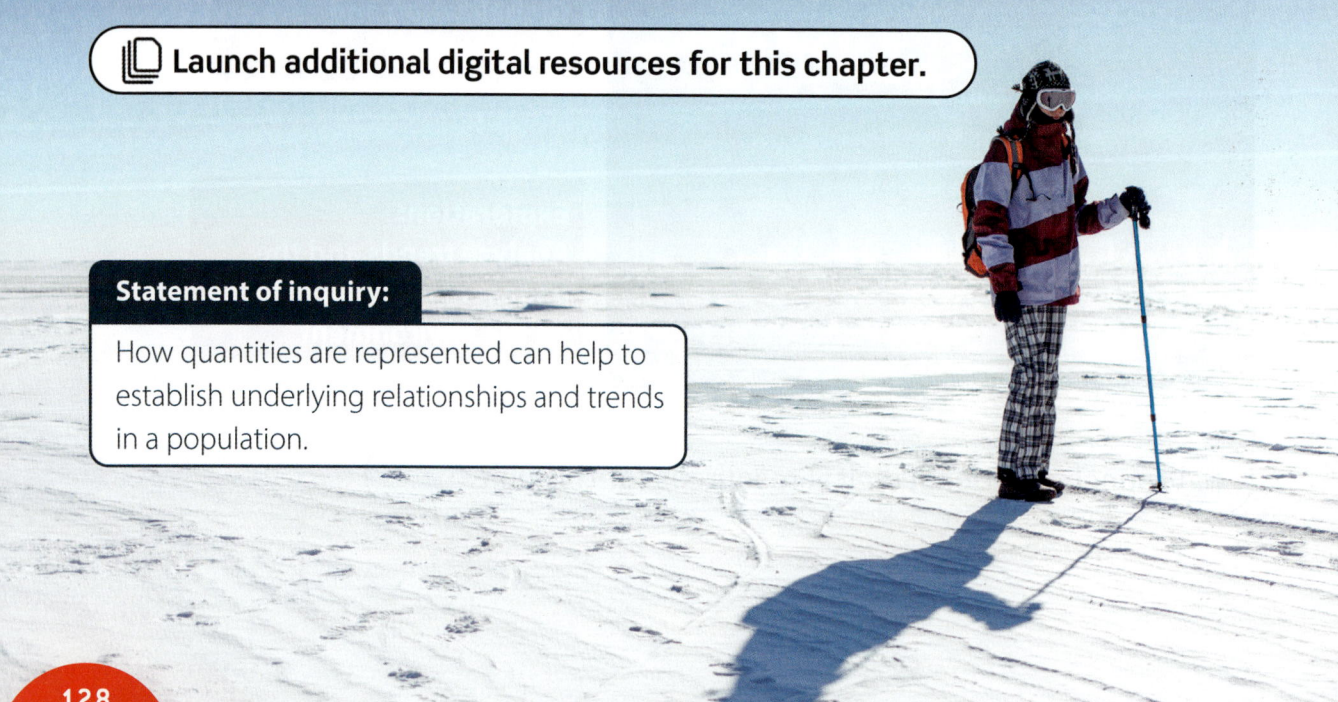

📖 **Launch additional digital resources for this chapter.**

Statement of inquiry:

How quantities are represented can help to establish underlying relationships and trends in a population.

You should already know how to:

• find the mean from frequency tables of discrete and grouped data	**1 a** This table gives the exam grades for 200 students. Calculate the mean grade. | **Grade**	1	2	3	4	5
---	---	---	---	---	---
Frequency	8	29	33	35	95 | **b** This table gives the mass in grams of 80 packets of chia seeds. Calculate an estimate for the mean mass. | **Mass, m (g)**	**Frequency**
$70 \leq m < 75$	10
$75 \leq m < 80$	22
$80 \leq m < 85$	38
$85 \leq m < 90$	10	
• understand the difference between a population and a sample	**2** Define these terms: **a** population **b** sample

 The ultimate measure of dispersion

- How do you calculate the standard deviation of a data set?
- What is the normal distribution?

Exploration 1

The temperature on the first day of the first five months of the year was recorded in La Crieux, France and Betzdorf, Luxembourg.

	Temperature (°C)	
	La Crieux, France	**Betzdorf, Luxembourg**
January	10	18
February	16	10
March	14	13.5
April	12	14
May	18	14.5

▶ Continued on next page

1   For this data, calculate the range and the three measures of central tendency (mean, mode and median). What do you notice?

When two sets of data in an experiment have the same mean and range, there is another statistical measure that you can use to help discover differences between the data sets. You will now explore this measure, called the standard deviation.

2   Copy and complete this table for the La Crieux data.
Calculate the mean of the differences, the mean of the squares of the differences and the square root of the mean of the squares.

Temperature (°C)	Difference between recorded temperature and mean temperature	Square of the difference
10	−4	16
16		
14		
12		
18		
	Mean of differences =	Mean of squares of differences =
		Square root of the mean of squares of differences =

> A tardigrade is a tiny animal that lives in a variety of environments, from the tropics to the polar regions. Also known as a water bears, this tiny creature can withstand temperatures ranging from −273 °C to 150 °C!

3   Determine the units for the mean of squares and for the square root of the mean of squares. Hence, explain why you need to take the square root of the mean of the squares of differences.

4   Decide, with reasons, whether the mean of the differences or the mean of the squares of the differences best represents the difference (deviation) from the mean of the original temperature values.

5   Generalize this algorithm using mathematical notation and vocabulary.

Reflect and discuss 1

- Why do we square the differences between the data and the mean?

- Squaring large numbers makes them even larger. How does that impact the mean? Why is that important?

In Exploration 1, squaring the differences from the mean gives positive values to represent the deviation from the mean. It also gives more weighting to the larger deviations, which is important because the data further away from the mean may be more significant. The square root of the mean of these squared deviations is a measure of dispersion called the standard deviation.

> The **standard deviation** is a measure of dispersion that gives an idea of how close the original data values are to the mean.
>
> A small standard deviation shows that the data values are close to the mean. A large standard deviation shows that the data values are further from the mean. The units of standard deviation are the same as the units of the original data.

The standard deviation shows how representative the mean is of the data.

The notation used for the standard deviation depends on whether it is calculated for a whole population or for a sample. The convention is:

Use Greek letters for populations

- μ = mean of the population
- σ = standard deviation of the population

Use Roman letters for samples

- $\bar{x}$ = mean of the sample
- s_n = standard deviation of the sample

Standard deviation formulae also use the Greek symbol $\sum$ (upper case sigma) to mean 'the sum of'.

> $\sum x$ means the sum of all the x-values.
>
> Using this notation (called sigma notation), the mean of a set of values is $\mu = \dfrac{\sum x}{n}$, the sum of all the values divided by the number of values.

In Exploration 1 you found the standard deviation by calculating:

$(x - \mu)$	the differences between the data values, x, and the mean, μ
$(x - \mu)^2$	the squares of the differences
$\dfrac{\sum (x - \mu)^2}{n}$	the mean of the squares of the differences
$\sqrt{\dfrac{\sum (x - \mu)^2}{n}}$	the square root of the mean of the squares

> A formula to calculate the standard deviation of a population is: $\sigma = \sqrt{\dfrac{\sum (x - \mu)^2}{n}}$

You can calculate standard deviation with your GDC.

Example 1

At a summer carnival, a small crowd of people are trying to guess the mass of a small goat. The first nine people to guess give the following amounts, in kilograms.

18.3, 21.6, 22.2, 24.0, 20.4, 17.4, 14.9, 26.7, 23.1

a Find the mean mass.

b Find the standard deviation of the masses.

c Write down what the standard deviation means in this context.

a Mean $\mu = \dfrac{\sum x}{n} = \dfrac{188.6}{9} = 20.96$ (2 d.p.) —— The nine masses are the population, so use Greek letters.

b $\sigma = \sqrt{\dfrac{\sum (x-\mu)^2}{n}}$ —————— Make a table to organize your calculations.

x	μ	$x - \mu$	$(x - \mu)^2$
18.3	20.96	−2.66	7.07
21.6	20.96	0.64	0.4096
22.2	20.96	1.24	1.5376
24.0	20.96	3.04	9.2419
20.4	20.96	−0.56	0.3136
17.4	20.96	−3.56	12.674
14.9	20.96	−6.06	36.724
26.7	20.96	5.74	32.948
23.1	20.96	2.14	4.5696
			$\sum (x-\mu)^2 = 105.5024$

$n = 9$

$\sigma = \sqrt{\dfrac{\sum (x-\mu)^2}{n}} = \sqrt{\dfrac{105.5024}{9}} = 3.4238 = 3.42$ kg (3 s.f.)

c This implies that the mean mass estimate is 20.96 kilograms, but with a spread of up to 3.42 kilograms heavier or lighter than the mean mass.

No, you are not looking at a photo that has been retouched and you are not seeing things either. This is an Argania tree, almost exclusive to Morocco. The goats who climb these trees do so because of their love for the nuts that grow on the thorny, twisted branches. When the nuts are ripe, the Argania trees are often seen with a dozen or more goats in them at a time.

Practice 1

1 For each set of data, first find the mean and the standard deviation by hand, then with a calculator.

a

2	2	4	4	4
5	6	6	8	9

b

13.1	20.4	17.4	16.5
21.0	14.8	12.6	

c

15 cm	17 cm	14 cm
12 cm	14 cm	18 cm
14 cm	13 cm	18 cm

d

44.3 kg	41.5 kg	36.5 kg
41.0 kg	33.6 kg	41.8 kg
51.2 kg	39.2 kg	37.9 kg

2 The duration, in minutes, for a train journey is recorded on 15 consecutive days:

21	24	30	21	25
27	24	27	25	29
23	22	26	28	29

  a Find the mean and standard deviation of the times for this train journey.

  b State the inferences that you can draw from the data.

3 Beatriz has a choice of routes to school. She timed her journeys along each route on five occasions. The times, recorded to the nearest minute, were:

Motorway	15	16	20	28	21
Country roads	19	21	20	22	18

  a Calculate the mean and standard deviation for each route.

  b State the route you would recommend and explain with reasons.

4 Find the mean and standard deviation of the set of integers 1, 2, 3, 4, …, 15.

5 The heights (in meters), of a squad of 12 basketball players are:

1.65	1.62	1.75	1.80	1.75	1.72
1.81	1.72	1.79	1.63	1.69	1.75

  a Find the mean and standard deviation of the heights of the players.

  b A new player whose height is 1.98 m joins the squad. Find the new mean and standard deviation of the heights of the squad.

ATL

ATL

Problem solving

6 a Calculate the mean and the standard deviation of this set of data:

| 3 | 6 | 7 | 9 | 10 |

Each number in the data set is then increased by 4.

b Predict what will happen to the mean and standard deviation.

c Calculate the new mean and standard deviation.

d Comment on your answers.

One of the numbers in the original data set has changed, so the data set is now: 3, 6, 7, 9, x. The new mean, y, is unknown but the standard deviation is known to be $\sqrt{34}$.

e Calculate the two possible values of the unknown values x and y.

Using $\sum$ notation, the **mean** of a set of discrete data values in a frequency table is $\dfrac{\sum fx}{n}$. This is the sum of all the fx values divided by the total frequency.

In different books xf and fx are interchangeable. Both ways of writing are equally valid.

A formula to calculate the standard deviation for discrete data presented in a frequency table is:

$$\sigma = \sqrt{\dfrac{\sum f(x-\mu)^2}{n}}$$

Reflect and discuss 2

How is the formula for the standard deviation of discrete data in a frequency table similar to the formula for the standard deviation of a population? How is it different?

Example 2

The scores for 25 players in a golf tournament are given in this frequency table. Find the mean and the standard deviation.

x	f
66	2
67	3
68	4
69	5
70	4
71	4
72	3

▶ Continued on next page

x	f	fx
66	2	132
67	3	201
68	4	272
69	5	345
70	4	280
71	4	284
72	3	216
	$n = 25$	$\sum fx = 1730$

$\mu = \dfrac{1730}{25} = 69.2$ ——————————————————— Use $\mu = \dfrac{\sum fx}{n}$ to find the mean.

x	f	$x - \mu$	$(x - \mu)^2$	$f(x - \mu)^2$
66	2	−3.2	10.24	20.48
67	3	−2.2	4.84	14.53
68	4	−1.2	1.44	5.76
69	5	−0.2	0.04	0.2
70	4	0.8	0.64	2.56
71	4	1.8	3.24	123.96
72	3	2.8	7.84	23.52
	$n = 25$			$\sum f(x - \mu)^2 = 80$

$\sigma = \sqrt{\dfrac{\sum f(x - \mu)^2}{n}} = \sqrt{\dfrac{80}{25}} = 1.789$ ————————— To find the standard deviation, use the formula.

The mean score is 69.2 and the standard deviation is 1.79 (3 s.f.)

Example 3

The table gives the frequency distribution of total penalty minutes in a season for all 20 players on a hockey team. Find the mean and the standard deviation.

Total penalty minutes (t)	Number of players
$0 \leq t < 10$	3
$10 \leq t < 20$	9
$20 \leq t < 30$	6
$30 \leq t < 40$	2

▶ Continued on next page

Total penalty minutes (t)	Mid-value (t)	f	ft
$0 \leq t < 10$	5	3	15
$10 \leq t < 20$	15	9	135
$20 \leq t < 30$	25	6	150
$30 \leq t < 40$	35	2	70
		$n = 20$	$\sum ft = 370$

$\mu = \frac{370}{20} = 18.5$ ⸻ Use $\mu = \frac{\sum fx}{n}$ to calculate an estimate for the mean.

Total penalty minutes (t)	Mid-value (t)	f	$t - \mu$	$(t - \mu)^2$	$f(t - \mu)^2$
$0 \leq t < 10$	5	3	−13.5	182.25	546.75
$10 \leq t < 20$	15	9	−3.5	12.25	110.25
$20 \leq t < 30$	25	6	6.5	42.25	253.5
$30 \leq t < 40$	35	2	16.5	272.25	544.5
		$n = 20$			$\sum f(t - \mu)^2 = 1455$

$\sigma = \sqrt{\dfrac{\sum f(t - \mu)^2}{\sum f}} = \sqrt{\dfrac{1455}{20}} = 8.529$ ⸻ Use the standard deviation formula.

The mean number of penalty minutes is 18.5 and the standard deviation is 8.53 (3 s.f.)

Practice 2

1 Find the mean and the standard deviation for each set of data.

a

x	1	2	3	4	5
f	3	4	4	5	2

b

Interval	1–4	5–8	9–12	13–16	17–20	21–24	25–28
f	2	0	3	3	4	2	1

c

Interval	$0 \leq x < 5$	$5 \leq x < 10$	$10 \leq x < 15$	$15 \leq x < 20$
Frequency	10	12	15	12

2 The masses of 90 cyclists in a bicycle race were recorded:

Mass (kg)	Number of cyclists
$40 \leq m < 50$	8
$50 \leq m < 60$	27
$60 \leq m < 70$	30
$70 \leq m < 80$	25

a Calculate an estimate for

  i the mean mass

  ii the standard deviation.

b A cyclist must wear a weight belt if their mass is 1 standard deviation or more below the mean. Find the minimum mass to compete without a weight belt.

Problem solving

3 Copy and complete this table:

$\sum f$	$\sum fx$	$\sum f(x-\mu)^2$	μ	σ
10	50			$\sqrt{2}$
20			6.15	$\sqrt{2.06}$
	197	80.34	5.05	
43	223	102.34		
		39.56	5	$\sqrt{1.72}$

4 Copy the table below and fill in the missing values. Then calculate the mean and standard deviation for the data.

Length (cm)	Mid-value (x)	f	fx	$x - \mu$	$f(x-\mu)^2$
$0 < x \leq 5$	2.5	3	7.5	-11.4	389.88
$5 < x \leq 10$	7.5	4	30	-6.4	163.84
$10 < x \leq 15$	12.5	6	75	-1.4	
$15 < x \leq 20$	17.5	7	122.5		90.72
$20 < x \leq 25$	22.5			8.6	369.8
		$n =$	$\sum fx = 347.5$		$\sum f(x-\mu)^2 =$

Exploration 2

32 students' test scores were recorded:

Test score	1	2	3	4	5	6	7	8	9
Frequency	1	2	3	6	9	6	3	2	1

1 The data is shown in this histogram. The curve joins the midpoints of the bars. Describe the shape of the curve.

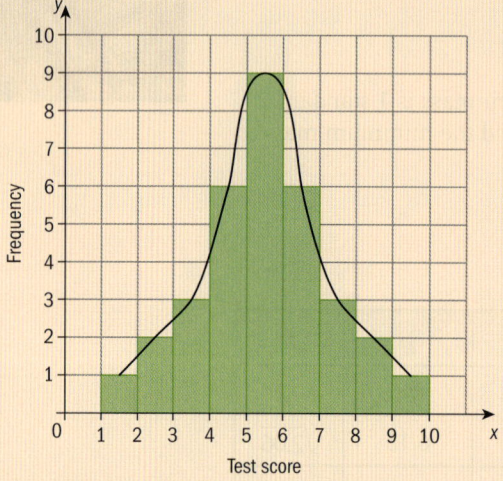

2 Calculate the mean and standard deviation for the data, to 1 d.p.

3 Determine where the mean lies on the curve.

4 From the original data:

   a State how many data items are more than 1 standard deviation from the mean.

   b State how many data items are within 1 standard deviation of the mean.

   c Find the percentage of the data items that are within 1 standard deviation of the mean.

The data in Exploration 2 follows a normal distribution.

The **normal distribution** is a symmetric distribution, with most values close to the mean and tailing off evenly in either direction. Its frequency graph is a bell-shaped curve.

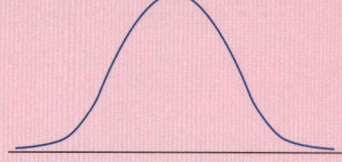

Data on natural attributes, such as height, mass, and age generally follow a normal distribution. The normal frequency distribution curve looks like this:

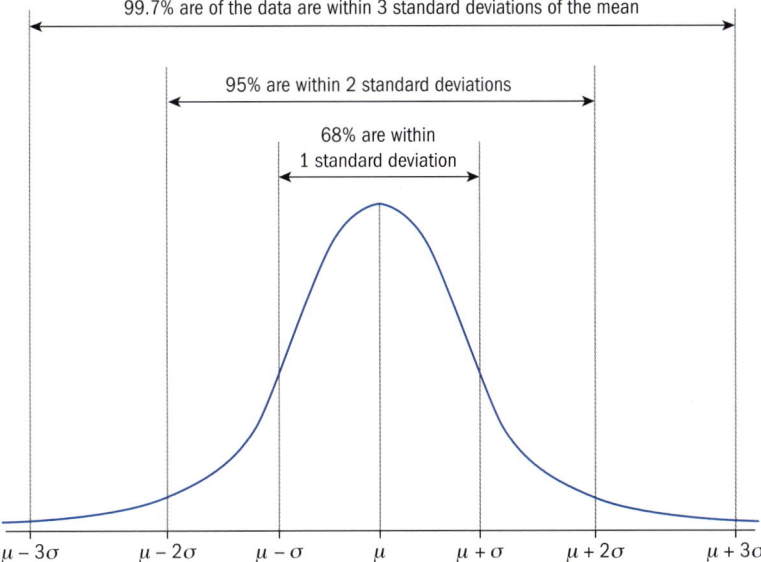

If you know that the frequency distribution follows a normal distribution then you can infer that:

- 68% of the data values lie within ±1 standard deviation of the mean.
- 95% lie within ±2 standard deviations of the mean.
- 99.7% lie within ±3 standard deviations of the mean.

This is extremely useful for making inferences about sets of data.

Reflect and discuss 3

Employees at La Salsa del Erizo have a mean starting salary of €45 000 with a standard deviation of €5000. Employees at rival company La Salsa del Zorro have a mean starting salary of €41 000 with a standard deviation of €8000. Which company would you rather work for?

C Different representations of a formula for different purposes

- How is the meaning of 'standard deviation' represented in its different formulae?

Sometimes you may not be given the whole set of data, but just some summary statistics taken from the raw data. Usually this includes $\sum x$ (the sum of all the data values) and $\sum x^2$ (the sum of the squares of all the data values).

Most GDCs have a summary statistics page, which gives $\sum x$ and $\sum x^2$ when you input a set of data.

Exploration 3

Here are the data values for two populations:

Population 1	**Population 2**
2, 4, 4, 5, 7	4, 6, 9, 10, 11, 14

1 Find μ_1, the mean of Population 1.

2 Find the mean of the squared values of Population 1.

3 Find μ_2, the mean of Population 2.

4 Find the mean of the squared values of Population 2.

5 Generalize your findings using sigma notation:

If $\mu = \dfrac{\sum x}{n}$, then $\mu^2 = $ _____

6 Find μ_{1+2}, the mean of the combined populations (Population 1 + Population 2).

7 Generalize your findings using sigma notation:

$\mu_{1+2} = $ _____

When you can manipulate this mathematical notation (called sigma notation), you can analyse the standard deviation formula and represent it in a variety of ways.

ATL

Exploration 4

1 Start with the formula for the population standard deviation: $\sigma = \sqrt{\dfrac{\sum (x - \mu)^2}{n}}$

2 Expand the numerator: $\sigma = \sqrt{\dfrac{\sum (x^2 - 2\mu x + \mu^2)}{n}}$

3 Distribute the sigma notation: $\sigma = \sqrt{\dfrac{\sum x^2 - \sum 2\mu x + \sum \mu^2}{n}}$

4 Distribute the n: $\sigma = \sqrt{\dfrac{\sum x^2}{n} - \dfrac{\sum 2\mu x}{n} + \dfrac{\sum \mu^2}{n}}$

5 Substitute $\mu = \dfrac{\sum x}{n}$ and $\mu^2 = \dfrac{\sum \mu^2}{n}$.

6 Collect like terms.

7 Substitute $\mu = \dfrac{\sum x}{n}$ again.

8 Write your new formula: $\sigma = $ _____

Reflect and discuss 4

What does your new formula for standard deviation mean?
What information do you need to use to calculate standard deviation?

ATL

Example 4

The length of time t, in minutes, for a skier to travel down a mountain follows a normal distribution and is recorded on 15 runs. The summary statistics are: $\sum x = 129$ and $\sum x^2 = 1181$.

a Find the mean and standard deviation of the times taken for this ski run.

b Make a generalization about the times for the ski run.

a Mean $= \dfrac{\sum x}{n} = \dfrac{129}{15} = 8.6$ min

Standard deviation $\sigma = \sqrt{\dfrac{\sum x^2}{n} - \left(\dfrac{\sum x}{n}\right)^2} = \sqrt{\dfrac{1181^2}{15} - (8.6)^2}$ ⎯⎯⎯⎯⎯⎯⎯⎯⎯⎯⎯ $\left(\dfrac{\sum x}{n}\right)^2 = \mu^2$

$= 2.18$ min

b $8.6 - 2.18 = 6.42$ ⎯⎯⎯⎯⎯⎯⎯⎯⎯⎯⎯⎯⎯⎯⎯⎯⎯⎯⎯⎯⎯⎯⎯

$8.6 + 2.18 = 10.78$

Calculate the values 1 standard deviation on either side of the mean. 68% of the data values lie between these.

68% of the runs will take between 6.42 min and 10.78 min.

ATL

Example 5

The summary statistics for a class of 15 students' test marks are $\sum x = 930$ and $\sum x^2 = 59\,146$.

a Calculate the mean and standard deviation of the marks for this class.

b A second class of 25 students had a mean of 63.5 and standard deviation of 12.5 marks for the same test. Calculate $\sum x^2$ for the second class.

c Calculate the mean mark of all the students in the two classes.

d Compare the performance of the two classes on this test.

(Assume test marks follow a normal distribution.)

a $\mu = \dfrac{930}{15} = 62$ marks ⎯⎯⎯⎯⎯⎯⎯⎯⎯⎯⎯⎯⎯⎯⎯⎯⎯⎯⎯⎯⎯⎯⎯⎯⎯ The mean is $\mu = \dfrac{\sum x}{n}$

$\sigma = \sqrt{\dfrac{\sum x^2}{n} - \left(\dfrac{\sum x}{n}\right)^2} = \sqrt{\dfrac{59\,146}{15} - (62)^2} = 9.95$ marks

▶ Continued on next page

b

$$\sigma = \sqrt{\frac{\sum x^2}{n} - \left(\frac{\sum x}{n}\right)^2}$$

Substitute known values into the formula for σ and solve for $\sum x^2$.

$$12.5 = \sqrt{\frac{\sum x^2}{25} - (63.5)^2}$$

$$156.25 = \frac{\sum x^2}{25} - 4032.25$$

$$4188.5 = \frac{\sum x^2}{25}$$

$$104\,712.5 = \sum x^2$$

c

$$\frac{\sum x_1 + \sum x_2}{n_1 + n_2} = \mu_{1+2}$$

$$\frac{930 + (63.5 \times 25)}{15 + 25} = \mu_{1+2}$$

$$63.5 = \mu_2 = \frac{\sum x_2}{n_2} = \frac{\sum x_2}{25}$$

so $\sum x_2 = 63.5 \times 25$

Therefore, $\mu_{1+2} = 62.9$ (3 s.f.)

d The mean and standard deviation were both slightly lower for the class of 15 than for the class of 25.

Assuming the test marks are normally distributed, 68% of the students' marks in the first class would be between 52.05 and 71.95. For the second class, 68% of the students' marks would be between 51 and 76.

Practice 3

In these questions, assume that all the data follow normal distributions.

1 The mute swan is the national bird of Denmark and has been a protected species since 1926. In a breeding farm in Copenhagen, data on the masses of 50 fully grown mute swans was collected:

$$\sum x = 550 \text{ kg} \qquad \sum x^2 = 6162.5 \text{ kg}$$

Find the mean and standard deviation for the data collected and make a generalization about the masses of mute swans.

2 The mean and standard deviation of the heights of a squad of 15 football players are 1.80 m and 0.0432 m respectively.

a Find $\sum x$ and $\sum x^2$.

b A new player whose height is 1.98 m joins the squad. Find the new mean and standard deviation of the heights of the squad.

c Provided this data is normally distributed, make generalizations from this data.

3 In Houston, Texas, the mean annual rainfall is 1264 mm with standard deviation of 155 mm.

a One year the rainfall was 1100 mm. Assuming that the rainfall in Houston follows a normal distribution, determine whether or not this was an exceptional year.

Exceptional results are more than 1 standard deviation from the mean.

b The next year saw a total of 1400 mm of rain. Determine whether or not this was an exceptional year.

4 In a year group, 45 students each recorded the number of minutes, x, they spent on their homework one night. The total was $\sum x = 2230$.

    a Find the mean number of minutes spent on homework.

    b Three new students joined the year group and reported that they spent 42 minutes, 25 minutes and 30 minutes respectively on their homework. Calculate the new mean including these three students.

    c State what extra information you would need to find the standard deviation.

Problem solving

5 Twenty five students were asked about the amount of monthly pocket money they received. The summary values were calculated to be $\sum x = \text{US\$2237}$ and $\sum x^2 = \text{US\$228\,361}$.

Two additional students gave their monthly pocket money: US\$85 and US\$125.

Find the mean and standard deviation for all this data.

- -

D   Sample versus population

- Can samples give reliable results?
- Do we want to be like everybody else?

A key purpose of statistics is to make inferences about a population by using data from a sample of the population. For a sample, you can calculate the sample mean $\bar{x}$ and the sample standard deviation s_x.

If, for example, you want to make inferences about a whole population of Elstar apples you can use the mean as an estimator for the average mass of all Elstar apples. But to make predictions about the standard deviation of the whole population you need to take into account that the population is much larger than the sample and, therefore, there is more likely to be a larger spread.

The masses (in grams) of a sample of 25 Elstar apples selected at random are:

132	122	132	125	134
129	130	131	133	129
126	132	133	133	131
133	138	135	135	134
142	140	136	132	135

The mean is $\bar{x} = \dfrac{\sum x}{n} = 132.48\,\text{g}$

The standard deviation is $s_n = \sqrt{\dfrac{\sum(x - \bar{x})^2}{n}} = 4.28\,\text{g}$

In statistics, you want the sample values (mean, standard deviation, etc.) to be good estimates of the same values for the entire population. When they are, these values are called 'unbiased estimators'. For example, the sample mean is an unbiased estimator of the population mean. The notation $\hat{\mu}$ shows that the value is an unbiased estimator for the mean. For the apples data, $\hat{\mu} = 132.48$ g.

When you calculate a population standard deviation, you divide the sum of squared deviations from the mean by the number of items in the population n.

When you calculate an estimate of the population standard deviation from a sample, you divide the sum of squared deviations from the mean by the number of items in the sample less one, $n-1$.

For a sample of n items:

- an unbiased estimate of the mean for the whole population is $\hat{\mu}$, the sample mean

- an estimate of the standard deviation for the whole population is:

$$s_{n-1} = \sqrt{\frac{\sum (x - \bar{x})^2}{n-1}}$$

As a result, the estimate of the standard deviation for the population is slightly higher than if you used the population standard deviation formula. This gives a better estimate of the population's standard deviation, by taking into account that the sample may not exactly represent the whole range of the population.

Dividing by $n-1$ compensates for the fact that you are working only with a sample rather than with the whole population.

The alternative formula for calculating an estimate of the population standard deviation from summary statistics is:

$$s_{n-1} = \sqrt{\frac{\sum x^2}{n-1} - \frac{n}{n-1}\left(\frac{\sum x}{n}\right)^2}$$

Reflect and discuss 5

- Would you trust inferences made from a sample? Explain.

- Are there times when sampling would be absolutely necessary? Give specific examples.

Example 6

A machine produces 1000 ball bearings each day with a mean diameter of 1 cm. A sample of 8 ball bearings is taken from the production line and the diameters measured. The results in centimeters are:

1.0   1.1   1.0   0.8   1.4   1.3   0.9   1.1

Determine the standard deviation of the diameters of the ball bearings produced by the machine that day.

▶ Continued on next page

$$\bar{x} = \frac{1.0+1.1+1.0+0.8+1.4+1.3+0.9+1.1}{8}$$

$$= 1.075$$

x	$x - \bar{x}$	$(x - \bar{x})^2$
1.0	−00.075	0.005 625
1.1	0.025	0.000 625
1.0	−0.075	0.005 625
0.8	−0.0275	0.075 625
1.4	0.325	0.105 625
1.3	0.225	0.050 625
0.9	−0.175	0.030 625
1.1	0.025	0.000 625
		$\sum(x - \bar{x})^2 = 0.275$

Calculate $\bar{x}$ and $\sum(x - \bar{x})^2$.

$$s_{n-1} = \sqrt{\frac{\sum(x - \bar{x})^2}{n-1}} = \sqrt{\frac{0.275}{7}} = 0.1982 \text{ cm (4 d.p.)}$$

To estimate the standard deviation of the population (day's production) from a sample use:

$$s_{n-1} = \sqrt{\frac{\sum(x - \bar{x})^2}{n-1}}$$

Objective D: Applying mathematics in real-life contexts
iii. apply the selected mathematical strategies successfully to reach a solution

You must decide whether you need the standard deviation of the data set or an estimate for the population standard deviation, and then correctly apply the appropriate formula.

ATL

Practice 4

1   Each day for 10 days, Auberon recorded how many minutes late his bus had arrived. The times in minutes are shown here:

   10   12   5   0   14   2   5   8   9   6

   Find an estimate for the standard deviation of how many minutes late buses arrive in the whole town.

2   On a farm, 25 baby rabbits are born one week. Their masses in grams are:

450	453	452	480	501
462	475	460	470	430
485	435	425	465	456
475	435	466	482	455
462	435	462	478	455

   From this information, make a prediction about the mean and standard deviations of the masses for the whole year.

3 The summary statistics for a sample of the life length of batteries are given in the table. Calculate the mean and standard deviation of the batteries in the factory.

n	25
$\sum x$	38 750
$\sum x^2$	60 100 000

Problem solving

4 Katie recorded the number of passengers in a carriage on her train each day for 50 days. The results are shown here:

1	7	6	7	7	6	7	6	7	8
8	2	10	6	10	10	5	12	5	8
6	8	10	8	9	3	7	12	9	5
8	6	7	5	9	11	12	4	9	6
7	8	9	7	9	11	7	13	14	15

a Construct a tally chart to represent the data.

b Comment on the shape of the distribution of the representation.

c Estimate the mean and standard deviation of the whole train.

d Make some inferences for Katie to report on her findings.

Summary

The **standard deviation** is a measure of dispersion that gives an idea of how close the original data values are to the mean, and thus how representative the mean is of the data.

A large standard deviation shows that the data values are far from the mean.

A small standard deviation shows that the data values are close to the mean. The units of standard deviation are the same as the units of the original data.

$\sum x$ means the sum of all the x-values.

Using this notation, the mean of a set of values is $\mu = \dfrac{\sum x}{n}$, the sum of all the values divided by the number of values.

A formula to calculate the standard deviation of a population is:

$$\sigma = \sqrt{\frac{\sum (x - \mu)^2}{n}}$$

Using $\sum$ notation, the mean of a set of discrete data values in a frequency table is $\dfrac{\sum fx}{n}$, the sum of all the fx values divided by the total frequency.

A formula to calculate the standard deviation for discrete data presented in a frequency table is:

$$\sigma = \sqrt{\frac{\sum f(x - \mu)^2}{n}}$$

The **normal distribution** is a symmetric distribution, with most values close to the mean and tailing off evenly in either direction. Its frequency graph is a bell-shaped curve.

A formula to calculate standard deviation from the summary statistics $\sum x$ and $\sum x^2$ is:

$$\sigma = \sqrt{\frac{\sum x^2}{n} - \left(\frac{\sum x}{n}\right)^2}$$

For a sample of n items:

- an estimate of the mean for the whole population is $\hat{\mu}$, the sample mean, $\bar{x}$.

- an estimate of the standard deviation for the whole population is:

$$s_{n-1} = \sqrt{\frac{\sum(x-\bar{x})^2}{n-1}}$$

The alternative formula for calculating an unbiased estimate of the population standard deviation from summary statistics is:

$$s_{n-1} = \sqrt{\frac{\sum x^2}{n-1} - \frac{n}{n-1}\left(\frac{\sum x}{n}\right)^2}$$

Mixed practice

In questions **1** and **2** the data provided is for the population.

1 **Find** the mean and the standard deviation of each data set:

  a 2, 3, 3, 4, 4, 5, 5, 6, 6, 6

  b 21 kg, 21 kg, 24 kg, 25 kg, 27 kg, 29 kg

  c

x	3	4	5
f	2	3	2

  d

Interval	Frequency
1 – 5	2
6 – 10	4
11 – 15	4
16 – 20	5
21 – 25	2

2 Charlotte buys 20 strawberry plants for her garden. She feeds half each day with water and the other half with a special strawberry plant food. After one month she records the amount of strawberries on each plant.

Number of strawberries on each plant fed with water									
15	13	12	15	17	16	12	10	11	15

Number of strawberries on each plant fed with special strawberry plant food									
14	15	17	17	19	19	12	14	15	15

Analyse the data to find whether there is an effect of using the special strawberry plant food.

3 Bernie recorded the mass of food in grams his hamster ate each day. Here are his results:

Day	1	2	3	4	5	6	7	8	9
Food (g)	55	64	45	54	60	50	59	61	49

  a **Find** the mean and standard deviation of the mass of food the hamster ate over the 9 days.

  b Bernie assumes that his hamster's food consumption is normally distributed. **Write down** the inferences he can make.

  c One day the hamster eats 25 g of food. Should Bernie be worried?

4 The summary statistics for the masses of 100 lambs on a farm were:

$$\sum x = 425 \text{ kg} \qquad \sum x^2 = 2031.25 \text{ kg}$$

  a **Show that** $\mu = 4.25$ and $\sigma = 1.5$.

  b The farmer wanted to produce guidelines for his staff to see if any lambs needed special attention. He decided that any lamb born weighing between 2 and 6.5 kg was fine. **Calculate** how many standard deviations away from the mean these values are.

5 For a particular data set, the summary statistics are: $n = 20$, $\sum fx = 563$, and $\sum fx^2 = 16143$. **Find** the values of the mean and the standard deviation.

6 In a biscuit factory a sample of 10 packets of biscuits were weighed.

Mass (g)	196	197	199	200	200	200	202	203	203	205

  a **Calculate** the mean and standard deviation.

  b To make predictions about the mean and standard deviations of all the packets of biscuits in the factory, which values of the mean and standard deviation would you use?

Problem solving

7 Samples of water were taken from a river near a chemical plant to see if there were raised levels of lead. Ten samples were collected, shown in the table below. The units are μg per liter.

6.3	9.6	12.2	12.3	10.3
12.1	10.3	8.4	9.2	4.3

  a **Use** this data to **predict** the mean and standard deviation for the amount of lead in the river.

  b Over 10 μg per liter of lead in water is dangerous. **Comment** on whether the lead levels should be investigated further.

Review in context

1 Dr Roussianos asked cardiology patients to measure their systolic blood pressure each Saturday morning for ten weeks.

> Systolic pressure is the pressure in the arteries between the beats of the heart, while the heart muscle is resting and refilling with blood.

Here is the data for three patients.

Patient 1

95	95	87	92	100
84	87	90	87	96

Patient 2

78	76	75	80	76
75	81	80	82	80

Patient 3

65	100	76	98	58
75	76	98	66	75

This table shows the treatments recommended for different values of the yearly mean and standard deviation.

Mean	Standard deviation	Treatment
<75	<10	low blood pressure treatment
75–85	<10	no treatment
>85	<10	high blood pressure treatment
any value	>10	more tests needed

Calculate the mean and use the sample data to **estimate** the yearly statistics and therefore help to **determine** the treatment for each patient.

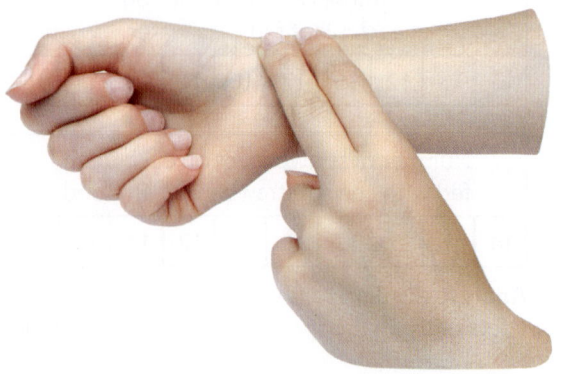

2 80 people were asked to measure their pulse rate as soon as they woke up in the morning.

The summary statistics are: $\sum x = 6000$ and $\sum x^2 = 452\,450$.

From this information, **find** the mean and the standard deviation of the data set. If this was a sample of the population, **state** the inferences which could be drawn from this sample data set.

3 Birth mass follows a normal distribution. The summary statistics for the masses of 50 babies in a hospital were $\sum x = 160$ kg and $\sum x^2 = 524$.

  a Calculate the mean baby mass and the standard deviation of the sample.

  b If a baby's mass is less than 2.5 times the standard deviation below the mean, the baby is at risk. **Find** a value x, so that babies who weigh less than x kg are considered to be at risk.

4 In one town, 300 mothers were asked their age at the birth of their first child. The results are given in the table.

Age at birth of first child	Number of mothers
18–20	15
21–23	20
24–26	30
27–29	42
30–32	53
33–35	52
36–38	43
39–41	25
42–44	12
45–47	8

  a Estimate the mean and standard deviation for a mother's age at the birth of her first child, for this town.

  b The summary statistics for 30 years ago, for a different sample of 300 women were $\sum x = 7500$ and $\sum x^2 = 190\,000$. **State** the inferences that can be drawn from the data.

Reflect and discuss 6

How have you explored the statement of inquiry? Give specific examples.

Statement of inquiry:

How quantities are represented can help to establish underlying relationships and trends in a population.

7 How do they measure up?

Statement of inquiry:

Systems use logic to validate generalizations and increase our appreciation of the aesthetic.

Key concept:

Logic is used as a process in making decisions about numbers, shapes and variables.

F **When is a measurement an approximation?**

How big is it?

Although we have sophisticated measuring tools and standard units, most people are not very good at visualizing or interpreting measurements.

- Would a sofa measuring 160 cm × 80 cm × 70 cm fit in a family car?

Models are depictions of real-life events using expressions, equations or graphs.

Modelling a problem

The length of a rectangular garden is twice as long as its width.

The area of the garden is 72 m².

Find the dimensions of the garden.

Drawing a diagram can help you write an equation to represent a situation.

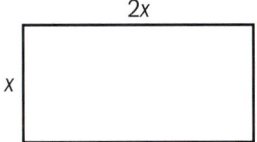

- For the rectangular garden, write and solve an equation to find x, and then find the length and width.

Translating a word problem into a mathematical expression or equation creates a model of the problem. Sometimes you can adapt a model to solve similar problems.

- Adapt your garden model to find the dimensions of a rectangular field whose length is three times as long as its width, and has an area of 7500 m².

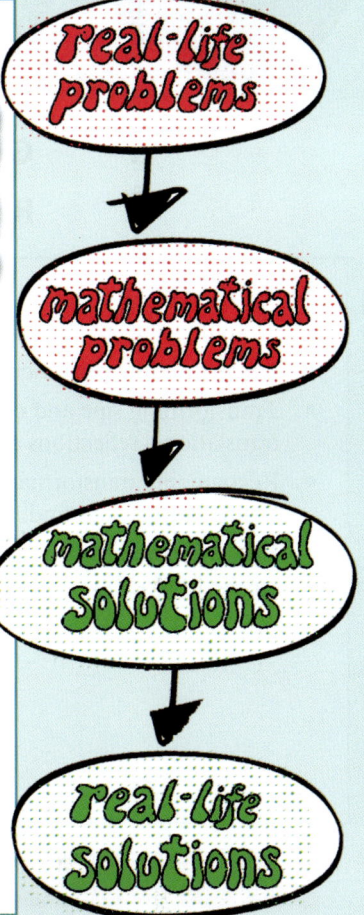

D To what extent does understanding systems help you make more aesthetic solutions?

Systems are groups of interrelated elements.

More than three dimensions

In the 1990s, mathematicians working on the string theories of physics discovered the likelihood of there being at least ten dimensions in existence. But what does this really mean? Mathematicians have always worked with any number of dimensional spaces, including infinite dimensional spaces. If mathematics is capable of explaining the inherent structure of our universe, then perhaps there are even more than ten dimensions waiting to be discovered.

Global context: Personal and cultural expression

Exploration: Explore your appreciation of the aesthetic

 Launch additional digital resources for this unit.

E7.1 Trigonometric functions

Global context: Personal and cultural expression

Related concept: Models

LOGIC

Objectives

- Graphing sine and cosine functions
- Understanding periodicity
- Transforming sine and cosine functions using translations, reflections and dilations
- Recognizing transformations of sine and cosine graphs, and finding equations of graphs
- Modelling real-life problems using sine and cosine functions

Inquiry questions

- What is a periodic function?
- What are the main characteristics of the graphs of $y = a \sin bx$ and $y = a \cos bx$?

- How do you translate, dilate and reflect periodic functions?
- How does the equation of a sinusoidal function represent the transformations performed on it?
- Does the order in which transformations are performed matter?

- What real-life phenomena can be modelled using periodic functions?
- Have scientific models and methods provided more answers or questions?

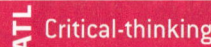

ATL Critical-thinking

Draw reasonable conclusions and generalizations

📑 **Launch additional digital resources for this chapter.**

Statement of inquiry:

Systems use logic to validate generalizations and increase our appreciation of the aesthetic.

You should already know how to:

• use the trigonometric ratios for sine and cosine	**1** Here is a right-angled triangle. $\begin{array}{c}\text{(triangle with hypotenuse } 13\text{, vertical side } 5\text{, base } 12\text{, angle } x)\end{array}$ Write down: **a** sin x **b** cos x
• find values of sine and cosine	**2** Use a calculator to find the value of: **a** sin 45° **b** cos 37° Make sure your GDC is in degree mode.
• transform functions using translations, reflections and dilations	**3** Here is the graph of $f(x)$. $\begin{array}{c}\text{(parabola graph on axes, vertex near } (-2, 0)\text{)}\end{array}$ On graph paper, sketch $f(x)$ and **a** $f(x) + 2$ **b** $3f(x)$ **c** $-f(x)$ **d** $f(x - 2)$ **e** $f(\tfrac{1}{2}x)$ **f** $f(2x)$

F   The sine and cosine curves

- What is a periodic function?
- What are the main characteristics of the graphs of $y = a \sin bx$ and $y = a \cos bx$?

You have used the trigonometric ratios sine, cosine and tangent in right-angled triangles. You can use your GDC to find these ratios for different angles.

Exploration 1

1 a Draw a table of values for angle $\theta = 0°$, 10°, 20°, ..., 360°, and sin θ.

θ	0°	10°	20°	30°	40°	50°	60°	...	360°
sin θ									

b Find sin 0°, sin 10°, sin 20°, and so on using your GDC. Round the values to 2 decimal places and write them in your table.

c On graph paper, plot the graph of sin θ, with θ from 0° to 360° on the x-axis and the sine values on the y-axis. Join your points with a smooth curve.

> Make sure your GDC is in degree mode.

▶ Continued on next page

2 Follow the instructions in step **1** to draw a table of values and plot the graph of $\cos\theta$.

3 Check your graphs by graphing $\sin\theta$ and $\cos\theta$ on your GDC.

4 For the domain $0° \leq \theta \leq 360°$, write down the range of

  a $\sin\theta$

  b $\cos\theta$.

Reflect and discuss 1

- What is similar about the graphs for sine and cosine? What is different?

- Predict how you think each curve will continue from:

  a $360°$ to $720°$ **b** $0°$ to $-360°$

- Describe the symmetry of each curve.
  Use your GDC to draw graphs to check your predictions.

The sine and cosine curves have the same shape. Translating the sine graph $90°$ to the left gives the cosine graph. Translating the cosine graph $90°$ to the right gives the sine graph.

The **amplitude** is the height from the mean value of the function to its maximum or minimum value. The graphs of $y = \sin x$ and $y = \cos x$ have amplitude 1.

The **period** is the horizontal length of one complete cycle. The graphs of $y = \sin x$ and $y = \cos x$ have period $360°$.

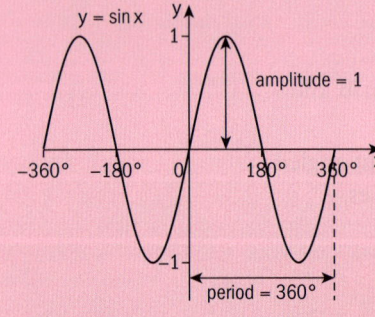

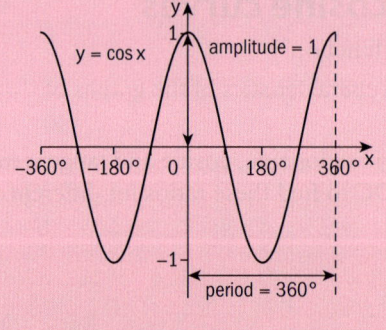

Sine and cosine graphs are also called sine and cosine waves. Waves have an amplitude and a period.

The graph of $y = \sin x$ passes through $(0, 0)$ and has a maximum at $(90°, 1)$.

The graph of $y = \cos x$ has a maximum at $(0, 1)$.

ATL

Exploration 2

1 Use what you know about transformations of functions from $f(x)$ to $af(x)$ to predict the shape of the graph of $y = 2\sin x$. Graph the function on your GDC to check your prediction.

2 Predict the shape of the graph of $y = \frac{1}{2}\sin x$. Graph the function on your GDC to check your prediction.

▶ Continued on next page

3 Find the amplitude of the graph of:

   a $y = 2\sin x$

   b $y = \frac{1}{2}\sin x$

   c $y = a\sin x$.

4 Predict the shapes of $y = 2\cos x$ and $y = \frac{1}{2}\cos x$. Graph the functions to check your predictions.

5 Find the amplitude of the graph of:

   a $y = 2\cos x$

   b $y = \frac{1}{2}\cos x$

   c $y = a\cos x$.

6 Make generalizations about the effect of parameter 'a' on the graphs of $y = a\sin x$ and $y = a\cos x$.

The graph of $y = a\sin x$ and the graph of $y = a\cos x$ both have amplitude a.

The amplitude of a curve is half the distance between the maximum and minimum values.

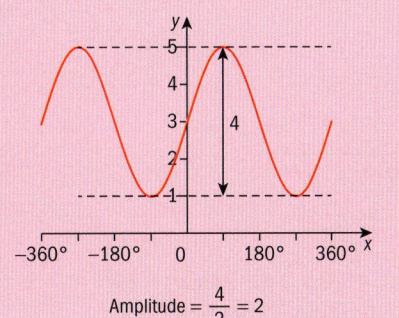

Amplitude $= \dfrac{4}{2} = 2$

Example 1

Write down the function represented by this graph:

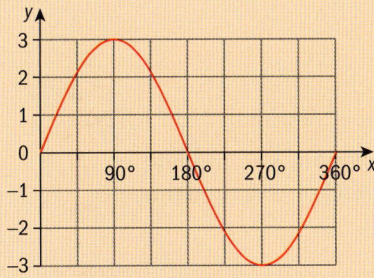

This is a sine graph. —————— Compare to the sine and cosine graphs. This passes through (0, 0).

The amplitude is 3. ————————————————————————— $a = \dfrac{3-(-3)}{2} = 3$

$\Rightarrow y = 3\sin x$

Practice 1

1 Sketch the graph of these functions. Label all the *x*-intercepts on your sketch graphs.

  a $y = 4\sin x$ **b** $y = 2\cos x$

Problem solving

2 Write down the function shown in each graph.

a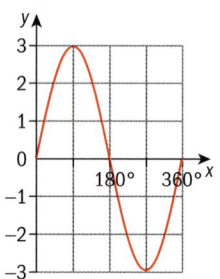

b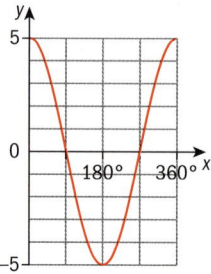

c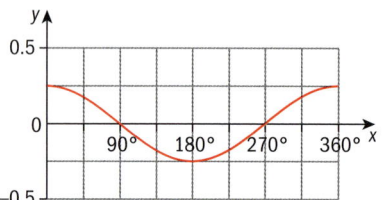

d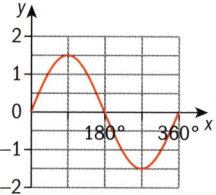

3 $y = 2\cos x$ $y = 0.5\sin x$ $y = 4\cos x$ $y = 2\sin x$
When graphed, choose which of the above function(s):

  a intersect the *y*-axis at (0, 2)
  b intersect the *x*-axis at (180°, 0) and (360°, 0)
  c intersect the *x*-axis at (90°, 0) and (270°, 0)
  d has the smallest amplitude.

Exploration 3

1 Describe the effect on the graph of $y = f(x)$ when it is transformed to $y = f(2x)$.

2 On the same axes, sketch the graphs of the functions $y = \sin x$ and $y = \sin 2x$ for $0 \leq x \leq 360°$. Check with your GDC or with dynamic geometry software.

3 Add the graph of $y = 2\sin 2x$ to your sketch.

4 Write down the amplitude and period of each graph, in a table like this:

Graph	$y = \sin x$	$y = \sin 2x$	$y = 2\sin 2x$
Period			

5 Predict how the graph of $y = \sin x$ changes when it is transformed to $y = \sin \frac{1}{2}x$. Predict the period of the graph of $y = \sin \frac{1}{2}x$. Check with your GDC or geometry software.

▶ Continued on next page

6 Add a column for $y = \sin\frac{1}{2}x$ to your table.

7 Repeat steps **1–6** for the graphs of $y = \cos x$, $y = \cos 2x$ and $y = \cos\frac{1}{2}x$.

8 Conjecture a rule for finding the period of a function $y = \sin bx$, $y = \cos bx$, $y = a\sin bx$ and $y = a\cos bx$, and explain why your rule makes sense.

Sine and cosine functions are periodic functions.

A **periodic function** repeats a pattern of y-values at regular intervals.

One complete repetition of the pattern is called a **cycle**.

The period of the functions $y = a\sin bx$ and $y = a\cos bx$ is $\frac{360}{b}$.

The parameter b is the **frequency**, or number of cycles between 0° and 360°.

The graph $y = 3\sin 2x$ has period $\frac{360}{2} = 180°$

The frequency is 2 and the amplitude is 3.

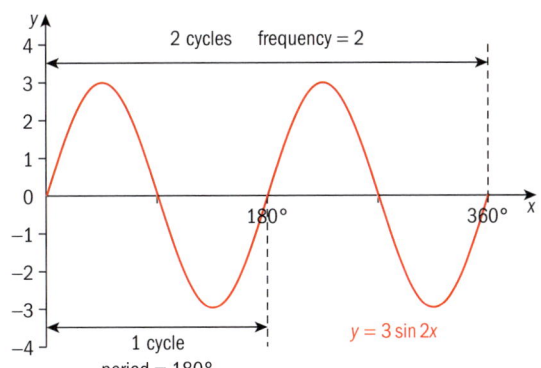

Practice 2

1 State the period and frequency of the graph of each function. Sketch the graph for the domain $0° \le x \le 360°$. Then check your graphs with a GDC or graphing software.

   a $y = \sin 3x$ **b** $y = \cos 4x$

Problem solving

2 State the period and frequency of the graph of each function. Sketch the graph for the domain $0° \le x \le 720°$. Then check your graphs with a GDC or graphing software.

   a $y = \sin\frac{1}{2}x$ **b** $y = \cos\frac{1}{3}x$

3 Write the equation of each graph.

a

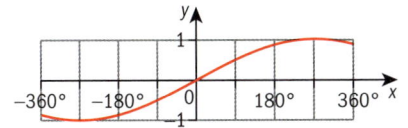

b

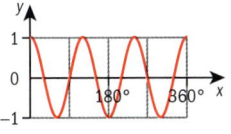

c

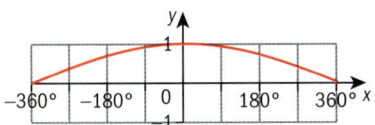

d

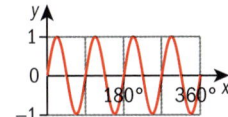

Problem solving

4 Match each equation to its graph.

$$y = 0.5\cos 3x \qquad y = 3\sin\frac{x}{2} \qquad y = 3\sin 2x \qquad y = 0.5\cos 0.5x$$

a
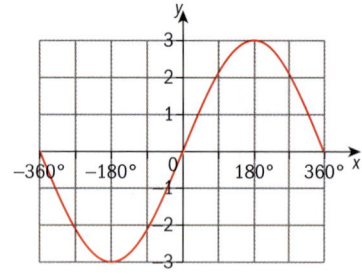

b
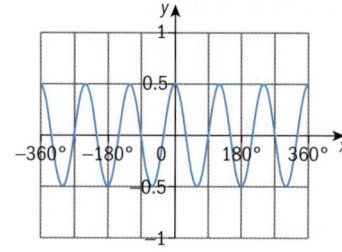

c
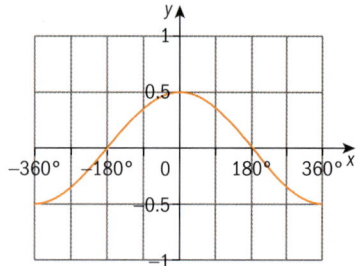

d
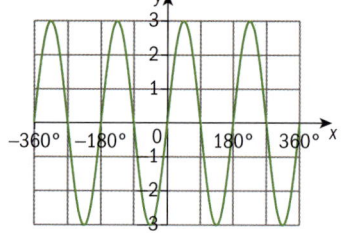

Example 2

Sketch the graph of each function on the domain given.

a $y = 0.5\sin 3x$, for $0° \le x \le 360°$

b $y = 3\cos 0.5x$, for $0° \le x \le 720°$

a amplitude $= 0.5$

frequency $= 3$

period $= \dfrac{360}{3} = 120°$

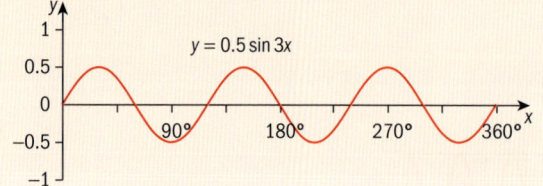

State the amplitude, frequency and period.

Draw axes for the domain.

The maximum and minimum y-values are 0.5 and −0.5 respectively.

Frequency $= 3$, so there are 3 complete sine curves between 0° and 360°.

Period $= 120°$, so there is a complete sine curve between 0° and 120°.

Sine curve passes through (0, 0).

▶ Continued on next page

b amplitude = 3

frequency = 0.5

period = $\frac{360}{0.5}$ = 720°

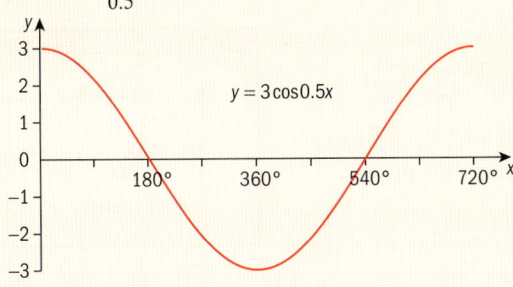

$y = 3\cos 0.5x$

Frequency = 0.5, so there is half a complete cosine curve between 0° and 360°.

Period = 720°, so there is a complete cosine curve between 0° and 720°.

Cosine curve has a maximum at $x = 0°$ and at 720°.

Practice 3

1 Write down the amplitude, frequency and period of each function, then sketch the graph for the given domain. Check your graphs on a GDC or graphing software.

a $y = 2\sin 4x$, for $0° \leq x \leq 360°$ **b** $y = 4\cos 3x$, for $0° \leq x \leq 360°$

c $y = \frac{1}{3}\sin\frac{x}{3}$, for $0° \leq x \leq 1080°$ **d** $y = 0.7\cos\frac{x}{4}$, for $0° \leq x \leq 1440°$

 Transformations of periodic functions

- How do you translate, dilate and reflect periodic functions?
- How does the equation of a sinusoidal function represent the transformations performed on it?
- Does the order in which transformations are performed matter?

A **sinusoidal function** is any function that can be obtained from a transformation of the sine function. For example, the graph of $y = \cos x$ can be obtained by translating the graph of $y = \sin x$ by 90° to the left. So $y = \cos x$ is a sinusoidal function.

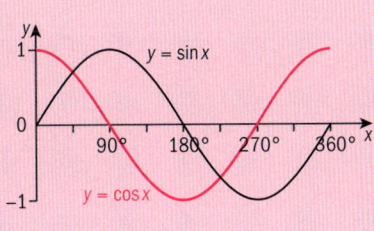

Exploration 4

Transforming $f(x)$ to $f(x) + d$

1 Use what you know about transformations of graphs from $f(x)$ to $f(x) + d$ to predict how the transformation of $y = \sin x$ to $y = \sin x + d$ will affect the graph.

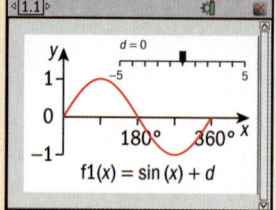

2 Graph the function $y = \sin x + d$ on the domain $0° \leq x \leq 360°$ for different values of d. Investigate how changing the value of d affects the graph. Was your prediction from step **1** correct?

3 Verify that the amplitude and period of the function $y = a \sin bx + d$ is not affected by the value of d.

4 Repeat steps **1** to **3** for the graph of $y = \cos x + d$.

Transforming $f(x)$ to $-f(x)$

5 Use what you know about transformations of graphs from $f(x)$ to $-f(x)$ to predict how the transformation of $y = \sin x$ to $y = -\sin x$ will affect the graph. Graph the functions $y = \sin x$ and $y = -\sin x$ on the domain $0° \leq x \leq 360°$ to check your prediction.

6 Verify that $y = a \sin bx$ and $y = -a \sin bx$ have the same amplitude and period.

7 Repeat steps **5** and **6** for the graphs of $y = \cos x$ and $y = -\cos x$.

Transforming $f(x)$ to $f(-x)$

8 Use what you know about transformations of graphs from $f(x)$ to $f(-x)$ to predict how the transformation of $y = \sin x$ to $y = \sin(-x)$ will affect the graph. Graph the functions $y = \sin x$ and $y = \sin(-x)$ on the domain $-360° \leq x \leq 360°$ to check your prediction.

9 Verify that $y = a \sin bx$ and $y = a \sin(-bx)$ have the same amplitude and period.

10 Repeat steps **8** and **9** for the graphs of $y = \cos x$ and $y = \cos(-x)$.

Transformations of sine and cosine functions

Reflection: For the sinusoidal functions $f(x) = \sin x$ and $f(x) = \cos x$:

The graph of $y = -f(x)$ is a reflection of the graph of $y = f(x)$ in the x-axis.

The graph of $y = f(-x)$ is a reflection of the graph of $y = f(x)$ in the y-axis.

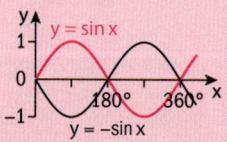

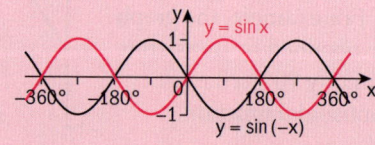

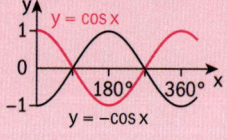

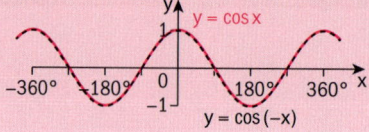

▶ Continued on next page

Translation: For the sinusoidal functions $f(x) = \sin x$ and $f(x) = \cos x$, $y = f(x) + d$ translates $y = f(x)$ by d units in the y-direction.

When $d > 0$, the graph moves in the positive y-direction (up).

When $d < 0$, the graph moves in the negative y-direction (down).

Dilation: For the sinusoidal functions $f(x) = a \sin bx$ and $f(x) = a \cos bx$:

$y = af(x)$ is a vertical dilation of $f(x)$, scale factor a, parallel to the y-axis. a is the amplitude.

$y = f(bx)$ is a horizontal dilation of $f(x)$, scale factor $\frac{1}{b}$, parallel to the x-axis. b is the frequency.

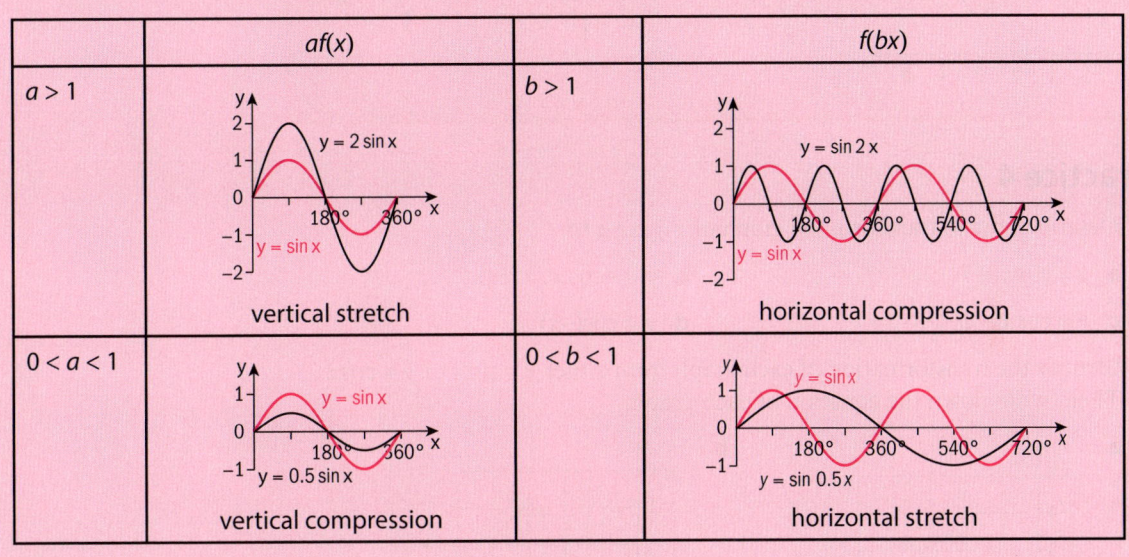

	$af(x)$		$f(bx)$
$a > 1$	vertical stretch	$b > 1$	horizontal compression
$0 < a < 1$	vertical compression	$0 < b < 1$	horizontal stretch

While the graphs of $y = \sin x$ and $y = \cos x$ share many similarities, they are easy to recognize by looking at a specific point on the graph. Exploration 5 will help you find that point.

Exploration 5

ATL

1. Sketch the graphs of $y = \sin x$ and $y = \cos x$.

2. In Reflect and discuss 1, you informally noted differences between the sine and cosine graphs. Now, using proper mathematical terminology, state the similarities and differences between the sine and cosine graphs.

You can recognize the graphs of $y = \sin x$ and $y = \cos x$ from their values at $x = 0$.

3. Use your GDC to graph several cosine functions with equations of the form $y = a \cos bx + d$. Generalize how to find the y-intercept from the equation.

4. Repeat step **3** with the function $y = a \sin bx + d$.

The y-intercept of a function is the y-value when $x = 0$. Specifically, for $y = a\sin bx + d$, the y-intercept is the average value of the function: $\dfrac{y_{max} + y_{min}}{2}$

For $y = a\cos bx + d$, the y-intercept is the maximum value of y.

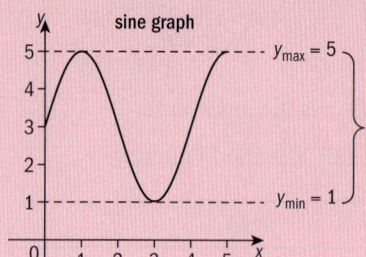

y-intercept is $\dfrac{5 + 1}{2} = 3$

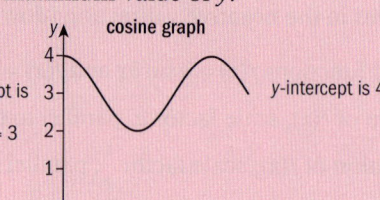

y-intercept is 4

Practice 4

1 Describe how to transform the graph of $y = \cos x$ to:

   a $y = \cos x + 7$ **b** $y = -\cos x$

   c $y = \cos x - 2$ **d** $y = \cos(-x)$

2 Identify the transformation of each graph from either $y = \sin x$ or $y = \cos x$. Then, write down the equation of each graph.

  a
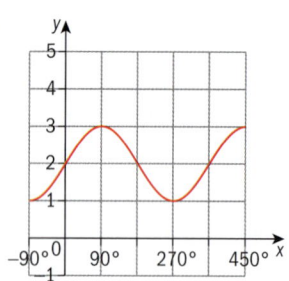

  b
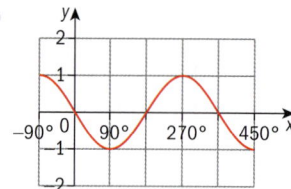

  c
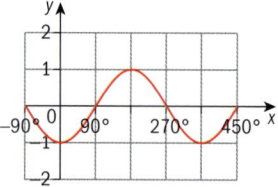

  d
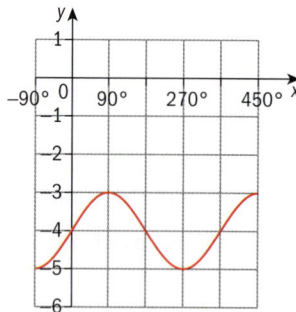

3 Draw the graph of each function for $0° \le x \le 360°$. Be sure to clearly indicate on your graph the amplitude, the y-intercept and the period.

   a $y = \sin x - 2$ **b** $y = -\cos x$

   c $y = \cos x + 11$ **d** $y = -\sin x$

   e $y = \cos x - 8$ **f** $y = \sin x + 1$

4 The graph of $y = \sin x$ was transformed to produce the following graph:

a Find the amplitude, frequency and period of the function.

b Write down the equation of the graph.

c Dennis wants to translate the graph so that its minimum value is $y = 0$. Describe a translation that will allow him to accomplish this.

d Write down the equation for Dennis's graph.

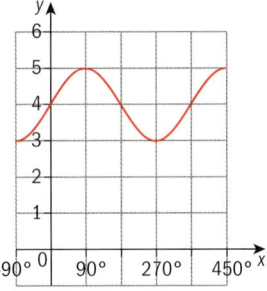

Problem solving

5 Jawad and Aaron disagree about the equation of the following graph:

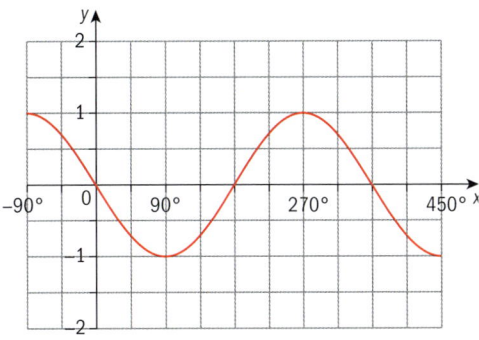

Aaron says the equation is $y = -\sin x$ while Jawad thinks it is $y = \sin(-x)$. State who is correct, and justify your answer.

- -

Example 3

By describing the transformations on the sinusoidal graph, determine the function for the graph.

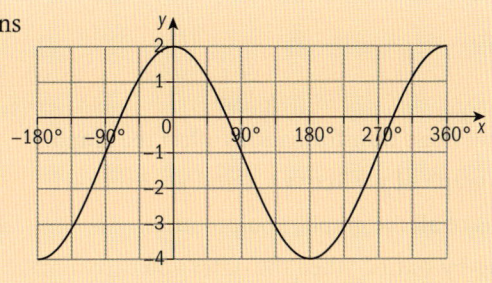

This is a cosine curve, form: $y = a \cos bx + d$ ——————— Cosine curve has maximum at $x = 0$.

The amplitude, a, is half the distance between the ——— Find the amplitude a and frequency b.
max and min points: $a = \frac{1}{2} \times 6 = 3$

The frequency, b, is the number of cycles between $0°$ and $360° = 1$

Since the amplitude is 3, the graph has shifted 1 unit downward, hence $d = -1$.

The amplitude is 3 but the maximum value is 2, so the graph is translated down 1 unit. Hence $d = -1$

Substitute your values for a, b and d into $y = a \cos bx + d$.

$y = 3\cos x - 1$ ———————————————

Example 4

Write a function that describes this sinusoidal graph.

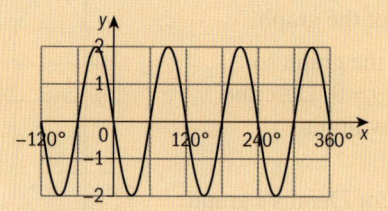

For the sine function, a reflection in the *x*-axis gives the same graph as a reflection in the *y*-axis.

This is a sine curve, reflected in either the *x*-axis or *y*-axis.

This is a sine curve because at $x = 0$ it has average value.

The amplitude, $a = \frac{4}{2} = 2$

There are 3 cycles from 0° to 360°, so $b = 3$.

y-intercept $c = 0$

$\Rightarrow y = -2\sin 3x$ or $y = 2\sin(-3x)$

Graph of $y = \sin(x)$ increases from 0° to 90° but this graph decreases over that range.

ATL

Exploration 6

1   **a**   Determine which two transformations transform $y = \sin x$ to $y = 3\sin 2x$.

   b   Start with the graph of $y = \sin x$ and apply the two transformations.

   c   Start with the graph of $y = \sin x$ and apply the two transformations in the opposite order.

   d   Do you get the same graph each time?

2   Repeat step **1** for the graphs of:

   a $y = -3\sin 2x$

   b $y = 3\sin(-2x)$

   c $y = -3\sin x$.

Does the order you carry out these transformations affect the graph?

3   **a**   Repeat step **1** for the graph of $y = 3\cos x + 1$ and $y = 3\sin x + 1$.

   b   Write down equations of all the graphs you produce.

4   Summarize your findings by stating when the order you carry out transformations is important, and when it doesn't matter.

Practice 5

1   Describe how to transform the graph of $y = \sin x$ to:

   a $y = -4\sin x$ **b** $y = 2\sin x - 9$ **c** $y = 0.5\sin x + 4$

   d $y = \sin\left(\frac{1}{2}x\right) + 3$ **e** $y = -\sin\left(\frac{1}{3}x\right)$ **f** $y = \sin(-2x) + 1$

2   Describe how to transform the graph of $y = \cos x$ to:

   a $y = -3\cos x$ **b** $y = 2\cos x + 1$ **c** $y = \cos\left(\frac{1}{2}x\right) + 2$

   d $y = 0.5\cos x - 1$ **e** $y = -\cos 3x$ **f** $y = \cos\left(-\frac{1}{2}x\right) - 3$

Problem solving

3 Each graph is a transformation of either $y = \sin x$ or $y = \cos x$.
For each graph, identify the transformations on the graph and write the function that describes the graph.

a
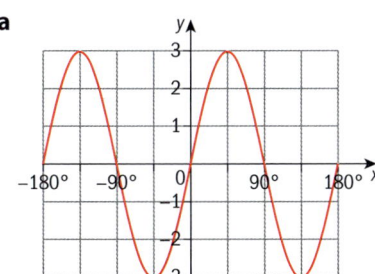

b
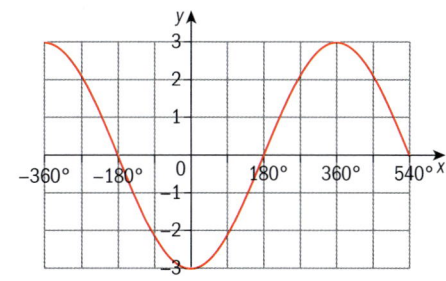

c
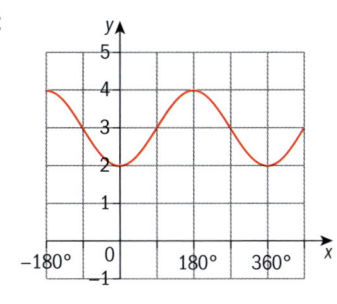

d
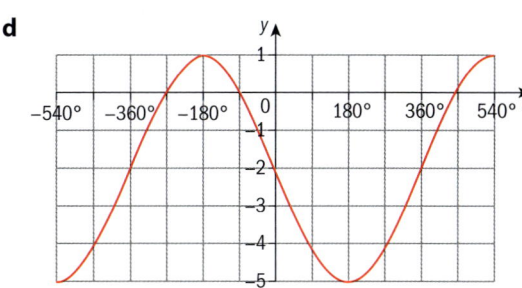

e
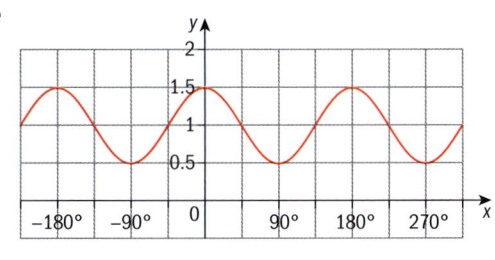

f
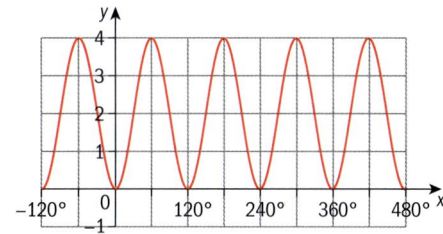

g
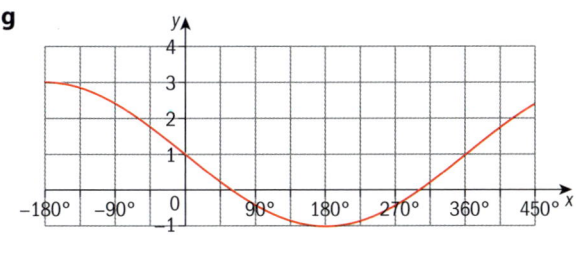

h
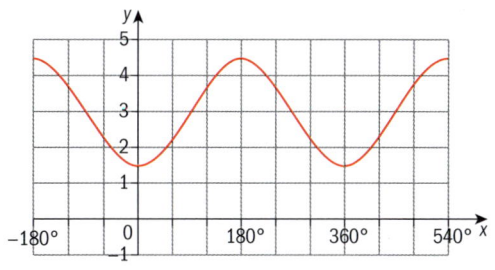

(D) Modelling real-life situations

- What real-life phenomena can be modelled using periodic functions?
- Have scientific models and methods provided more answers or questions?

In the sinusoidal graphs you have worked with so far, the x-axis has shown degrees, and the y-axis shows the sine or cosine function for each angle.
In sinusoidal curves representing real-life situations, the x and y axes may show other units, such as time on the x-axis and height on the y-axis.

The graph shows the distance (in meters) of a wrecking ball from its original position as it swings left and then right.

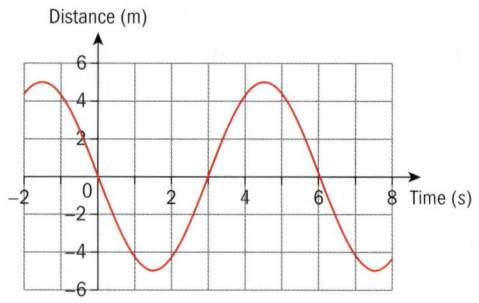

From the graph:

- The amplitude is 5, so the maximum distance the wrecking ball reaches from its original position is 5 m.
- The negative y-values represent the distance when it swings to the left, and the positive values represent the distance when it swings to the right.
- The period is 6 seconds (the time needed for one cycle).

To find the equation of the graph:

The graph is a sine curve. It has been reflected in the x- or y-axis.

Frequency $b = \dfrac{360°}{\text{period}} = \dfrac{360°}{6} = 60°$

Amplitude $a = 5$

$c = 0$

So, $y = 5\sin(-60°x)$ or $y = -5\sin 60°x$

> When graphing sinusoidal curves with degrees in the function, make sure to type the degree symbol on the $y =$ line.

Exploration 7

A Ferris wheel has 18 seats arranged every 20°. Its diameter is 75 m and the lowest seat is 2 m above the ground. As you ride the Ferris wheel your height above the ground changes continuously. Draw an accurate scale drawing of the wheel. Determine the kind of function that describes its motion.

1 Suppose you get on at the bottom and the wheel rotates so that it takes 5 seconds between positions of the seats. Use a ruler to determine your height above the ground as the wheel passes through each position. Record your results in a table. Graph height h (m) above the ground against time t (seconds) for $0 \le t \le 180$.

2 Find the amplitude, period and frequency of your graph.

3 Use your results to write down the equation of your graph.

4 Identify the transformations of the graph $y = \cos x$.

5 Determine the changes that would need to be made to the Ferris wheel in order for the relationship to be described by transformations of $y = \sin x$.

Practice 6

1 After you exercise, the velocity of air flow (in liters per second) into your lungs can be modelled by the equation $y = 2\sin(90°t)$.

  a Find the velocity of air flow at:

    i 1 s   **ii** 2.5 s   **iii** 4 s

  b Explain what you think negative velocities represent.

  c Find the period of the function, and what it represents.

d Find the amplitude and maximum velocity.

e Draw the graph of the function in the first 8 seconds.

2 The graph here shows how a buoy's distance from the ocean floor changes with the waves. Find a sinusoidal function that models the graph.

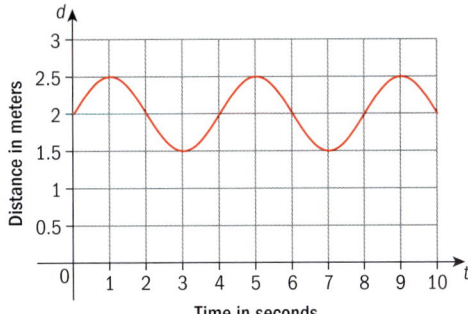

Problem solving

3 Find a sinusoidal function that models the relationship shown in each graph.

a

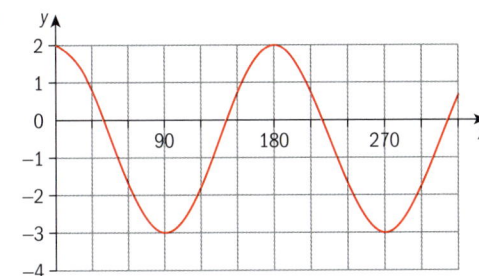

b

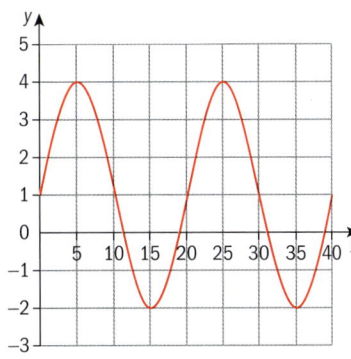

c

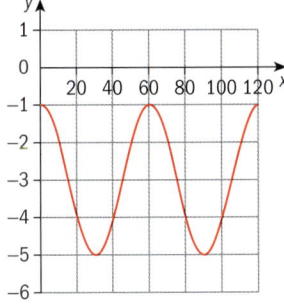

d

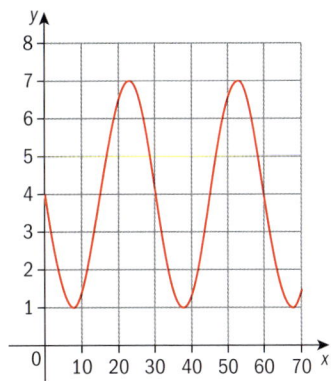

4 The height in meters (from its position at rest) of a spring as it bounces up and down can be modelled by the function $h(t) = 2\sin 60°t + 1$, where t is measured in seconds.

a Find the amplitude of $h(t)$.

b Sketch the graph of the function.

c Determine if the amplitude is the same as the maximum height from its position at rest.

5 When you ride a Ferris wheel, your vertical height above the ground changes. The relationship between your height above the ground and the time for a complete revolution of the wheel can be modelled with a sinusoidal graph like this:

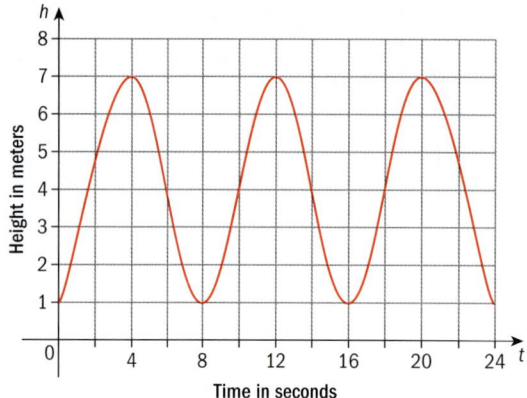

a State the height at which you board the Ferris wheel.

b State the maximum height you reach on the Ferris wheel.

c Determine how long it takes to rise to approximately 5 m above the ground for the first time.

d Determine your height above the ground after 8 seconds.

e Determine how long it takes for one complete revolution of the wheel.

f The Ferris wheel is circular. Determine its radius.

g Find a function that models this graph.

6 The height in meters of the tide above the mean sea level one day at Bal Harbour can be modelled by the function $h(t) = 3\sin30°t$, where t is the number of hours after midnight.

a Find h when $t = 0$, 6, 12, 18 and 24 hours.

b Draw the graph of the function for a 24 hour cycle.

c Determine the time of high tides, and their maximum heights.

d Determine the height of the tide at 4 o'clock in the afternoon.

e A ship can cross the harbour if the tide is at least 2 m above the average sea level. Determine the times when it can cross the harbour.

Problem solving

7 One day, high tide in Venice, Italy was at midnight. The water level at high tide was 3.3 m, and later at low tide the water level was 0.1 m. Assume that the next high tide is 12 hours later and that the height of the water level can be modelled with a sinusoidal function.

a Find a function that models this situation.

b Draw a graph of your function.

Summary

The **amplitude** is the height from the mean value of the function to its maximum or minimum value. The graphs of $y = \sin x$ and $y = \cos x$ have amplitude 1.

The **period** is the horizontal length of one complete cycle. The graphs of $y = \sin x$ and $y = \cos x$ have period $360°$.

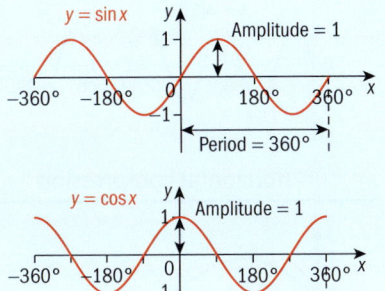

The graph of $y = a \sin x$ has amplitude a.
The graph of $y = a \cos x$ has amplitude a.

A periodic function repeats a pattern of y-values at regular intervals.

The period of the functions $y = a \sin bx$ and $y = a \cos bx$ is $\dfrac{360}{b}$.

$$\text{Period} = \frac{360}{\text{frequency}}$$

One complete repetition of the pattern is called a **cycle**. The parameter b is the **frequency**, or number of cycles between $0°$ and $360°$.

The amplitude is $\left(\dfrac{y_{max} - y_{min}}{2} \right)$.

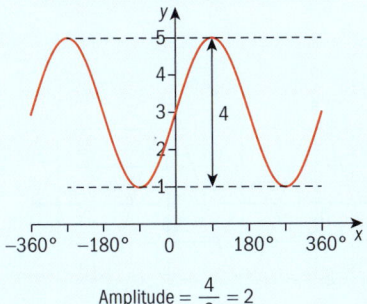

$$\text{Amplitude} = \frac{4}{2} = 2$$

A **sinusoidal function** is any function that can be obtained from a transformation of the sine function. The graph of $y = \cos x$ can be obtained by translating the graph of $y = \sin x$ by $90°$ to the left. So $y = \cos x$ is a sinusoidal function.

Reflection: For the sinusoidal functions $f(x) = \sin x$ and $f(x) = \cos x$:

The graph of $y = -f(x)$ is a reflection of the graph of $y = f(x)$ in the x-axis.

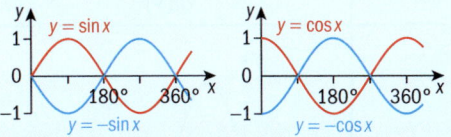

The graph of $y = f(-x)$ is a reflection of the graph of $y = f(x)$ in the y-axis.

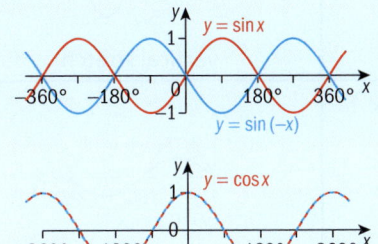

Translation: For the sinusoidal functions $f(x) = \sin x$ and $f(x) = \cos x$:

- $y = f(x) + d$ translates $y = f(x)$ by d units in the y-direction.
  When $d > 0$, the graph moves in the positive y-direction, up.
  When $d < 0$, the graph moves in the negative y-direction, down.

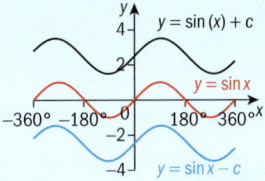

- $y = f(x - h)$ translates $y = f(x)$ by h units in the x-direction.
  When $h > 0$, the graph moves in the positive x-direction, to the right.
  When $h < 0$, the graph moves in the negative x-direction, to the left.

> Horizontal translation of cosine and sine graphs is an extended topic, but here you can see that the rules are the same as for translations of all functions $f(x)$.

Dilation: For the sinusoidal functions $f(x) = a \sin bx$ and $f(x) = a \cos bx$:

$y = af(x)$ is a vertical dilation of $f(x)$, scale factor a, parallel to the y-axis. a is the amplitude.

$y = f(bx)$ is a horizontal dilation of $f(x)$, scale factor $\frac{1}{b}$, parallel to the x-axis. b is the frequency.

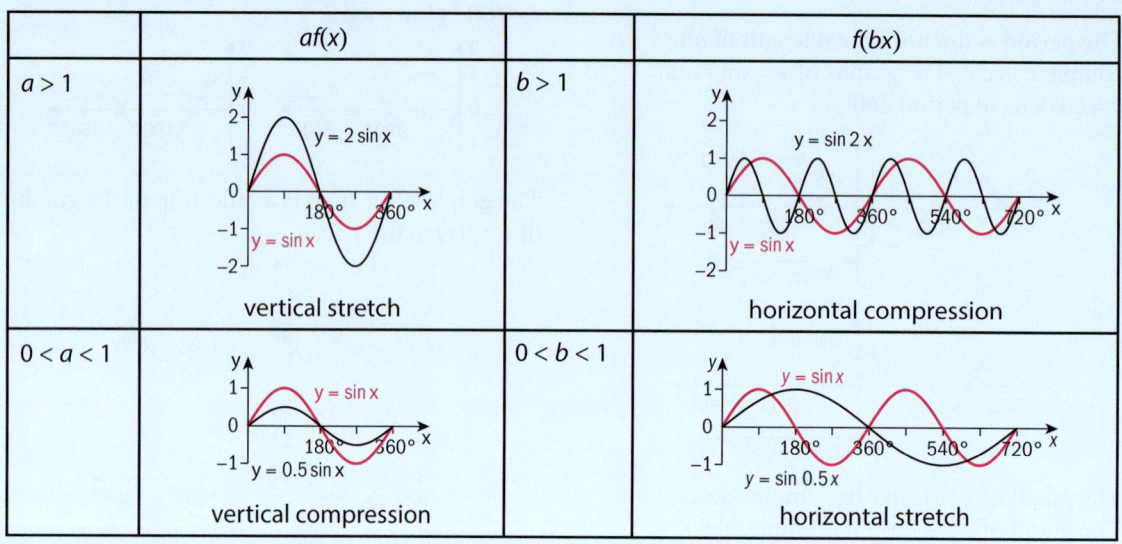

For $y = a \sin bx + d$, the y-intercept is the average value of the function: $\frac{y_{max} + y_{max}}{2}$

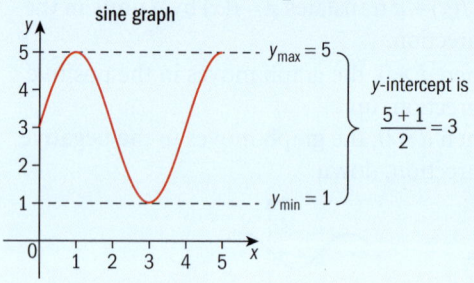

For $y = a \cos bx + d$, the y-intercept is the maximum value of y.

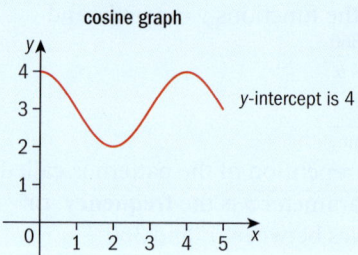

Mixed practice

1 For each of the following graphs, **find** the amplitude, frequency and period. Then, **write down** the equation that represents the function.

a

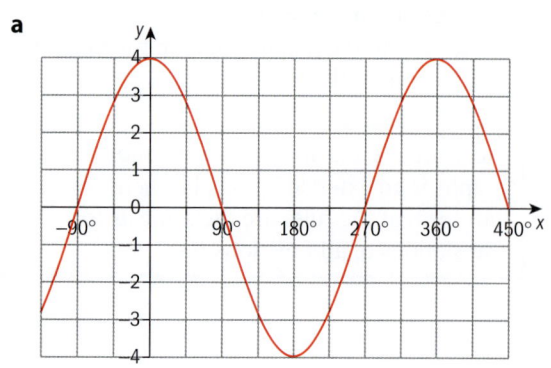

b

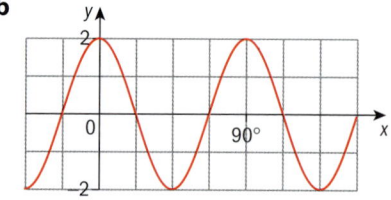

c

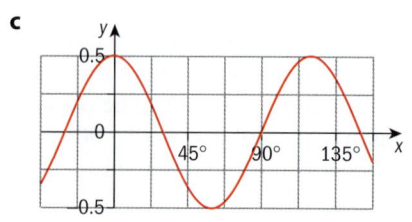

2 Draw the graph of each function showing at least two cycles. Be sure to clearly indicate the amplitude and period.

   a $y = 0.4 \sin 2x$ **b** $y = 7 \cos 5x$

   c $y = \frac{2}{3} \cos 8x$ **d** $y = \frac{5}{2} \sin \left(\frac{-x}{3} \right)$

3 State the amplitude, frequency and period of each graph. **Sketch** the graph for $-360° \le x \le 360°$.

   a $y = 4 \cos 3x$

   b $y = -\sin 0.5x$

   c $y = 0.5 \sin 2x + 3$

   d $y = 3 \cos 0.5x - 1$

4 This graph is a result of a transformation on $y = \sin x$ or $y = \cos x$.

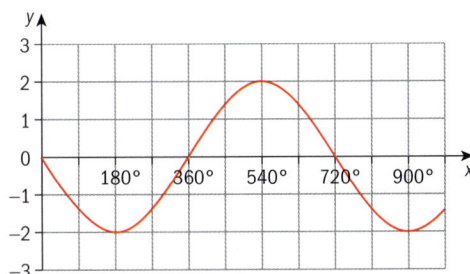

   Identify the transformation, and determine the function of the transformed graph.

5 Sketch the graph of each of the following, indicating the amplitude and period, and showing at least two cycles:

   a $y = \sin x + 12$ **b** $y = \sin (-x)$

   c $y = \cos x - 1$ **d** $y = \cos x + 6$

6 Find the amplitude, period and equation of the following graphs:

   a

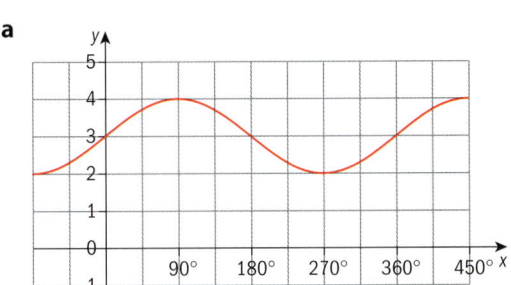

   b

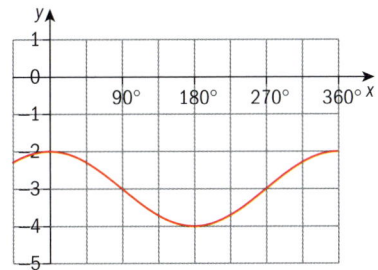

   c

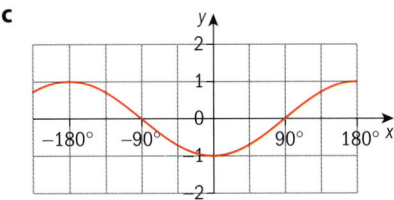

   d

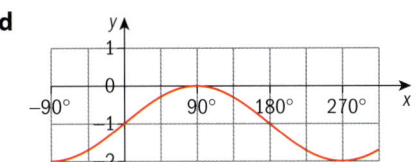

7 Describe in words how to transform the graph of $y = \sin x$ to:

   a $y = 3 \sin x + 2$ **b** $y = -2 \sin 4x$

   c $y = -\sin 2x - 3$ **d** $y = \frac{1}{2} \sin \left(\frac{x}{3} \right) - 4$

   e $y = -3 \sin 3x + 3$ **f** $y = \frac{3}{4} \sin \left(\frac{3x}{4} \right)$

8 Each graph is a result of a combination of transformations on $y = \sin x$ or $y = \cos x$.

   Identify the transformations, and **determine** the function of the transformed graph.

   a

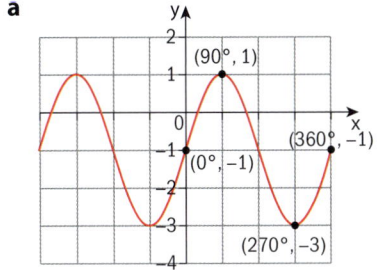

   b

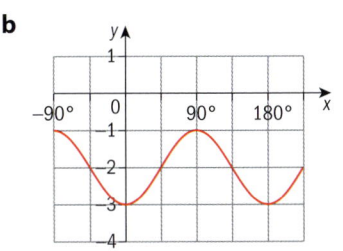

c

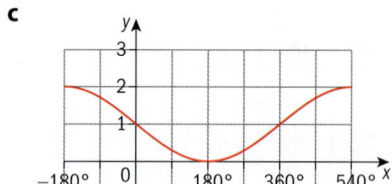

d

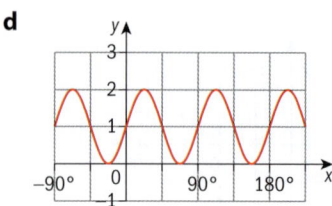

e

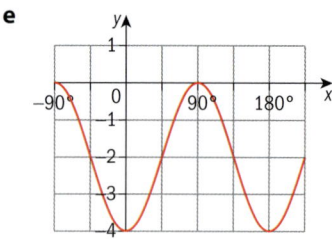

Problem solving

9 a A Ferris wheel has a radius of 10 meters. The bottom of the wheel is 2 meters above the ground. The wheel, rotating at a constant speed, takes 100 seconds to complete one revolution.

   i Find a function that models the height above the ground of a seat starting at the bottom of this Ferris wheel.

   ii Draw a graph of your function.

b Another Ferris wheel has a radius of 5 meters and the bottom of the wheel is 1 meter above the ground. It takes 2 minutes to make one complete revolution.

   i Find a function that models the height above the ground of a seat starting at the bottom of this Ferris wheel.

   ii Draw a graph of your function.

   iii For which age group do you think this Ferris wheel has been designed?

10 The graph shows the motion of a tall building as it sways to and fro in the wind.

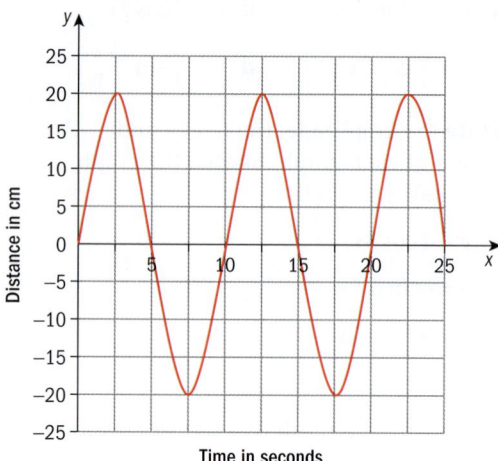

a Determine the period, and explain what it means in this problem.

b State the maximum number of centimeters that the tall building sways from its vertical position.

c Find a sinusoidal function to model this situation.

11 A nail is stuck in a car tire. The height of the nail above the ground varies as the wheel turns and can be modelled by this graph.

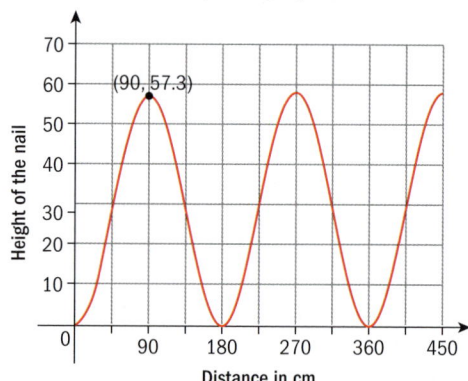

Find:

a the period of the graph, and explain what it means in this situation

b the amplitude, and explain what it means in this situation

c the radius of the wheel

d a sinusoidal function to describe the relationship between the distance the tire travels and its height above the ground.

Problem solving

12 When the Sun first rises, the angle of elevation increases rapidly at first, then more slowly, until the maximum angle is reached at about noon. The angle then decreases until sunset.

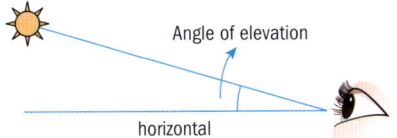

Assume that the relationship between the time of day and the angle of elevation is sinusoidal.

- Let t be the number of hours since midnight.

- Let the amplitude be 60 degrees.
- The maximum angle of elevation occurs at noon.
- The period is 24 hours.
- The angle of elevation at midnight is −65 degrees.

a **Sketch** a graph of hours after midnight against angle of elevation.

b **Explain** the significance of the t-intercepts.

c **Explain** what the values below the t-axis mean.

d **Predict** the angle of elevation at 9.00 in the morning and 2.00 in the afternoon.

e **Predict** the time of sunrise.

Objective D: Applying mathematics in real-life contexts
iii. apply the selected mathematical strategies successfully to reach a solution

In this Review you will apply the strategies of interpreting amplitude, period and dilation to sketch the graphs and reach appropriate solutions.

Review in context
Scientific and technical innovation

1 A tsunami, or monster tidal wave, can have a period anywhere between ten minutes and 2 hours, with a wavelength well over 500 km. Because of its incredible destructive powers, warning systems have been developed in regions where tsunamis are most likely to happen. A particular tsunami to hit a coastal town in Japan had a period of about a quarter of an hour. The normal ocean depth in this town was 9 m, and a tsunami of amplitude 10 m hit the coast.

a Write a sinusoidal function to describe the relationship of the depth of water and time, given that when $t = 0$, the sinusoidal function is at a minimum.

b Use your function to predict the depth of the water after:
  i 1 minute
  ii 5 minutes
  iii 10 minutes.

c Use your function to determine the minimum depth of the water.

d Interpret your answer to **c** in terms of the real world.

2 In 2005, the United States had one of the worst hurricane seasons on record. Computer models were continuously generated and updated in order to try to predict the path of oncoming storms. For almost five days, a portion of Hurricane Franklin's path could be approximated by a sinusoidal function, as seen in the following data:

Time (hours)	0	20	40	60	80	100	120
Longitude (degrees)	−78	−77	−74.5	−71.5	−69	−68	−69

a **Draw** a graph of the data and clearly indicate the amplitude and period.

b **Write down** the function representing this model.

c At what longitude was the hurricane at $t = 50$ hours?

d **Describe** how the graph of $y = \cos x$ was transformed to obtain this graph.

e Do you think the latitude of the hurricane followed a similar model? **Explain**.

3 The Bay of Fundy and Ungava Bay, both in Canada, have some of the highest tides in the world. Tides show periodic behaviour, with their constant shift from high to low tide and back again. Suppose a low tide of 1.5 m occurs at 6 am and a high tide of 18.5 m occurs twelve hours later.

  a Draw a graph to represent the height of the tide as a function of the number of hours, t, after 6am.

  b Write down the equation for this model.

  c Find the height of the tide at 3am and at 3pm.

  d Find the time(s) at which the height of the tide is 10 m.

  e Explain why harnessing electricity from this tidal energy is considered more reliable than wind energy.

4 A chemotherapy treatment is designed to kill cancer cells but it also kills red blood cells which are vital in the transport of oxygen in the body. The amount of red blood cells can be modelled by a sinusoidal function since it decreases after the treatment and then steadily increases until the next treatment. Suppose a patient's red blood cell count is 5 million cells per microliter on the day of treatment and hits a low of 2 million cells per microliter 10 days after treatment. If treatments occur every 20 days:

  a Draw a graph to represent the patient's red blood cell count over the course of 30 days.

  b From the graph, **state** the amplitude, period and frequency, and **write down** the function that models the situation.

  c Determine whether the patient has more or less than half of their maximum red blood cell count on day 15. **Justify** your answer.

  d If the 20th day were a holiday, would you rather go in for the treatment before the holiday or after? **Explain**.

Problem solving

5 The electricity delivered to your home is called 'alternating current' because it alternates back and forth between positive and negative voltage. It does so with regularity and so it can be described by a sinusoidal function.

  a The voltage in many European countries is 220 V with a frequency of 50 Hz (which means that 50 cycles occur in one second). **Draw** a graph of the amount of voltage over time, assuming at $t = 0$ you have 220 V.

  > Draw the graph between $t = 0$ seconds and $t = 0.02$ seconds.

  b Write down the period of your graph.

  c Write down the equation of your graph.

  d In North America, the typical voltage is 120 V at 60 Hz. **Draw** a graph of voltage as a function of time, assuming at $t = 0$ you have 120 V.

  e Write down the period, amplitude and equation for your graph.

  f Describe the transformations that occur from the European model to the North American model.

Reflect and discuss 2

How have you explored the statement of inquiry? Give specific examples.

Statement of inquiry:

Systems use logic to validate generalizations and increase our appreciation of the aesthetic.

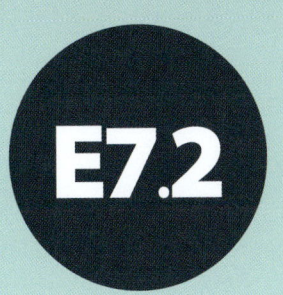

E7.2 Sine and cosine rules

Global context: Personal and cultural expression

Related concept: Space

Objectives

- Using the sine rule
- Using the cosine rule
- Using the sine and cosine rules to solve problems involving bearings

Inquiry questions

F
- How are non right-angled triangles labelled?
- What is the sine rule?

C
- How is the cosine rule related to the Pythagorean theorem?

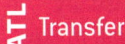

D
- Which is more useful, the sine rule or the cosine rule?
- How do the sine and cosine rules help define the space we live in?

LOGIC

ATL Transfer

Apply skills and knowledge in unfamiliar situations

Launch additional digital resources for this chapter.

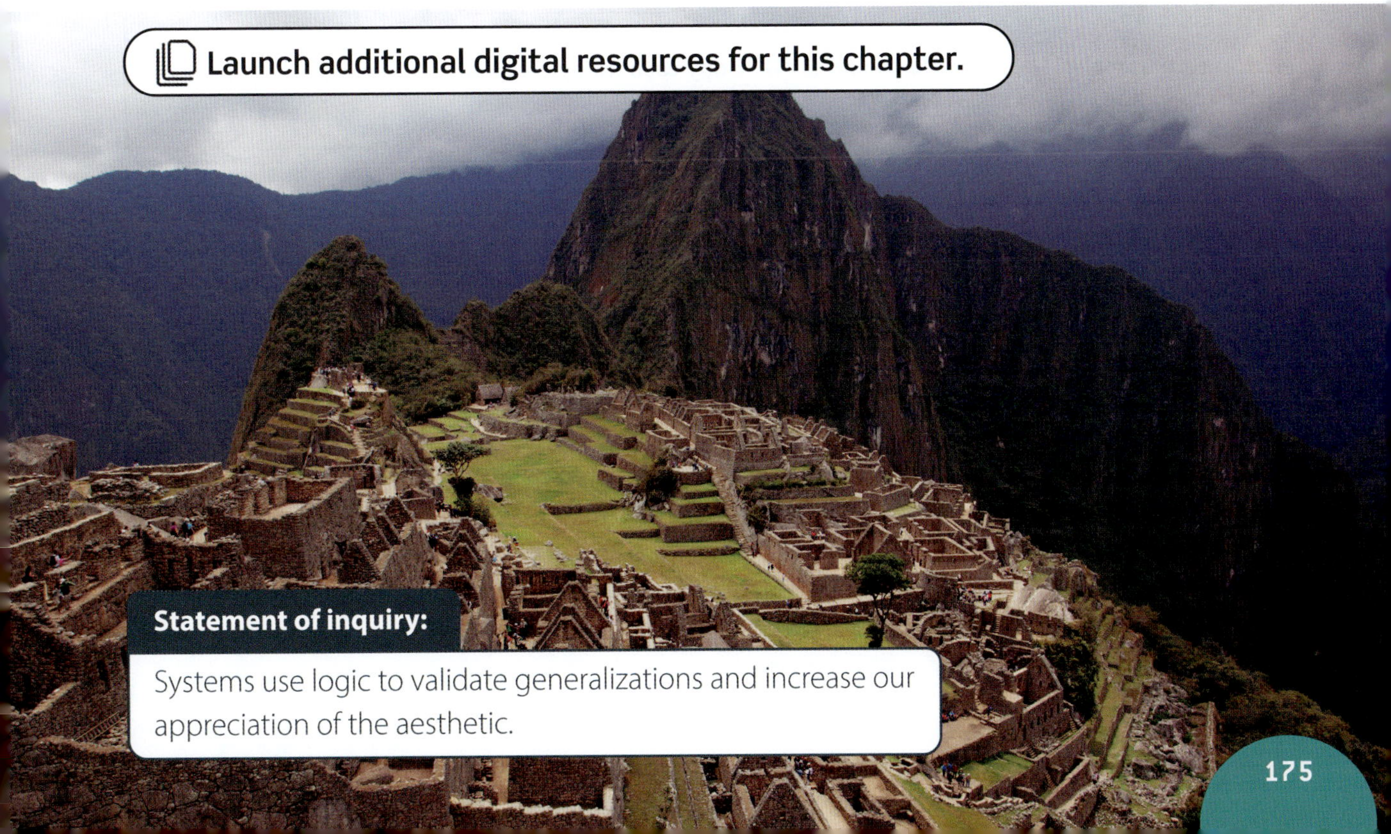

Statement of inquiry:

Systems use logic to validate generalizations and increase our appreciation of the aesthetic.

You should already know how to:

• find the area of a triangle given two perpendicular measurements	**1** Find the area of each triangle. **a** 3 cm, 7 cm **b** 6 cm, ←14 cm→
• use trigonometry in right-angled triangles	**2** Find x in each triangle. **a** 8 cm, 62°, x **b** x, 7 cm, 5 cm
• find the area of a sector of a circle	**3** Find the area of this sector. 115°, 6 cm

F Area of a triangle

- How are non right-angled triangles labelled?
- What is the sine rule?

When working with triangles, the convention is to label vertices and the interior angle at each vertex with a capital letter, and the side opposite that vertex with the same letter in lower case, like this:

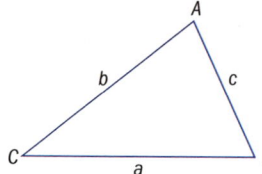

> A **convention** is a practice which, although usually not essential, makes things easier if everybody follows it. For example, in algebra, the convention is to write variables in alphabetical order.

Practice 1

1 Here are triangles *ABC*, *DEF*, *LMN* and *UVW*. Copy each triangle and label the remaining vertices and sides.

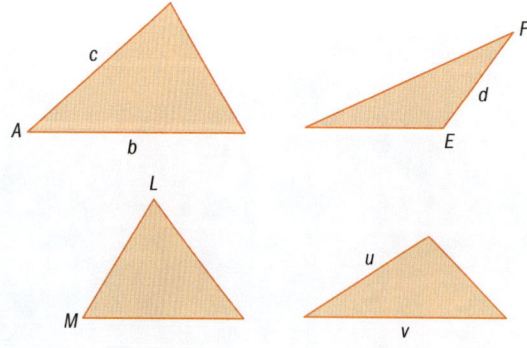

Exploration 1

1 Consider the triangle opposite.
Lengths are in centimeters.

   a Use trigonometry to work out the
length of the dotted line, given that it
meets BC at right angles.

   b Hence find the size of angle at B.

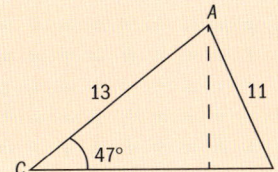

2 Consider the triangle opposite.
Lengths are in centimeters.

   Find the size of angle at B.

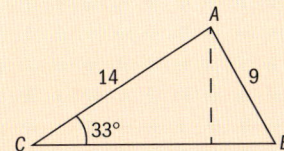

3 Triangle ABC has sides $BC = 7$ cm,
$AB = 8$ cm and $\angle ACB = 42°$.

   a Sketch triangle ABC.

   b Hence find the size of the angle at A.

4 Consider the triangle opposite.

   By considering the length of the line
through A perpendicular to BC, show
that $\dfrac{\sin B}{b} = \dfrac{\sin C}{c}$.

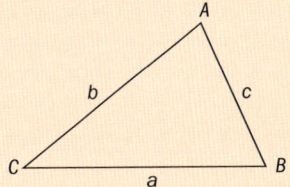

5 Show also that $\dfrac{\sin B}{b} = \dfrac{\sin A}{a}$.

6 Hence show that $\dfrac{\sin A}{a} = \dfrac{\sin B}{b} = \dfrac{\sin C}{c}$ and

   also that $\dfrac{a}{\sin A} = \dfrac{b}{\sin B} = \dfrac{c}{\sin C}$.

7 Consider the triangle opposite. Use
this formula to find the size of the angle
at B without first finding the triangle's
height. Lengths are given in centimeters.

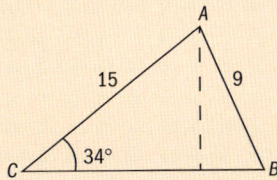

Reflect and discuss 1

Question 1 and question 7 from Exploration 1 both asked you to
find an angle given the same information. Why would it be more
convenient to use the formula from question 6 than to follow the
steps of question 1?

The sine rule

For a triangle ABC:

$$\frac{\sin A}{a} = \frac{\sin B}{b} = \frac{\sin C}{c}$$

and

$$\frac{a}{\sin A} = \frac{b}{\sin B} = \frac{c}{\sin C}$$

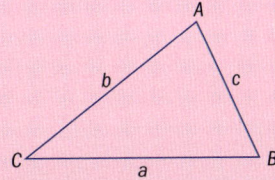

Example 1

Find the value of a, giving your answer correct to 3 significant figures.

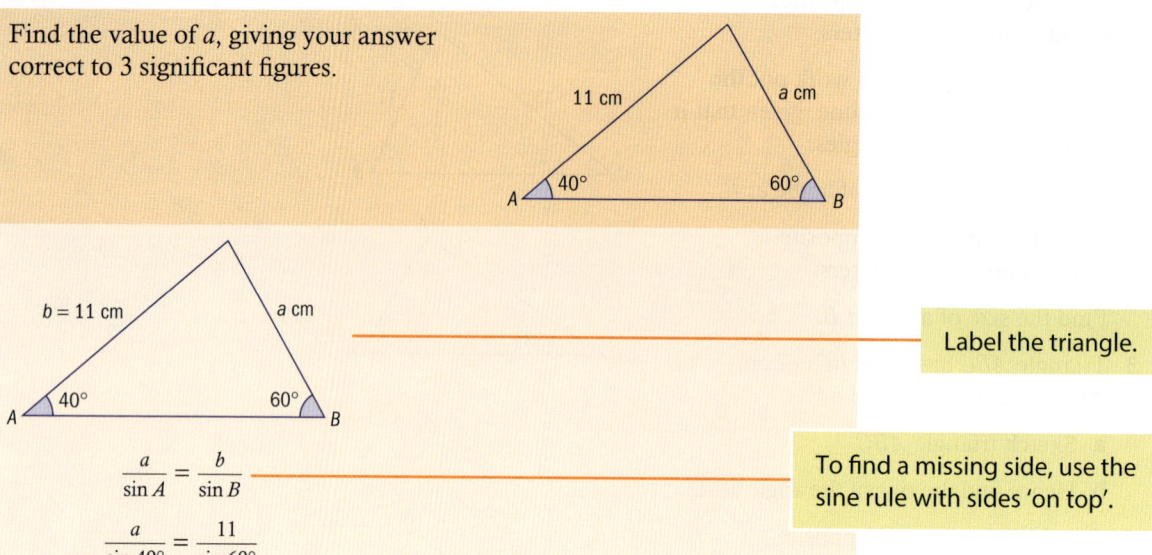

Label the triangle.

$$\frac{a}{\sin A} = \frac{b}{\sin B}$$

To find a missing side, use the sine rule with sides 'on top'.

$$\frac{a}{\sin 40°} = \frac{11}{\sin 60°}$$

$$\Rightarrow a = \frac{11\sin 40°}{\sin 60°} = 8.16 \text{ cm (3 s.f.)}$$

Example 2

Find the size of $\angle B$ correct to the nearest degree.

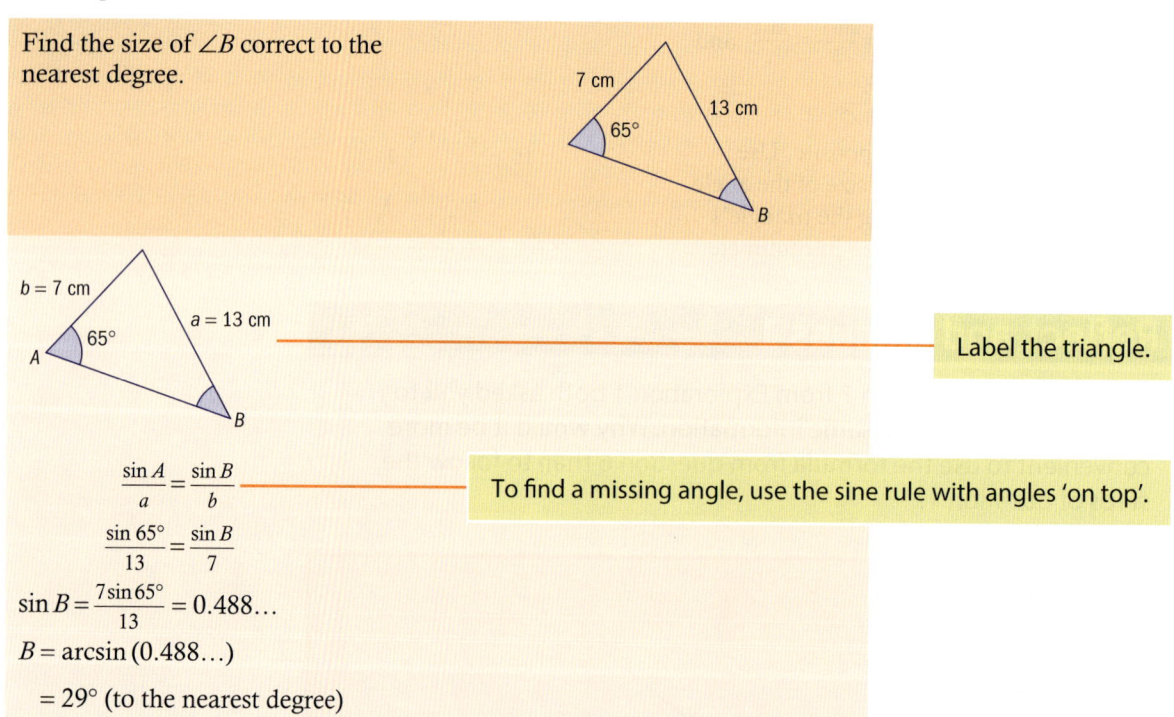

Label the triangle.

$$\frac{\sin A}{a} = \frac{\sin B}{b}$$

To find a missing angle, use the sine rule with angles 'on top'.

$$\frac{\sin 65°}{13} = \frac{\sin B}{7}$$

$$\sin B = \frac{7\sin 65°}{13} = 0.488\ldots$$

$$B = \arcsin(0.488\ldots)$$

$$= 29° \text{ (to the nearest degree)}$$

Practice 2

1 Find the length of the sides marked with letters, correct to 3 s.f.

a
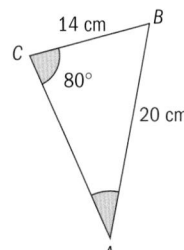

b
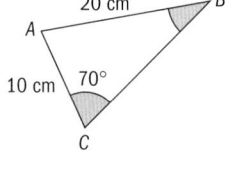

c
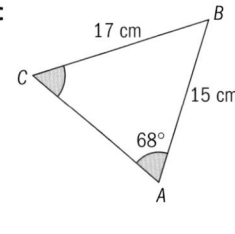

2 For each triangle, find the size of the unknown marked angles, correct to the nearest degree.

a
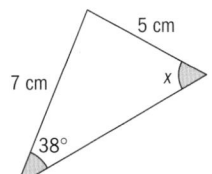

b
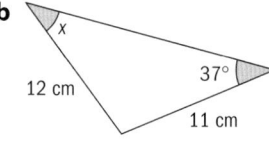

c
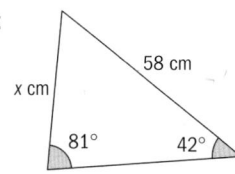

3 Find the value of *x* for each triangle. Give each answer correct to 1 d.p.

a

b

c

4 In triangle *XYZ*, *x* = 16 cm, ∠*Y* = 44° and ∠*Z* = 72°. Find the length of side *y*.

Problem solving

5 A yacht crosses the starting line of a race at *C* and sails on a bearing of 026°. After sailing 2.6 km, it rounds a buoy *B* and sails on a bearing of 335° until it reaches another buoy *A* that is due north of *C*.

  a Sketch a diagram to show the path followed by the yacht.

  b Calculate the size of ∠*CBA* and find the size of ∠*CAB*.

  c Calculate the total distance sailed by the yacht correct to 3 s.f.

6 From point *X*, a ship sights a lighthouse *L* on a bearing of 350°. The ship is moving on a bearing of 020° at 10 km/h. Thirty minutes later it is at point *Y* and sights the lighthouse again, this time on a bearing of 325°.

  a Sketch a triangle to illustrate this information.

  b Determine the size of all three angles in the triangle.

  c Calculate the distance from point *Y* to the lighthouse. Give your answer in km, accurate to 3 significant figures.

C The sine and cosine rules

- How is the cosine rule related to the Pythagorean theorem?

Reflect and discuss 2

Explain why you cannot use the sine rule to find length x in this triangle.

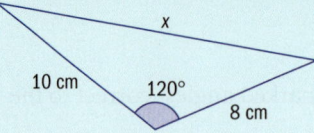

Exploration 2

1 a Copy triangle ABC, with the altitude through C meeting AB at right angles at point P.

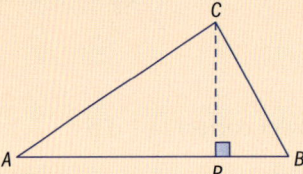

Label the sides a, b and c.

b Label length AP as x. Hence label length PB in terms of c and x.

c Use the Pythagorean theorem to write two expressions for CP. Hence show that $b^2 - x^2 = a^2 - (c - x)^2$.

Expand the brackets and simplify this equation as far as possible.

d Use trigonometry to express x in terms of A and b.

e Hence show that $a^2 = b^2 + c^2 - 2bc \cos A$.

2 Explain why it is possible to rewrite the formula from step **1e** so that it uses angle B as $b^2 = a^2 + c^2 - 2ac \cos B$.

Rewrite the formula so that it uses angle C.

The cosine rule

For a triangle ABC:

$a^2 = b^2 + c^2 - 2bc \cos A$

$b^2 = a^2 + c^2 - 2ac \cos B$

$c^2 = a^2 + b^2 - 2ab \cos C$

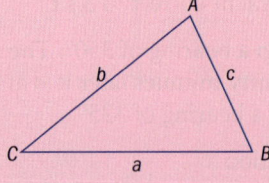

Reflect and discuss 3

- How would you modify the formula if the triangle is labelled MNP and you wanted to use the cosine rule to find the measure of side p?

- How is the cosine rule related to the Pythagorean theorem? Explain.

Example 3

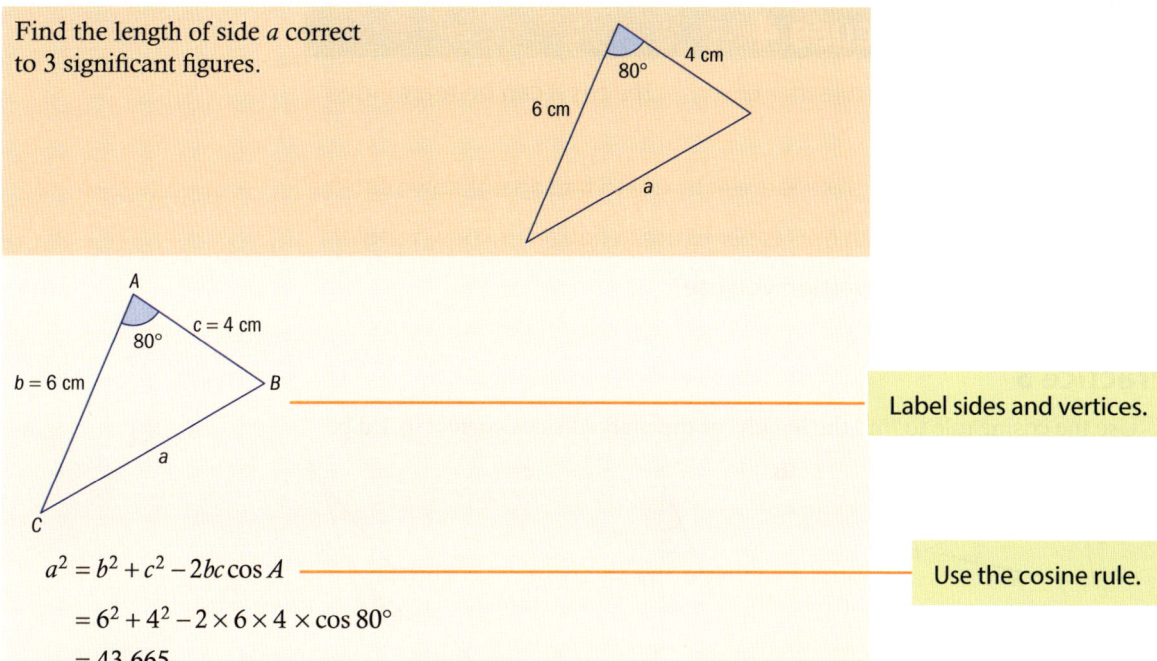

Find the length of side a correct to 3 significant figures.

$a^2 = b^2 + c^2 - 2bc \cos A$ ———————————————— Use the cosine rule.

Label sides and vertices.

$= 6^2 + 4^2 - 2 \times 6 \times 4 \times \cos 80°$

$= 43.665...$

$\Rightarrow a = 6.61$ cm (3 s.f.) ———————————— Check that your answer seems sensible.

Example 4

Find the value of x correct to the nearest degree.

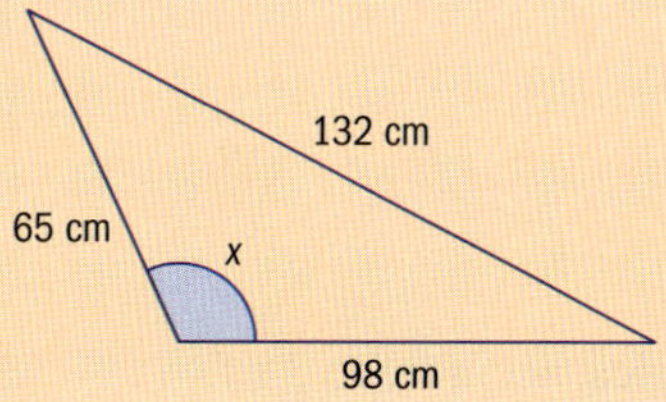

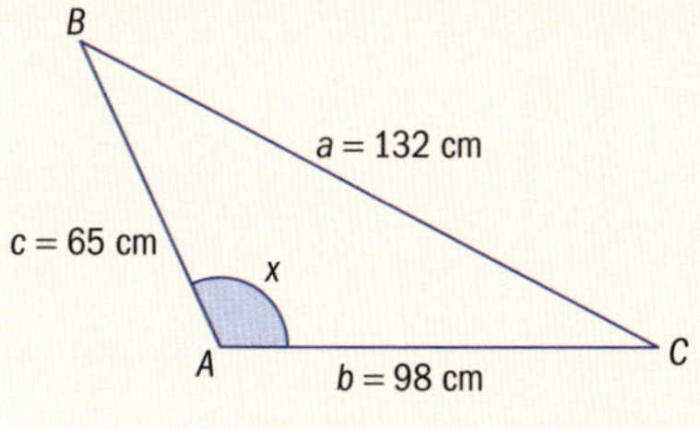

Label sides and vertices.

$a^2 = b^2 + c^2 - 2bc \cos A$ ———————————————— Use the cosine rule.

$132^2 = 98^2 + 65^2 - 2 \times 98 \times 65 \times \cos x$

$17\,424 = 9604 + 4225 - 12\,740 \cos x$ ———————————— Rearrange.

$12\,740 \cos x = -3595$

$\cos x = -0.28218...$

$x = \arccos(-0.28218...)$

$= 106°$ (to the nearest degree)

Reflect and discuss 4

- Show that the cosine rule $a^2 = b^2 + c^2 - 2bc \cos A$ can be rearranged to $\cos A = \dfrac{b^2 + c^2 - a^2}{2bc}$.
- Which version do you think is easier to use to find an unknown side?
- Which version do you think is easier to use to find an unknown angle?
- Does it matter which version you use?

Practice 3

1 Use the cosine rule to find the lengths of the marked sides correct to 1 d.p.

a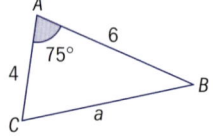

b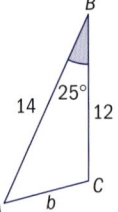

c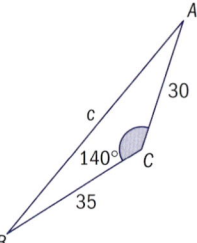

2 Use the cosine rule to find the size of the marked angles correct to the nearest degree.

a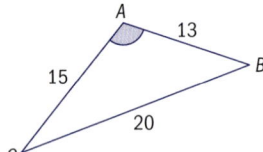

b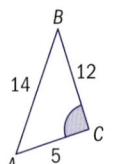

c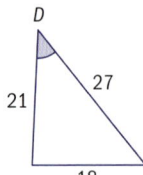

3 Find these side lengths and angles, accurate to 3 s.f.

  a $\triangle PQR$, $p = 14$, $q = 11$, $R = 98°$. Find side r.

  b $\triangle DEF$, $d = 6$, $e = 12$, $f = 9$. Find angle E.

  c $\triangle XYZ$, $x = 7.2$, $z = 5.4$, $Y = 121°$. Find side y.

  d $\triangle BCD$, $b = 25$, $c = 31$, $d = 34$. Find angle D.

4 Two boats leave the same harbour. One travels on a bearing of 060° for 13 km, the other on a bearing of 135° for 8 km.

  a Draw a diagram illustrating their positions.

  b Find the angle between their courses.

  c Find the distance between the two boats.

Problem solving

5 A triangle has sides of length 4 cm, 6 cm and 7 cm.

  a Find the size of the largest angle in the triangle.

  b Find the size of the smallest angle in the triangle.

D Applying the sine and cosine rules

- Which is more useful, the sine rule or the cosine rule?
- How do the sine and cosine rules help define the space we live in?

You can use the sine and cosine rules to find missing lengths and angles in triangles. To decide which rule to use, look at the information you have and the information you are trying to find.

Reflect and discuss 5

Referring to the triangle here:

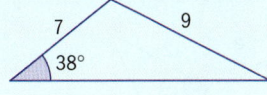

- Which measurements can you calculate?
  What rule will you use? Explain your selection.

- What information needs to be given in order to be able to use the sine rule?

- What information leads you to use the cosine rule?

By examining the sine rule and cosine rule carefully, you can work out when you should use each one. For the sine rule, you only ever use two of the three parts, so only two are shown here.

Cosine rule: $a^2 = b^2 + c^2 - 2bc \cos A$ **Sine rule:**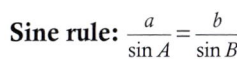

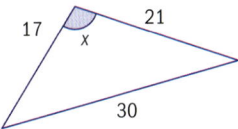

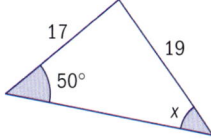

> If an angle and the side opposite are known, then the sine rule can be used. If not, then use the cosine rule.

The cosine rule involves three sides and one angle.

The sine rule involves two sides and two angles.

This triangle problem involves three sides and one angle (the unknown), so use the cosine rule.

This triangle problem involves two sides and two angles (one is the unknown), so use the sine rule.

Example 5

Find the size of the angle at A.

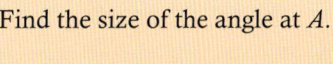

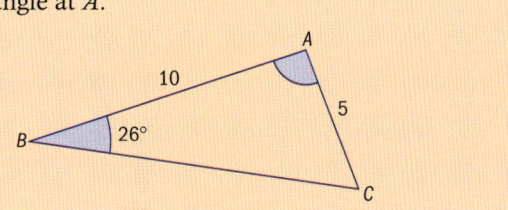

$\dfrac{\sin B}{b} = \dfrac{\sin C}{c}$ ——————— The problem involves two sides and two angles, so use the sine rule.

$\dfrac{\sin 26°}{5} = \dfrac{\sin C}{10}$

$C = \arcsin(2 \sin 26°)$ ——————————— Rearrange to make C the subject.

$\quad = 61.25°$

$\Rightarrow A = 180° - 26° - 61.25°$ ——————— The angles in a triangle add up to $180°$.

$\quad = 92.7°$ (3 s.f.)

Practice 4

1 In each triangle, determine whether the cosine rule or sine rule should be used to find the value of x. Explain how you have made your decision.

a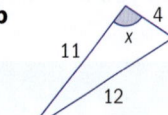

b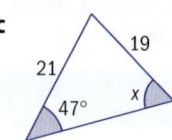

c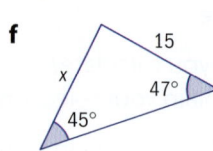

d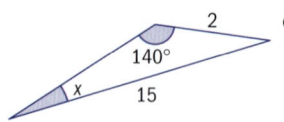

e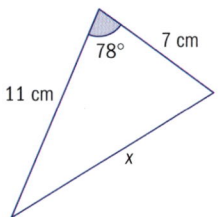

f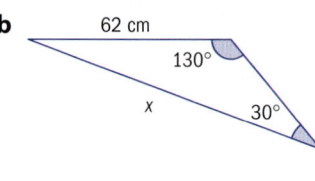

2 In each triangle, find the value of x, giving your answer correct to 3 s.f.

a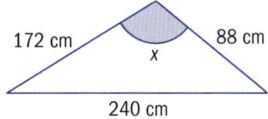

b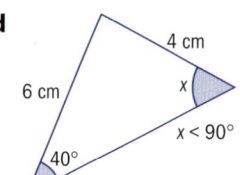

c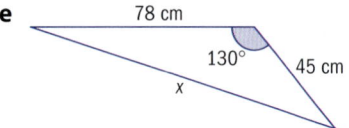

d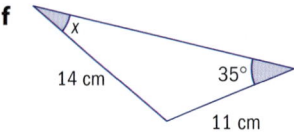

e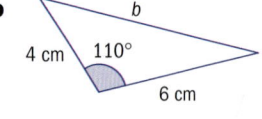

f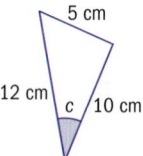

3 Use the sine rule or cosine rule to find the marked sides and angles. Give answers correct to 3 significant figures.

a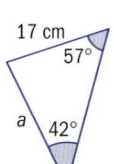

b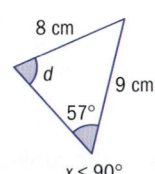

c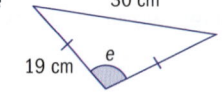

d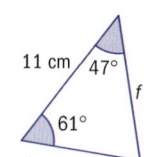

e

f

Problem solving

4 Find the value of x.

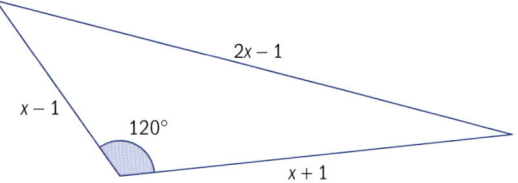

5 Circles of radius 10 cm and 6 cm overlap as shown:

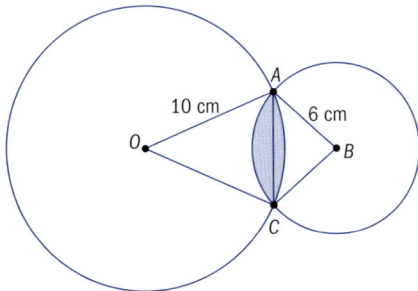

The circles meet at points A and C, and $\angle AOC = 45°$.

a Find the length of the straight line segment joining A to C.

b Hence find $\angle ABC$.

c Hence find the shaded area.

- -

One handy and beneficial use of trigonometry is to help you calculate measurements in space that you cannot measure directly.

Objective D: Applying mathematics in real-life contexts
iv. justify the degree of accuracy of a solution

In the Activity, comment on the accuracy of the original measurements and the effect that inaccuracy in the original measurements would have on your calculations.

ATL

Activity

1 Telephone cables from a house are connected to a telegraph pole C at the roadside, but C is not yet connected to the network.

▶ Continued on next page

On the other side of the road, two other telegraph poles *A* and *B* are 30 meters apart.

An engineer uses a theodolite to measure $\angle CAB = 27°$ and $\angle ABC = 68°$.

a Copy and complete this aerial view of the street, adding the size of angle *B* and the length *AB*.

b Find the size of angle *C*.

c Hence calculate the lengths of *BC* and *AC*. Explain why the telegraph pole at *C* should be connected to pole *B*.

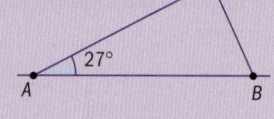

d The engineer discovers an error in the measurements. The angle at *A* is actually 23°.

  i Calculate the true length of *BC*. Justify your degree of accuracy.

  ii Find the percentage error in your original calculated value of *BC*.

  iii Suggest three reasons why the engineer should bring more cable than the calculated value to connect *B* to *C*.

A theodolite is a tool used to measure angles when making maps or surveying construction sites.

Practice 5

1 From point *P*, a ship sails 5.5 km to point *Q* on a bearing of 039°. It then sails 4.1 km to point *R* on a bearing of 072°.

  a Show this information on a diagram.

  b Calculate the size of angle *PQR*.

  c Find the distance from *R* to *P*.

2 Two boats leave a harbour: one travels on a bearing of 050° for 14 km, the other on a bearing of 145° for 18 km.

  a Draw a diagram illustrating their positions.

  b Find the angle between their courses.

  c Find the distance between the two boats.

Problem solving

3 Peter, Alex and Mary are sea-kayaking. Peter is 430 m from Alex on a bearing of 113°. Mary is on a bearing of 210° and a distance of 310 m from Alex. Find the distance between Peter and Mary.

4 I am standing at point *O*, near a major road. Along the road there are markers every 100 m. I can see three consecutive markers: *P*, *Q* and *R*. I am 20 m away from marker *P*. The bearing of *P* from my current position is 340° and the bearing of *Q* from my current position is 030°.

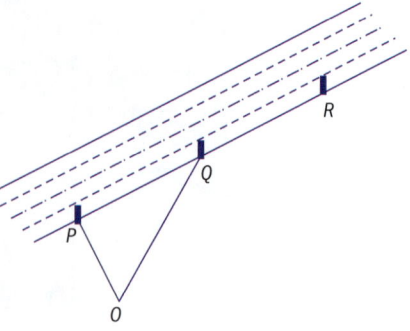

  a Find the angle *POQ*.

  b Find the bearing of *Q* from *P*.

  c Find my distance from *Q*.

  d Find my distance from *R*.

Summary

When working with a triangle ABC, side a is opposite vertex A and so on.

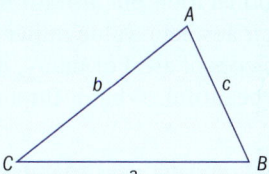

The sine rule

$$\frac{\sin A}{a} = \frac{\sin B}{b} = \frac{\sin C}{c}$$

and

$$\frac{a}{\sin A} = \frac{b}{\sin B} = \frac{c}{\sin C}$$

The cosine rule

$$a^2 = b^2 + c^2 - 2bc \cos A$$
$$b^2 = a^2 + c^2 - 2ac \cos B$$
$$c^2 = a^2 + b^2 - 2ab \cos C$$

Mixed practice

1 Find the labelled side correct to 3 s.f.

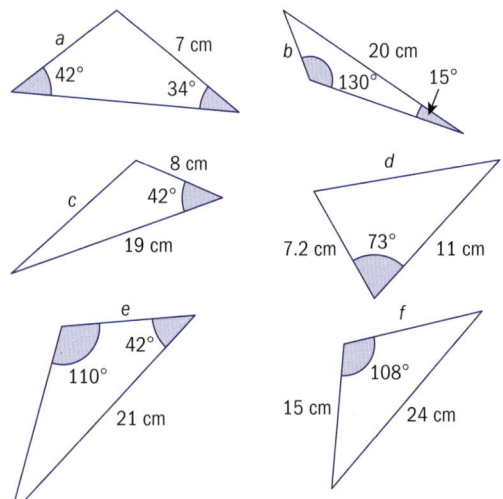

2 Find the labelled angle correct to 3 s.f.

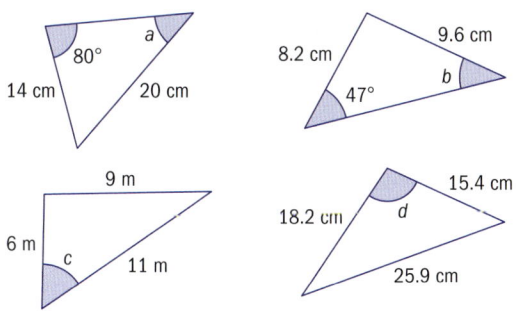

3 Find the labelled angle.

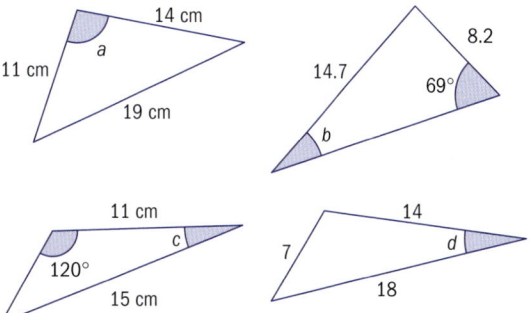

4 Find the size of the smallest angle in a triangle with sides 4 cm, 9 cm and 11 cm.

5 Two friends start walking from the same spot. One walks 50 meters due north. The other walks 35 meters on a bearing of 057°.

Find the distance between their final positions, correct to 3 s.f.

Review in context

Global context: Personal and cultural expression

Throughout history, maps have been cherished not only as essential navigational tools but also for their intricacy and beauty. Ancient maps are often highly desirable because of their aesthetic value rather than their accuracy but it is not uncommon for people to hang modern maps as pieces of art. For many, if the map represents a location of personal significance, this is enough to make it beautiful. What is important when making a map: accuracy or aesthetics?

Many maps are created by **triangulation**; this is when a network of points are joined across a landscape. Surveyors measure distances and bearings to a high degree of accuracy and use them to form the skeleton that underpins the map, as illustrated here in this triangulation of the Hawaiian island of Oahu.

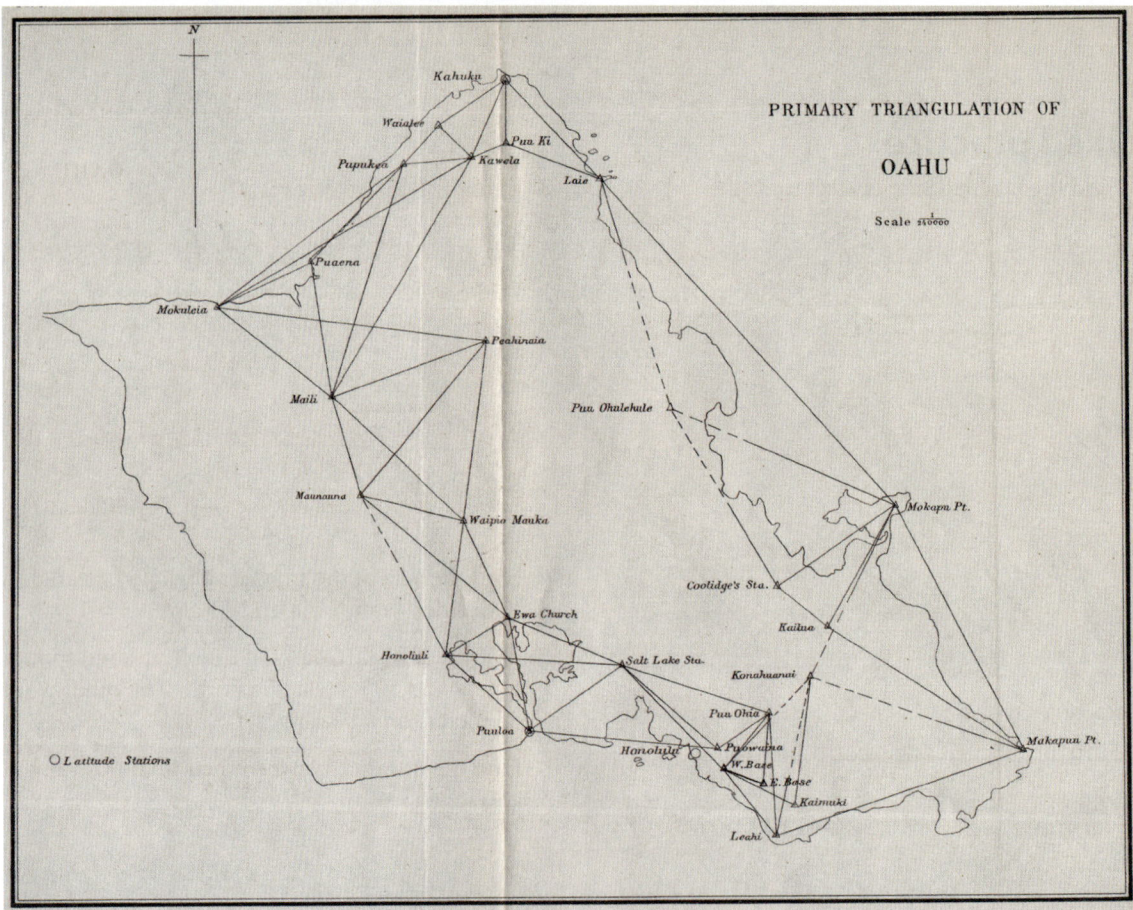

The map on the next page shows some key towns on the banks of Lac Léman, which lies on the French-Swiss border – it is known as Lake Geneva in most English-speaking countries. Because of the presence of the lake itself, and the mountains that surround it, finding point-to-point distance measurements between places on the shores of the lake is difficult.

Use the map of Lac Léman to help you answer these questions. Give your answers correct to a sensible degree of accuracy.

1 It is 9.5 km from Rolle to Saint-Prex on a bearing of 076°. Thonon-les-Bains lies on a bearing of 130° from Rolle, and on a bearing of 170° from Saint-Prex.

   a Using the letters R, S and T to denote the three towns, **sketch** triangle RST to show their positions relative to each other.

b Find and label the size of angles ∠RST, ∠STR and ∠TRS.

c Hence find the distances from Rolle to Thonon-les-Bains and from Saint-Prex to Thonon-les-Bains.

d When standing in Saint-Prex, there is an angle of 100° between Lausanne and Thonon-les-Bains. Lausanne lies on a bearing of 038° from Thonon-les-Bains. Add this information to your diagram.

e Hence find the distance from Lausanne to Saint-Prex and Thonon-les-Bains.

Map of Lac Léman

Problem solving

2 The distance from Évian-les-Bains to Saint-Gingolph is measured to be 16.9 kilometers. Viewed from Lausanne, there is an angle of 54° between Évian-les-Bains and Saint-Gingolph. Viewed from Évian-les-Bains, there is an angle of 66° between Lausanne and Saint-Gingolph. Évian-les-Bains lies on a bearing of 200° from Lausanne.

a Find the bearing of Saint-Gingolph from Lausanne.

b Find the distance from Lausanne to Évian-les-Bains.

3 The distance from Vevey to Montreux is 6.5 km. The distance from Montreux to Saint-Gingolph is 9.6 km. The distance from Vevey to Saint-Gingolph is 8.6 km on a bearing of 200°.

a Find the angle between Montreux and Saint-Gingolph as viewed from Vevey.

b Hence find the bearing of Montreux from Vevey.

c Find the bearing of Saint-Gingolph from Montreux.

4 Nyon is 7.0 km from Chens-sur-Léman. Coppet is 6.1 km from Chens-sur-Léman. As viewed from Chens-sur-Léman, there is an angle of 84° between Nyon and Coppet.
Find the distance from Nyon to Coppet.

Reflect and discuss 6

How have you explored the statement of inquiry? Give specific examples.

Statement of inquiry:

Systems use logic to validate generalizations and increase our appreciation of the aesthetic.

Statement of inquiry:

Representing patterns and change in a variety of forms has helped humans apply their understanding of scientific principles.

Key concept:

Form is the shape and underlying structure of an entity or piece of work.

F **Which patterns exist in real-life situations?**

Patterns are sets of numbers or objects that follow a specific order or rule.

Patterns in music

Steve Reich is an American composer who experiments with pattern and structure in his music. One of his famous works is titled 'Clapping Music for two people', and consists of a single rhythm repeated over 150 times, but with variation created by one musician starting half a beat later every 8 bars.

Search online for 'Steve Reich clapping music' to listen to a live performance and see if you can follow any patterns.

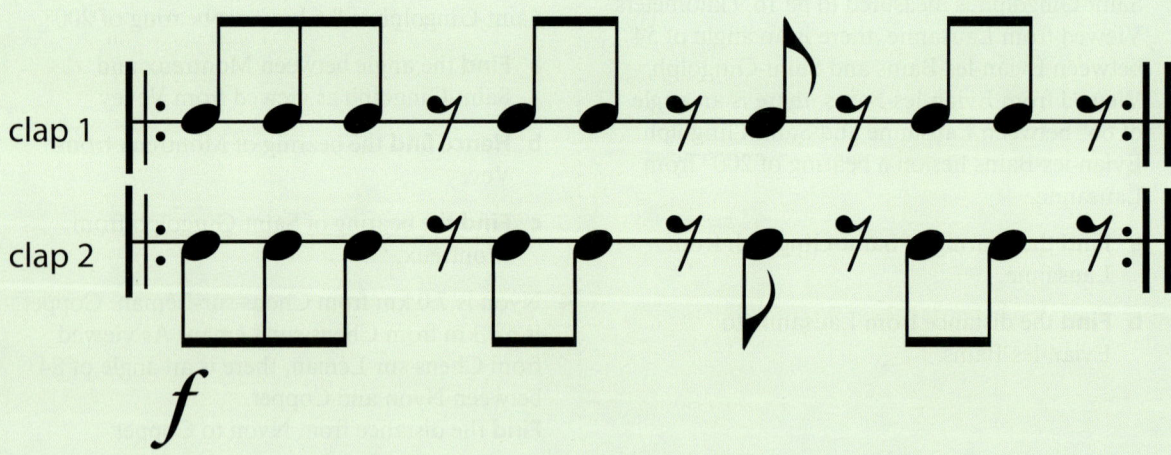

clap 1

clap 2

f

C How can changing the form help to visualise a pattern?

Change is a variation in size, amount or behavior.

Hilbert's Hotel Infinity

Are there different *forms* of infinity denoting different *sizes* of infinity? David Hilbert's thought experiment imagined a hotel with an infinite number of rooms – with the motto 'always room for one more!'

- What if a guest arrives, but all the infinite number of rooms in the hotel are already occupied? No problem – the guest in room 1 moves to room 2, the guest in room 2 moves to room 3, and so on. Room 1 is now free, and everyone is happy.

- And what if an *infinite* number of guests arrive at the same time but all rooms are occupied? Still no problem – the guest in room 1 moves to room 2, the guest in room 2 moves to room 4, and so on, so that the one in room n moves to room $2n$. All the even-numbered rooms are now occupied, but all the odd numbered rooms are free.

D To what extent does changing the form help you understand the scientific principles in real-life situations?

The symbol for infinity is called a lemniscate. The word lemniscate is of Latin origin, and means 'pendant ribbon'.

- Why do you think this form was chosen to symbolize infinity?

- Can you design an alternative symbol that would effectively signify infinity?

This curve is known as the Lemniscate of Bernoulli; on the Cartesian plane its equation is:

$$(x^2 + y^2)^2 = 2a^2(x^2 - y^2)$$

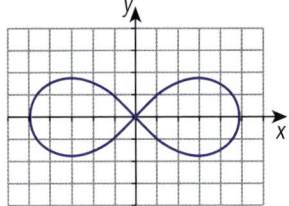

- Use a GDC to graph this equation and create a slider for the variable a from −5 to 5. What effect does the variable a have on the graph?

Global context: Scientific and technical innovation

Exploration: Explore how humans apply their understanding of scientific principles to real-life situations

 Launch additional digital resources for this unit.

Global context: Scientific and technical innovation

Related concept: Patterns

Objectives

- Finding and justifying (or proving) general rules and formulae for sequences
- Using explicit and recursive formulae to describe arithmetic sequences and geometric sequences
- Recognizing arithmetic and geometric sequences in context

FORM

Inquiry questions

F
- What is an arithmetic sequence?
- What is a geometric sequence?
- What are the recursive and explicit formulae for arithmetic and geometric sequences?

C
- How do patterns help you recognize arithmetic and geometric sequences in real-life problems?
- How can you solve problems involving arithmetic and geometric sequences?

D
- How does the behavior of a geometric sequence vary depending on the value of the common ratio?
- How can you use the general patterns for arithmetic and geometric sequences to predict future terms?

ATL Critical-thinking

Identify trends and forecast possibilities

Statement of inquiry:

Representing patterns and change in a variety of forms has helped humans apply their understanding of scientific principles.

📖 **Launch additional digital resources for this chapter.**

You should already know how to:

• use notation to describe sequences	**1** Write down the first three terms of each sequence. **a** $u_{n+1} = u_n + 1, u_1 = 5$ **b** $v_n = 2n - 1$ **c** $w_{n+1} = 2w_n, w_1 = 2$
• write recursive and explicit formulae	**2** Write a recursive and an explicit formula for the sequence that begins 1, 4, 9, 16, …
• use the laws of indices for positive integer powers	**3** Simplify: **a** $3^5 \times 3^2$ **b** $6^5 \div 6^3$ **c** $2 \times 5^1 \times 5^{n-1}$ **d** $\dfrac{4^7}{4^2}$
• solve simultaneous equations	**4** By hand, or using a GDC, solve the simultaneous equations: $y = x + 6$ and $y = 3x$
• calculate compound interest	**5** Find the value of \$150 invested at a compound interest rate of 5% per year for 3 years.

F General formulae for arithmetic and geometric sequences

- What is an arithmetic sequence?
- What is a geometric sequence?
- What are the recursive and explicit formulae for arithmetic and geometric sequences?

ATL

Exploration 1

1 Here are four different sequences.

    4, 7, 10, 13, 16, 19, …

    23, 30, 37, 44, 51, 58, …

    48, 42, 36, 30, 24, …

    11, 42, 73, 104, 135, …

Copy each sequence and write down anything you notice about it.

Describe any similarities about the way you think the sequences could have been be generated.

Suggest ways in which the sequences might continue.

▶ Continued on next page

2 Here are four more sequences.

4, 12, 36, 108, 324, …

5, −10, 20, −40, 80, …

−96, −48, −24, −12, …

100, 25, 6.25, 1.5625, …

Write down each sequence and anything you notice about it.

Describe any similarities about the way you think the sequences have been generated.

Suggest ways in which the sequences might continue.

3 Discuss your conclusions with others.

4 The sequences in step **1** are **arithmetic** sequences.

The sequences in step **2** are **geometric** sequences.

Consider each of the following sequences and decide if it is an arithmetic sequence, a geometric sequence, or neither.

a 17, 19, 21, 23, 25, …   **b** 18, 9, 4.5, 2.25, …

c 1, 4, 9, 16, 25, …   **d** 5, 10, 20, 40, 80, …

e $1, \frac{1}{2}, \frac{1}{3}, \frac{1}{4}, …$ **f** 13, 39, 117, 351, …

g 64, 56, 48, 40, 32, …   **h** 1, 5.5, 10, 14.5, 19, …

i 3, 3, 3, 3, 3, …   **j** $\sqrt{1}, \sqrt{2}, \sqrt{3}, \sqrt{4}, …$

5 The following recursive formulae each define a sequence.

In each case, list the first few terms of the sequence and determine if it is an arithmetic sequence, a geometric sequence, or neither.

> A recursive formula is sometimes called a **term-to-term** formula.

a $a_{n+1} = a_n + 3, a_1 = 4$ **b** $b_{n+1} = b_n - 2, b_1 = 5$

c $c_{n+1} = 2c_n, c_1 = 3$ **d** $d_{n+1} = \frac{1}{4}d_n, d_1 = 1024$

e $e_{n+1} = 3e_n - 1, e_1 = 1$ **f** $f_{n+1} = (f_n + 2)(f_n - 3), f_1 = 5$

g $g_{n+1} = 4 - g_n, g_1 = 1$ **h** $h_{n+1} = h_n - 6.4, h_1 = 13.5$

In an **arithmetic** sequence the *difference* between consecutive terms is constant.

In a **geometric** sequence the *ratio* between consecutive terms is constant.

> If d is positive the series is **increasing**, and if d is negative it is **decreasing**.

When working with arithmetic sequences, we typically use u_1 for the first term, and n for the term number. The constant difference between consecutive terms is d. Therefore you could write:

$$u_{n+1} - u_n = d$$

or, rearranging the equation:

$$u_{n+1} = u_n + d.$$

The difference d is usually called the **common difference**.

> You will sometimes see a used instead of u_1 for the first term of an arithmetic sequence.

Exploration 2

1 Use the recursive formula to write each of the terms u_1, u_2, ... u_6 of an arithmetic sequence with first term u_1 and common difference d.

2 Look for patterns as the sequence moves from one term to the next.

Describe briefly how these patterns relate to what you know about arithmetic sequences.

3 Now look for patterns linking the term number to the right-hand side of the formula. Generalizing from the patterns you observe, write down a conjecture for a formula for u_n in terms of n. This is an **explicit** formula.

4 Verify that your explicit formula gives $u_7 = u_1 + 6d$.

5 Use your conjecture to find explicit formulae for these recursive formulae:

   a $s_{n+1} = s_n + 3,\ s_1 = 4$

   b $t_{n+1} = t_n - 2,\ t_1 = 5$

> An explicit formula is sometimes called a **position-to-term** formula.

Mathematicians often use r to represent the constant ratio between consecutive terms of a geometric sequence. So when n is the term number, you can write:

$$\frac{u_{n+1}}{u_n} = r$$

or, rearranging the equation:

$$u_{n+1} = ru_n$$

r is usually called the **common ratio**.

Looking again at Exploration 1, step **5**, which of the formulae given are of the same form as the formula above?

Exploration 3

1 Use the recursive formula to write each of the terms u_1, u_2, ... u_6 of a geometric sequence with first term u_1 and common ratio r.

2 By considering the pattern you obtain, and generalizing from it, write down a conjecture for an explicit formula for u_n, the nth term of a geometric sequence with first term u_1 and common ratio r.

3 Use your conjecture to find explicit formulae for the geometric sequences described by these recursive formulae:

   a $c_{n+1} = 2c_n,\ c_1 = 3$

   b $d_{n+1} = \frac{1}{4}d_n,\ d_1 = 1024$

An **arithmetic sequence** with first term u_1 and common difference d has recursive formula $u_{n+1} = u_n + d$ and explicit formula $u_n = u_1 + (n-1)d$ for the nth term.

A **geometric sequence** with first term u_1 and common ratio r has recursive formula $u_{n+1} = ru_n$ and explicit formula $u_n = u_1 r^{n-1}$ for the nth term.

> Sometimes arithmetic sequences are called **arithmetic progressions**, and geometric sequences are called **geometric progressions**. The names are interchangeable.

Example 1

An arithmetic sequence has first term 7 and common difference -3.
Find a general formula for u_n, the nth term. Simplify your answer.

$u_1 = 7, d = -3$

$u_n = 7 + (n-1)(-3)$ ——— Substitute the given information into $u_n = u_1 + (n-1)d$.

$u_n = 7 - 3n + 3$ ——— Expand the brackets.

$u_n = 10 - 3n$ ——— Simplify.

Example 2

A geometric sequence has first term 2 and common ratio 5.
Find a general formula for u_n, the nth term.

$u_1 = 2, r = 5$

$u_n = u_1 r^{n-1}$

$u_n = 2 \times 5^{n-1}$ ——— Substitute the given information into $u_n = u_1 r^{n-1}$.

Example 3

A geometric sequence has the general formula $u_n = 3 \times 6^n$.

a Express the formula in the form $u_n = u_1 r^{n-1}$.

b Hence write down its first term (u_1) and common ratio.

a $u_n = 3 \times 6^n$ ——— You are given the formula, but it is not in the form $u_n = u_1 r^{n-1}$.

$u_n = 3 \times 6^1 \times 6^{n-1}$ ——— Use the laws of indices.

$u_n = 18 \times 6^{n-1}$ ——— This is now in the form $u_n = u_1 r^{n-1}$.

b The first term is 18 and the common ratio is 6. ——— The general form is $u_n = u_1 r^{n-1}$, so $u_1 = 18$ and $r = 6$.

Example 4

A geometric sequence has the general formula $u_n = 2 \times (-4)^n$.
Find its first term and common ratio.

$u_1 = 2 \times (-4)^1 = -8$ ——————————— Using the given formula, you can find the first term directly.

The first term is –8.

Using the formula again gives u_2.

$u_2 = 2 \times (-4)^2 = 32$ ——————————— The common ratio r is equal to $u_2 \div u_1$.

$r = u_2 \div u_1 = 32 \div -8 = -4$

The common ratio is –4.

Practice 1

1 Find explicit formulae for the nth term of:

     a an arithmetic sequence with first term 5 and common difference 7
     b an arithmetic sequence with first term 4 and second term 7
     c a geometric sequence with first term 10 and common ratio 4
     d a geometric sequence with first term 3 and second term 1
     e a geometric sequence with first term 20 and common ratio $\frac{1}{4}$

2 Find the first term and common difference of each arithmetic progression.

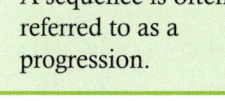

A sequence is often referred to as a progression.

     a $u_n = 3 + 5(n - 1)$ **b** $u_n = 2n - 4$
     c $u_{n+1} = u_n - 4,\ u_1 = 11$ **d** $u_n = -8 - 5n$

3 Find the first term and common ratio of each geometric sequence.

     a $u_n = 4 \times 5^{n-1}$ **b** $u_n = \frac{1}{2} \times 7^{n-1}$

     c $u_n = 3 \times 5^n$ **d** $u_n = \frac{8}{3^n}$

     e $u_n = 0.4 \times 10^{n+3}$ **f** $u_1 = 7,\ u_{n+1} = \frac{1}{2} u_n$

4 A Norwegian glacier was 6.4 km long in 1995. Since then it has been retreating at a constant rate of 80 m per year. Write an explicit formula for the length l_n of the glacier n years after 1995. Use this formula to predict the length of the glacier in 2025 if the retreat continues at the same rate.

5 Moore's law showed that, between 1965 and 1975, the power of computers doubled every year. In 1965 a microprocessor contained around 60 transistors.

     a Write an explicit formula for the number of transistors t_n in a microprocessor n years after 1965.
     b Moore later revised his law, saying that after 1971 doubling would occur every two years. How many transistors did the law predict that there would be in a processor in 1993?

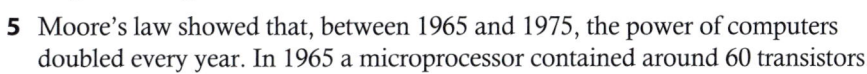

C   Using arithmetic and geometric sequences in context

- How do patterns help you recognize arithmetic and geometric sequences in real-life problems.
- How can you solve problems involving arithmetic and geometric sequences?

In this section you will explore how the general formulae for arithmetic and geometric progressions can help solve problems involving sequences.

Example 5

An arithmetic sequence has terms $u_1 = 7$ and $u_2 = 18$. Find u_{10}.

$d = u_2 - u_1 = 18 - 7 = 11$ —————————— The common difference is the difference between any two consecutive terms.

$u_n = 7 + 11(n - 1)$ ————————— Although the question did not ask you to, it is useful to find the explicit formula for the nth term.

$u_{10} = 7 + 11(10 - 1)$ ————————— For the 10th term, let $n = 10$ in the general formula.
$u_{10} = 7 + 99 = 106$

Example 6

An arithmetic sequence has terms $u_3 = 14.2$ and $u_5 = 19.6$. Find u_{11}.

$14.2 = u_1 + 2d$ (1)
$19.6 = u_1 + 4d$ (2) ————————— Use $u_n = u_1 + (n - 1)d$ to write two simultaneous equations.

$2d = 5.4$ ————————— Subtract (1) from (2) and rearrange.
$d = 2.7$
$u_1 = 14.2 - 2 \times 2.7 = 8.8$ ————————— Solve the simultaneous equations to find u_1.

$u_n = 8.8 + 2.7(n - 1)$ ————————— Write a general formula for u_n.

$u_{11} = 8.8 + 2.7(11 - 1)$ ————————— Use $n = 11$ to find u_{11}.
$u_{11} = 8.8 + 27 = 35.8$

Example 7

The second term of a geometric progression is 4 more than the first term. The common ratio is 3. Find the first term.

$u_2 = u_1 + 4$ ————————— u_2 is 4 greater than u_1.

$u_2 = 3u_1$ ————————— Since the common ratio is 3, u_2 is 3 times u_1.

$\Rightarrow 3u_1 = u_1 + 4$
$u_1 = 2$

Practice 2

1 An arithmetic sequence has first term 4 and second term 7.
Find its tenth term.

2 An arithmetic sequence has second term 19 and common difference 4.
Find its eighth term.

3 An arithmetic sequence has third term 11 and fifth term 6.
Find its first term, tenth term and common difference.

4 An arithmetic sequence has first term 3. The third term is three times the second term. Find the value of the second and third terms.

5 An arithmetic sequence has sixth term 15 and ninth term 16.
Find its common difference. Determine which term has value 22.

6 A geometric sequence has first term 8 and second term 24.
Find its common ratio and fifth term.

7 A geometric sequence has third term 48 and fourth term 96.
Find its common ratio and fifth term.

> You could solve simultaneous equations by hand, or use your GDC.

Problem solving

8 A geometric sequence has second term 30 and third term 45. Find its first term, and write down an expression for the nth term. By using trial and improvement, or otherwise, find the first term in the sequence that is greater than 1000.

9 Two arithmetic sequences have the same first term. The 5th term of the first sequence and the 4th term of the second are both equal to 16. The 9th term of the first sequence and the 7th term of the second are both equal to 28. Find the first term of each sequence and their common differences.

Objective: D. Applying mathematics in real-life contexts
i. identify relevant elements of authentic real-life situations

To identify whether each of the following should be modelled with an arithmetic or a geometric sequence, you must first decide whether the real life factors lead to growth at a constant rate or by a constant scale factor.

ATL

Exploration 4

Sometimes a real-life problem can be modelled using an arithmetic or geometric sequence. Consider each of the following scenarios and decide if it could be described using an arithmetic or a geometric sequence, and explain why.
In each case, write down what the terms of the sequence would represent.

1 You are saving up for a summer trip. Your parents give you $10 to get you started, and then you save half your pocket money each month. (Your pocket money is the same amount every month.)

2 The population of the Earth is increasing by 1.13% per year. This means that next year it will have increased by a factor of 1.0113.

3 The developers of a new website are trying to predict how its number of active users will grow. The developers believe that every month, each existing user will introduce three new users to the site.

▶ Continued on next page

4 The owners of a new coffee shop are trying to work out how their customer numbers will grow in the first year. They think that each month, 20 new customers will find their business.

5 A population of Chloroflexi bacteria doubles in number every 27 minutes. A researcher records the size of the population every hour after the start of the experiment.

6 Outside my house the snow is 15 cm deep one morning. As the snow melts, the total depth of snow decreases by 15% every hour.

Reflect and discuss 1

- Explain to others why you chose either arithmetic or geometric sequences to describe each of the scenarios in Exploration 4.

- Assumptions sometimes need to be made in order to make real-life problems simpler so that they can be successfully modelled. How has this happened in the examples in Exploration 4?

- What is it about a real-life problem that means:
  i an arithmetic sequence will be appropriate, or
  ii a geometric sequence will be appropriate?

Example 8

At a certain ski resort, some guests stay overnight and all the other skiers arrive in full coaches of equal size during the day. One coach arrives every 10 minutes, starting at 08:10, ten minutes after the resort opens. After the 7th coach has arrived, there are 785 skiers at the resort. After the 10th coach has arrived, there are 920 skiers at the resort.

a Find the number of skiers that will be at the resort once the 12th coach has arrived.

b Find the number of skiers that stayed overnight.

a Let u_n be the number of skiers in the resort after the nth coach has arrived.

An arithmetic sequence models this problem because each coach brings the same number of people.

$$u_n = u_1 + (n-1)d$$

$$u_7 = 785 = u_1 + 6d$$

$$u_{10} = 920 = u_1 + 9d$$

Form two equations.

so $135 = 3d$

$$\Rightarrow d = 45, \text{ and } u_1 = 515$$

Solve to find the values of u_1 and d.

$$u_{12} = 515 + 11 \times 45 = 1010$$

Use the formula to find the twelfth term.

b The number of skiers before the first coach is given by $u_0 = 515 - 45 = 470$.

Since the number of overnight guests is the number of guests when 0 coaches have arrived, finding u_0 tells you the number of overnight guests.

Practice 3

1 Some money is invested in an account which pays compound interest annually. At the end of 20 years the account is worth \$29 136.22. At the end of 21 years it is worth \$29 718.95. Find the amount of money in the account at the end of the 30th year.

2 When standing vertically upright, a ladder's 11th rung is 170 cm above the ground and its 14th rung is 215 cm above the ground.

   a Explain why the heights of the rungs could be expected to form an arithmetic sequence.

   b Find the height of the first rung above the ground and the distance from one rung to the next.

   c Find the height of the 20th rung.

   d Given that the top rung is 350 cm above the ground, determine the total number of rungs that the ladder has.

3 After being cleaned, a swimming pool is being refilled with water. The water level is rising at a constant rate. After three hours the water is 16 cm deep and after five hours it is 19.5 cm deep.

   a Determine how deep the water is after only one hour.

   b Find the number of hours it will take for the pool to fill to a depth of 25 cm.

4 A computer virus spreads via emails from an infected computer. Each infected computer successfully manages to infect five new computers every day.

   a If u_n represents the number of infected computers at the start of day n, explain why $u_{n+1} = 6u_n$.

   b Given that there are 2592 computers infected at the start of day 5, find the number of computers from which the virus was initially launched at the start of day 1.

   c Determine on what day the virus will infect the millionth computer.

5 The seats in an arena are arranged so that each row is longer than the row in front of it by the same number of seats. The 13th row has 71 seats and the 19th row has 95 seats. Determine the total number of seats in the front three rows combined.

6 In the 2014 Ebola outbreak, the number of deaths from the disease was doubling every month from April. In June there were 252 deaths.

   a If u_n represents the number of deaths n months after April explain why $u_{n+1} = 2u_n$.

   b Find the number of deaths in April and write an explicit formula for finding the number of deaths in any month after April.

   c Find the number of deaths from Ebola in September.

   d Explain why this model does not fully explain the outbreak and the continued number of deaths over a longer period of time.

D ## When do geometric sequences defy expectations?

- How does the behavior of a geometric sequence vary depending on the value of the common ratio?
- How can you use the general formulae for arithmetic and geometric sequences to predict future terms?

ATL

Exploration 5

For each of the sequences described in steps **1** to **4**:

- **a** find the first ten terms of the sequence
- **b** describe what you notice about the terms
- **c** predict what will happen to the value of u_n, the nth term, as n becomes very large.

1 A geometric sequence, first term 10, common ratio 0.8

2 A geometric sequence, first term 10, common ratio –0.8

3 A geometric sequence, first term 10, common ratio 1.2

4 A geometric sequence, first term 10, common ratio –1.2

Reflect and discuss 2

- Compare and contrast the geometric sequences in steps **1** and **2**.
- Do the same for those in steps **3** and **4**.

Exploration 6

A sequence has terms 10, 10, 10, 10, 10, 10, …

Another sequence has terms 10, –10, 10, –10, 10, –10, …

For each sequence:

- **a** determine whether or not there is a common ratio between successive terms
- **b** explain whether or not it is a geometric sequence.

Reflect and discuss 3

- How would you best describe the behavior of the sequences?
- Is the sequence 0, 0, 0, 0, 0, … a geometric sequence? What happens if you try to find the common ratio by dividing any term by the term before it?

The sequence 0, 0, 0, 0, … has a lot in common with geometric sequences but is not normally regarded as geometric because of the problems involved with dividing by zero.

Geometric sequences either become larger and larger or smaller and smaller depending on the common ratio. If r is between –1 and 1, the values will get closer to zero. If r is greater than 1 or less than –1, the terms will become infinitely large. When r is negative, the terms of a geometric sequence alternate between being positive or negative.

Summary

- In an **arithmetic sequence** the difference between consecutive terms is constant.
- An arithmetic sequence with first term u_1 and common difference d has recursive formula $u_{n+1} = u_n + d$ and explicit formula $u_n = u_1 + (n-1)d$ for the nth term.
- In a **geometric sequence** the ratio between consecutive terms is constant.

- A geometric sequence with first term a and common ratio r has recursive formula $u_{n+1} = ru_n$ and explicit formula $u_n = u_1 r^{n-1}$ for the nth term.
- In a geometric sequence, the common ratio, r, cannot be equal to 0.

Mixed practice

1 An arithmetic sequence begins 7, 25, 43, …

  a **Find** the common difference.

  b **Write down** a recursive formula linking the nth term to the $(n+1)$th term.

  c **Write down** an explicit formula for the nth term.

  d **Find** the value of the 15th term.

  e **Find** the term number of the term with value 367.

2 An arithmetic sequence has fourth term 253 and fifth term 291.

  a **Write down** the value of the common difference.

  b **Hence find** the first term.

  c **Find** the sum of the first three terms.

3 An arithmetic sequence has third term 31 and sixth term 52. Let the first term be u_1 and the common difference be d.

  a Form two simultaneous equations in terms of u_1 and d.

  b **Hence find** u_1, d and the value of the 10th term.

4 An arithmetic sequence has common difference 6. The product of the first two terms is 91. **Find** the value of the first term, given that it is negative.

5 The third term of an arithmetic sequence is twice the first term. The second term is 45.

  a **Find** the value of the first term and the common difference.

  b **Determine** whether or not 310 is a term of the sequence.

6 A geometric sequence begins 6, 42, 294, …

  a **Write down** the value of the first term and the common ratio.

  b **Write down** a recursive formula linking the nth term to the $(n+1)$th term.

  c **Write down** an explicit formula for the nth term.

  d **Find** the value of the fifth term.

  e **Find** the value of the first term to exceed one million.

7 A geometric sequence begins 6, 3, 1.5, …

  a **Write down** the value of the first term and the common difference.

  b **Write down** a recursive formula linking the nth term to the $(n+1)$th term.

  c **Write down** an explicit formula for the nth term.

  d **Find** the value of the tenth term, correct to three significant figures.

8 A geometric sequence has common ratio 4. The second term is 9 more than the first term.

  a **Write down** two different expressions for the second term in terms of u_1, the first term.

  b **Hence** write an equation using this information and **find** the value of u_1.

  c **Find** how many terms there are in the sequence that are less than 1000.

9 A geometric sequence has first term 12 and third term 48. The common ratio is r.

  a **Show that** $r^2 = 4$.

  b **Hence find** two possible values for the common ratio.

  c **Find** the possible values of the sixth term.

Review in context
Scientific and technical innovation

1 Consider the following diagram, which illustrates the chemical structure of methane, ethane and propane, three examples of chemicals known as alkanes.

methane   ethane   propane

a **Show that** the number of hydrogen atoms (represented by an H) in the three alkanes pictured forms an arithmetic sequence.

b Let u_n be the number of hydrogen atoms in an alkane with n carbon (C) atoms. **Write down** an explicit formula for u_n.

c **Find** the number of hydrogen atoms in an alkane with 20 carbon atoms.

d **Find** the number of carbon atoms in an alkane with 142 hydrogen atoms.

2 The developers of a new social media website think that its membership will grow by the same scale factor every month. At the end of the first month it has 20 000 members, and at the end of the second month it has 25 000 members.

a **Explain** which information in the statement above suggests that this can be modelled with a geometric sequence.

b **Determine** how many members this model would predict for the website to have at the end of the 12th month.

c **Determine** how many members this model predicts for the end of the second year.

3 A design company produces business cards. They charge a set fee for design, and then sell the cards in boxes of 100 cards. Each box costs the same amount.

The total cost (including the design fee) for 400 cards is $108.

The total cost (including the design fee) for 600 cards is $133.

Find the cost for 1000 cards, and **calculate** the design fee.

4 A machine produces a constant number of components per hour, except in the first hour of operation.

By the end of the second hour of operation, it has made 6000 components. By the end of the seventh hour, it has made 24 000 components.

a **Explain** why the number of components made by the nth hour forms an arithmetic sequence.

b **Find** the number of components made in the first hour.

c **Find** the number of components made in total over a nine-hour working day.

Reflect and discuss 4

How have you explored the statement of inquiry? Give specific examples.

Statement of inquiry:

Representing patterns and change in a variety of forms has helped humans apply their understanding of scientific principles.

Rational algebraic expressions

Global context: Scientific and technical innovation

Related concept: Change

Objectives

- Simplifying rational algebraic expressions
- Performing mathematical operations on rational algebraic expressions

Inquiry questions

F
- How can you simplify a rational expression?

C
- What does it mean to simplify a rational algebraic expression?
- How do operations on rational algebraic expressions compare to operations on rational numerical expressions?

D
- Does technology help or hinder understanding?

FORM

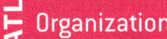

ATL Organization

Use appropriate strategies for organizing complex information

Statement of inquiry:

Representing patterns and change in a variety of forms has helped humans apply their understanding of scientific principles.

📖 **Launch additional digital resources for this chapter.**

You should already know how to:

• simplify fractions	**1** Simplify each fraction. **a** $\dfrac{20}{100}$ **b** $\dfrac{27}{72}$ **c** $\dfrac{x^5y}{x^8}$ **d** $\dfrac{24x^3}{(3x^2)^2}$

• factorize quadratic expressions	**2** Factorize:
	  a $x^2 + 5x + 6$
	  b $x^2 - 3x - 10$
	  c $x^2 - 9$

F   Rearranging formulae

• How can you simplify a rational expression?

> A **rational algebraic expression** is a fraction that contains variables.

Factorizing can change rational algebraic fractions to a simpler form. When the numerator and the denominator have a common factor, you can divide to simplify the fraction, as you would a numerical fraction. For example,

$$\frac{12}{20} = \frac{(4 \times 3)}{(4 \times 5)} = \frac{3}{5} \qquad \text{and} \qquad \frac{x\,\cancel{(x-2)}}{\cancel{(x-2)}(x+5)} = \frac{x}{x+5}$$

> The expression $(x - 2)$ is being cancelled in both the numerator and denominator, since $\dfrac{(x-2)}{(x-2)} = 1$

ATL

Exploration 1

1 Simplify these fractions completely. Justify each step.

  a $\dfrac{25}{100}$ **b** $\dfrac{45}{75}$ **c** $\dfrac{64}{80}$

  d $\dfrac{91}{105}$ **e** $\dfrac{12a}{3a}$ **f** $\dfrac{15a^3}{60a}$

  g $\dfrac{3(x+1)}{5(x+1)}$ **h** $\dfrac{(x+y)(x-y)}{4(x+y)}$ **i** $\dfrac{(a+b)(c-d)(e+f)(g-h)}{(a+b)(e+f)(g+h)}$

2 State the one value that you are not allowed to have in the denominator of a fraction. Explain why that is.

3 For each of these rational expressions, explain the steps needed to simplify it to the given expression.

  a $\dfrac{x^2-9}{x-3} = x+3$ **b** $\dfrac{x^2-9}{x+3} = x-3$ **c** $\dfrac{x^2+3x}{x+3} = x$

4 For each expression in step **3**, state any value that x cannot take.

5 Based on your answers to steps **1** and **3**, write down the steps for simplifying a rational algebraic expression.

The Ancient Egyptians used images to represent fractions in the same way they did to represent words. Horus was a sky god whose eye was shattered into six pieces. Each part of his shattered eye represented a different fraction. Interestingly if you add the six fractions together you get $\dfrac{63}{64}$ rather than 1. Some consider this to demonstrate that perfection is not possible.

To simplify a rational expression, you may need to factorize the numerator and/or denominator first.

Example 1

Simplify completely and state any restrictions on x.

$$\frac{x^2 - 3x - 28}{x^3 - 9x^2 + 14x}$$

$$\frac{x^2 - 3x - 28}{x^3 - 9x^2 + 14x} = \frac{(x+4)\cancel{(x-7)}}{x(x-2)\cancel{(x-7)}}$$ ——— Factorize the numerator and denominator completely.

$$= \frac{(x+4)}{x(x-2)} \quad x \notin \{0, 2, 7\}$$ ——— The restrictions are any values that make the expressions in the denominator 0, including any cancelled when simplifying.

Practice 1

ATL

Write these expressions in their simplest form. State any restriction(s) on the variable.

1 $\dfrac{10a^3}{2a}$

2 $\dfrac{5x^5 + 3x^4}{2x^4}$

3 $\dfrac{42x^6 y^5}{35x^3 y^7}$

4 $\dfrac{(x-7)(x+8)}{(x+7)(x+8)}$

5 $\dfrac{(a-b)(a+2b)}{(a-2b)(b-a)}$

6 $\dfrac{x^2 + 6x + 8}{x^2 + 7x + 10}$

7 $\dfrac{x^2 + x - 12}{x^2 - x - 6}$

8 $\dfrac{x^2 - 3x - 10}{x^2 + 2x - 35}$

9 $\dfrac{x^3 - 12x^2 + 32x}{x^2 - 7x + 12}$

10 $\dfrac{x^2 + 4x - 21}{x^2 - 3x - 18}$

> In simplest form the numerator and denominator have no common factors.

Problem solving

11 Write an unsimplified rational expression in x that has a quadratic expression in the numerator and the restriction on x that $x \notin \{-2, 5\}$.

12 Write a rational expression in x which simplifies to $\dfrac{x+3}{x-10}$, and where $x \notin \{6, 10\}$.

C Operations on rational algebraic expressions

- What does it mean to simplify a rational algebraic expression?
- How do operations on rational algebraic expressions compare to operations on rational numerical expressions?

You can multiply and divide algebraic fractions in the same way as numeric fractions.

Exploration 2

1 Multiply these fractions by:

   i   simplifying first, and then multiplying,

   ii multiplying first, and then simplifying.

   Explain which method you found easier.

   a $\dfrac{3}{10} \times \dfrac{2}{9}$ **b** $\dfrac{-4}{12} \times \dfrac{2}{6}$ **c** $\dfrac{12}{75} \times \dfrac{18}{60}$

2 Use your preferred method from step **1** to multiply these algebraic fractions.

   a $\dfrac{x-5}{x+3} \times \dfrac{3x+9}{x+5}, \; x \neq -3, \; x \neq -5$

   b $\dfrac{(x-2)(x-3)}{(x+2)(x+3)} \times \dfrac{(x+1)(x+2)}{(x-1)(x-2)}, \; x \notin \{-3, 1, \pm 2\}$

   c $\dfrac{x^2+3x-4}{2x^2-14x+24} \times \dfrac{4x^2-16x+12}{2x^2+4x-16}, \; x \notin \{2, 3, \pm 4\}$

3 Divide these fractions, leaving your answers in simplest form. Explain your method.

   a $\dfrac{5}{3} \div \dfrac{1}{6}$ **b** $\dfrac{4}{5} \div \dfrac{2}{10}$ **c** $\dfrac{12}{75} \div \dfrac{18}{60}$

4 Use your method in step **3** to divide these algebraic fractions. Explain your method.

   a $\dfrac{x+5}{x+6} \div \dfrac{5x+25}{x+3}, \; x \neq -6, \; x \neq -5$

   b $\dfrac{(x-8)(x-2)}{x(x+4)(x+3)} \div \dfrac{x(x+4)(x-2)}{(x+3)(x-5)}, \; x \notin \{-4, -3, 0, 2, 5\}$

   c $\dfrac{x^2+3x-4}{2x^2-14x+24} \div \dfrac{4x^2-16x+12}{2x^2+4x-16}, \; x \notin \{-4, 1, 2, 3, 4\}$

Reflect and discuss 2

- Write down two equivalent fractions. Take the reciprocal of each. Are the new fractions also equivalent?

- What are the differences between multiplying and dividing algebraic fractions and multiplying and dividing numeric fractions?

> The *reciprocal* of $\dfrac{a}{b}$ is $\dfrac{b}{a}$. It is the multiplicative inverse.

Example 2

Simplify completely and state the restrictions on the variable.

$$\frac{x^2-9}{x^2-8x+16} \div \frac{x^2+6x+9}{x^2-7x+12}$$

$\dfrac{x^2-9}{x^2-8x+16} \div \dfrac{x^2+6x+9}{x^2-7x+12}$ — Factorize the quadratic expressions.

$= \dfrac{(x+3)(x-3)}{(x-4)(x-4)} \div \dfrac{(x+3)(x+3)}{(x-3)(x-4)}$ — To divide by a fraction, multiply by its reciprocal.

$= \dfrac{\cancel{(x+3)}(x-3)}{\cancel{(x-4)}(x-4)} \times \dfrac{(x-3)\cancel{(x-4)}}{\cancel{(x+3)}(x+3)}$ — Simplify.

$= \dfrac{(x+3)^2}{(x-4)(x+3)}, \; x \notin \{\pm 3, 4\}$ — Include values of x that make the denominators of the *original expressions* equal to 0.

Practice 2

Simplify each rational expression. State any restrictions on the variables.

1 $\dfrac{25p}{55k} \times \dfrac{66p}{5k}$

2 $\dfrac{3p^3c^4}{5c^5} \div \dfrac{24p^5c}{10c^3}$

3 $\dfrac{5x+10}{3x-9} \times \dfrac{6x-18}{4x+8}$

4 $\dfrac{6x-12y}{x+3y} \div \dfrac{3}{2x+9y}$

5 $\dfrac{x^2-x-2}{x^2-2x+1} \times \dfrac{x-1}{x+1}$

6 $\dfrac{a^3+ab^2}{a^3-2a^2b} \div \dfrac{a^2+b^2}{(a-2b)^2}$

7 $\dfrac{x^2-3x-10}{x^2+x-6} \times \dfrac{x^2+2x-3}{x^2+x-2}$

8 $\dfrac{x^2+5x-24}{x^2-9x+18} \div \dfrac{x^2+2x-48}{x^2+3x-18}$

9 $\dfrac{x^2-9}{x^2-4x+3} \times \dfrac{2x-2}{x^2+5x+6} \div \dfrac{6x}{2x^2+4x}$

10 $\left(\dfrac{x^2-3x-10}{x^2-4} \div \dfrac{2x^2-2}{6x+12}\right) \div \dfrac{x^2-6x+5}{2x^2+6x+4}$

Reflect and discuss 3

- Should you find the restrictions on the variable in a multiplication before or after multiplying? Explain your reasoning.

- In a division question, when would you find the restrictions – before or after finding the reciprocal? Explain your reasoning.

Exploration 3

There are two possible ways of connecting electrical components together: in series or in parallel. For components connected in parallel, the total resistance (R_{tot}) of the circuit is: $\frac{1}{R_1}+\frac{1}{R_2}+\frac{1}{R_3}+\cdots=\frac{1}{R_{tot}}$ (where R_1, R_2, ... are the resistances of the components).

1 Find the total resistance in a circuit with:

    a $R_1 = 4$ ohms, $R_2 = 8$ ohms

    b $R_1 = 2$ ohms, $R_2 = 6$ ohms

    c $R_1 = 3$ ohms, $R_2 = 5$ ohms

2 When two components are connected in parallel, determine if the combined resistance is greater or less than the individual resistances.

3 Write down a necessary step before adding fractions together, and explain.

4 Find an expression for the total resistance when one component has twice the resistance of the other.

5 Find an expression for the total resistance when one component has a resistance 2 ohms more than the other.

Example 3

Find each rational expression in simplest form.

a $\dfrac{1}{x+5}-\dfrac{2}{x-3}$ **b** $\dfrac{2}{x-2}+\dfrac{x}{x^2-5x+6}$

a $\dfrac{1}{x+5}-\dfrac{2}{x-3}=\dfrac{1}{x+5}\times\dfrac{x-3}{x-3}-\dfrac{2}{x-3}\times\dfrac{x+5}{x+5}$

               If there is no common factor between the denominators then the LCM is simply the product of the denominators.

$=\dfrac{x-3}{(x+5)(x-3)}-\dfrac{2(x+5)}{(x-3)(x+5)}$

$=\dfrac{x-3-2x-10}{(x+5)(x-3)}$

               Simplify your final answer completely.

$=\dfrac{-x-13}{(x+5)(x-3)}\ x\notin\{-5,\ 3\}$

b $\dfrac{2}{x-2}+\dfrac{x}{x^2-5x+6}=\dfrac{2}{x-2}+\dfrac{x}{(x-2)(x-3)}$

               There is a common factor between the two denominators: $(x-2)$.

$=\dfrac{2}{x-2}\times\dfrac{x-3}{x-3}+\dfrac{x}{(x-2)(x-3)}$

               With a common denominator, you can now add the terms.

$=\dfrac{2(x-3)+x}{(x-2)(x-3)}$

$=\dfrac{2x-6+x}{(x-2)(x-3)}$

$=\dfrac{x-6}{(x-2)(x-3)}\ x\notin\{2,\ 3\}$

Practice 3

Objective: C. Communicating
v. organize information using a logical structure.

In Practice 3, show the steps in your working in a logical order. Remember to include any restrictions on the variables.

Simplify each rational expression. State any restrictions on the variables.

1 $\dfrac{3}{x}+\dfrac{4}{y}$ **2** $\dfrac{3}{2x}-\dfrac{1}{4x}$ **3** $\dfrac{1}{3x}+\dfrac{1}{6x^2}$ **4** $\dfrac{2}{ab}+\dfrac{3}{ac}-\dfrac{5}{bc}$

5 $\dfrac{1}{x+2}+\dfrac{1}{x-2}$ **6** $\dfrac{x}{x+4}-\dfrac{5}{x-3}$ **7** $\dfrac{x-2}{x+4}+\dfrac{x+3}{x-2}$ **8** $\dfrac{x^2-2x+1}{x-3}-x$

9 $\dfrac{1}{x+5}-\dfrac{2x}{x^2+3x-10}$ **10** $\dfrac{5x}{x-8}+\dfrac{4}{x^2-5x-24}$ **11** $\dfrac{7}{x-1}+\dfrac{6}{x}-\dfrac{5}{x+1}$ **12** $\dfrac{3}{x+3}-\dfrac{x}{4}+\dfrac{5}{x-5}$

- -

You have seen that algebraic fractions behave in much the same way as numerical fractions. Simplifying, multiplying, and dividing involve very similar processes:

- Simplify rational expressions by first factorizing the expression, and then dividing by common factors in the numerator and denominator.

- To multiply rational expressions, multiply the numerator and multiply the denominator. It is more efficient to simplify the rational expressions before multiplying them.

- To divide rational expressions, multiply by the reciprocal of the divisor.

- To add and subtract rational expressions, first rewrite the fractions with a common denominator.

 ## Finding restrictions on variables using technology

- Does technology help or hinder understanding?

Exploration 4

1 In Exploration 1 you saw that $\dfrac{x^2-9}{x+3}$ simplifies to $x-3$. Use your GDC or graphing software to draw the graphs of both expressions.

2 Describe any similarities or differences between the graphs.

3 State whether or not the GDC or graphing software has graphed both expressions correctly.

4 Explain whether or not you think both expressions are equal.

5 Repeat steps **2** to **4** for $\dfrac{x^2+3x}{x+3}$ which simplifies to x.

6 Explain whether you should always trust results you obtain using technology.

Summary

- A **formula** is an equation that describes an algebraic relationship between two or more sets of values. Each variable in a formula can take different values, depending on the values of the other variables.

- Changing the subject of the formula is a way of changing, or **rearranging** algebraic relationships. It usually involves isolating a different variable in the formula.

- A **rational algebraic expression** is a fraction that contains variables.

Rational expressions:

- must exclude all the values of x that make a denominator in the expression equal to 0

- can be simplified by dividing common factors

- can be multiplied, divided, added, or subtracted using similar rules as for numerical fractions.

Mixed practice

Simplify each rational expression. **State** any restrictions on the variables.

1 $\dfrac{12x^4 y}{36xy}$

2 $\dfrac{5x^7 - 6x^5}{4x^3}$

3 $\dfrac{x^2 - 4x - 21}{x^2 - 8x - 33}$

4 $\dfrac{x+4}{x^2 - 16}$

5 $\dfrac{2}{x} + \dfrac{y}{5}$

6 $\dfrac{16x^3 y^2}{5z^3} \times \dfrac{15z}{8xy}$

7 $\dfrac{x^3 y^2 + x^2 y^3}{x^3 y^3} \div \dfrac{x^2 - y^2}{x^4 y^4}$

Simplify these expressions. **State** the restrictions on the variable.

8 $\dfrac{x - 2y}{4} - \dfrac{1 + 2xy}{x}$

9 $\dfrac{7}{x - 7} + \dfrac{5}{x + 5}$

10 $\dfrac{-3}{x + 9} + \dfrac{-2}{x - 8}$

11 $\dfrac{x+1}{x-1} - \dfrac{x-4}{x+4}$

12 $\dfrac{9}{x - 1} - \dfrac{9x - 4}{x^2 - 1}$

13 $\dfrac{3}{a} + \dfrac{5}{b} - \dfrac{a+b}{4}$

14 $\dfrac{x+1}{6} + \dfrac{2}{x} - \dfrac{x}{x-2}$

Review in context

Context: Scientific and technical innovation

1 When resistors are connected in parallel, the total resistance R_{tot} is given by $\dfrac{1}{R_1} + \dfrac{1}{R_2} + \dfrac{1}{R_3} + \cdots = \dfrac{1}{R_{tot}}$.

When connected in series, the total resistance is simply the sum of the individual resistances.

a Three resistors, A, B and C, are connected in parallel. Resistor A has resistance r ohms. Resistor B's resistance is 4 ohms larger than resistor A's. Resistor C, the largest, has a resistance two ohms more than twice that of resistor A. **Write down** an expression for the total resistance of the circuit. **Simplify** the expression into a single fraction.

b A fourth resistor, D, has the same resistance as resistor C. It is connected in series with resistors A, B, and C. **Write down** an expression for the total resistance of the circuit. **Simplify** the expression into a single fraction.

2 Ohm's Law states that the voltage (V), in an electrical circuit with current (I) and total resistance, R, is given by $V = IR$

a Make I the subject of the formula.

b Circuit A has a resistor of 6 ohms and a second resistor with resistance r, connected in series. Circuit B has a resistor of 5 ohms and a second resistor with resistance $3r$. Circuit A and circuit B are connected in parallel. The voltage in the complete circuit is 12 volts. **Find** the total resistance of the circuit and hence find an expression for the total current flowing through the complete circuit in terms of r.

Problem solving

3 Scientists calculate the gravitational force between *any* two masses (m_1 and m_2) using the formula $F = \frac{Gm_1m_2}{r^2}$, where r is the distance between them and G is the gravitational constant.

a **Determine** how many times larger the force of gravity is when the distance between the two masses is halved.

b One mass is doubled and the distance between the masses is increased by scale factor 4. **Determine** the effect on the gravitational force between them.

c One mass is doubled, the other is tripled and the distance between them is reduced by scale factor 4. **Determine** the effect on the gravitational force between them.

d One mass is halved and the other is made eight times larger. **Find** how the distance r needs to change to keep the gravitational force the same.

The minimum speed required for an object (usually a rocket) to break free of Earth's gravitational field is called 'escape velocity'. The equation for the escape velocity v_e of an object is given by: $v_e = \sqrt{\frac{2Gm_E}{r}}$ where G is the gravitational constant, m_E is Earth's mass, and r is the distance between Earth's center of mass and the object.

The escape velocity for objects leaving the Earth is approximately 25 000 miles per hour.

Now, rockets require a tremendous amount of fuel to break away from Earth's gravitational pull. This fuel adds considerable mass to the rocket, and thus it takes more thrust to lift it. But to create more thrust, you need more fuel. It's a vicious circle that scientists hope to overcome by building lighter vehicles, discovering more efficient fuels and new methods of propulsion.

Reflect and discuss 4

How have you explored the statement of inquiry? Give specific examples.

Statement of inquiry:

Representing patterns and change in a variety of forms has helped humans apply their understanding of scientific principles.

E8.3 Graphs of rational functions

Global context: Scientific and technical innovation

Related concept: Change

Objectives

- Graphing rational functions of the form $f(x) = \dfrac{a}{x-h} + k$
- Finding asymptotes of graphs of rational functions
- Transforming rational functions using translations, reflections and dilations
- Identifying transformations of graphs
- Finding the inverse of a rational function

Inquiry questions

- What is a rational function?
- How are asymptotes linked to domain and range?

- How can understanding transformations of rational functions help you graph them?

D
- Can a function be its own inverse?
- Does science solve problems or create them?

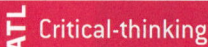

ATL Critical-thinking

Revise understanding based on new information and evidence

Statement of inquiry:

Representing patterns and change in a variety of forms has helped humans apply their understanding of scientific principles.

📄 **Launch additional digital resources for this chapter.**

You should already know how to:

• find the domain and range of a function	**1** State the domain and range of these functions. **a** $f(x) = 2x + 5$ **b** $f(x) = x^2$ **c** $f(x) = \dfrac{2}{1-x}$
• write statements of proportionality	**2** Write the statement of proportionality for: **a** y is proportional to x **b** y is inversely proportional to x.
• transform functions	**3** State the combination of transformations applied to $f(x)$ to get $g(x)$: $f(x) = x^2,\ g(x) = -2(x+3)^2 + 5$
• find an inverse function algebraically	**4** Find the inverse relation of each function algebraically, and state whether or not the inverse relation is also a function. **a** $f(x) = \dfrac{3}{4}x + 2$ **b** $f(x) = (x-2)^2$

 F   # Introducing rational functions

- What is a rational function?
- How are asymptotes linked to domain and range?

A **rational function** is any function which can be expressed as a quotient $\dfrac{f(x)}{g(x)}$ where $f(x)$ and $g(x)$ are functions of x, and $g(x) \neq 0$.

The function $f(x) = \dfrac{1}{x}$, $x \neq 0$, called the **reciprocal function**, is one type of rational function. Its domain is the set of real numbers excluding zero, and its range is the set of real numbers excluding zero.

One practical application of a reciprocal function is the design and layout of the cables used on a suspension bridge. The cables help keep the bridge stable, and this is achieved by engineers who design the bridge so that the opposing forces of tension and compression work together. This is a photo of the Clifton Suspension Bridge, which spans the Avon Gorge and the River Avon, in Bristol, England.

Exploration 1

1 Complete the table of values for the function $y = \frac{1}{x}$.

x	−8	−4	−2	−1	$-\frac{1}{2}$	$-\frac{1}{4}$	$-\frac{1}{8}$	$\frac{1}{8}$	$\frac{1}{4}$	$\frac{1}{2}$	1	2	4	8
y	$-\frac{1}{8}$			−2										

2 Use the table in step **1** to help you draw the graph of $y = \frac{1}{x}$ for values of x from −8 to 8.

3 a Explain what happens as x gets closer to 0. Think about what happens for both positive and negative values of x that approach 0.

   b Describe the behavior of y as x gets closer and closer to 0 on the graph. Think about positive and negative values for x.

   c In a different color, draw a vertical line on your graph that the curve never touches.

   d Explain why x can never be equal to 0. Hence, state the domain of the function $y = \frac{1}{x}$.

4 a Find the values of x for which y gets closer to 0. Think about positive and negative values for x.

   b Explain why y can never be equal to 0. How is this represented on the graph?

   c In a different color, draw a horizontal line on your graph that the curve never touches.

   d State the range of the function $y = \frac{1}{x}$.

For a reciprocal function:

- The **horizontal asymptote** is the horizontal line that the graph of $f(x)$ approaches as x approaches positive or negative infinity.

- The **vertical asymptote** is the vertical line that the graph of $f(x)$ approaches as x approaches 0. (The denominator can never equal zero.)

Reflect and discuss 1

- Find the equation of the horizontal asymptote and the vertical asymptote for the graph of $y = \frac{1}{x}$.

- How are the domain and range of this function related to the equations of the asymptotes?

Exploration 2

1 a Copy and complete this table of values for $y = -\dfrac{1}{x}$.

x	-8	-4	-2	-1	$-\frac{1}{2}$	$-\frac{1}{4}$	$-\frac{1}{8}$	$\frac{1}{8}$	$\frac{1}{4}$	$\frac{1}{2}$	1	2	4	8
y														

  b Draw the graph of $y = -\dfrac{1}{x}$ for values of x between -8 and 8.

  c State the domain and range of this function.

  d State the equation of the horizontal and vertical asymptotes. How do they relate to the domain and range?

  e Look back at your graph of $y = \dfrac{1}{x}$ from Exploration 1. Explain why that graph is only in quadrants 1 and 3.

  f Explain why the graph of $y = -\dfrac{1}{x}$ is only in quadrants 2 and 4.

  g Write down a conjecture for which quadrants the graph of $y = \dfrac{a}{x}$ will be in for $a > 0$, and for $a < 0$. Test your conjecture with a GDC.

Reflect and discuss 2

- If $f(x) = \dfrac{1}{x}$ and $g(x) = -\dfrac{1}{x}$, is $g(x) = -f(x)$ or is $g(x) = f(-x)$? How do the effects of the two transformations $-f(x)$ and $f(-x)$ compare when $f(x) = \dfrac{1}{x}$?

Exploration 3

1 Graph the function $y = \dfrac{a}{x}$ and insert a slider for the parameter a for values from -10 to $+10$.

2 Move the slider to explore what happens to the graph for different values of a (positive, negative, fraction, zero).

3 Generalize the effect of the parameter a on the graph of $y = \dfrac{a}{x}, a \neq 0$. Write conclusions for when $a > 0$, and for $a < 0$.

4 Explain why the case when $a = 0$ is ignored in step 3.

The graph of a reciprocal function $y = \dfrac{a}{x}$, $a \neq 0$ is a special case of a curve called a **hyperbola**. It has a horizontal asymptote at $y = 0$ and a vertical asymptote at $x = 0$. Because the asymptotes are perpendicular, it is also known as a **rectangular hyperbola**.

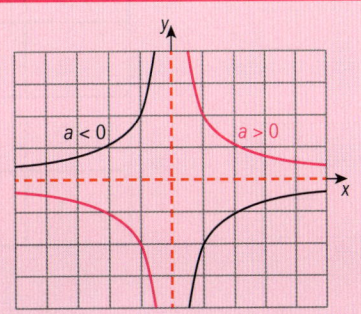

Reflect and discuss 3

- Compare the effect of parameter a on the graph of $y = \dfrac{a}{x}$ with its effect on:

  a linear function $(y = ax)$

  a quadratic function $(y = ax^2)$

- For the rational function $f(x) = \dfrac{1}{x}$, is $y = \dfrac{1}{2x}$ the same as $y = \dfrac{1}{2}f(x)$ or $y = f(2x)$? What does this mean about the effects of these transformations on the graphs of rational functions?

Example 1

For each function below:

- state the domain and range
- write down the equations of the asymptotes
- draw the graph of the function.

a $f(x) = \dfrac{3}{x}$ **b** $f(x) = -\dfrac{2}{x}$

a $f(x) = \dfrac{3}{x}$

Domain: $x \in \mathbb{R},\ x \neq 0$; range: $y \in \mathbb{R},\ y \neq 0$

Horizontal asymptote: $y = 0$

Vertical asymptote: $x = 0$

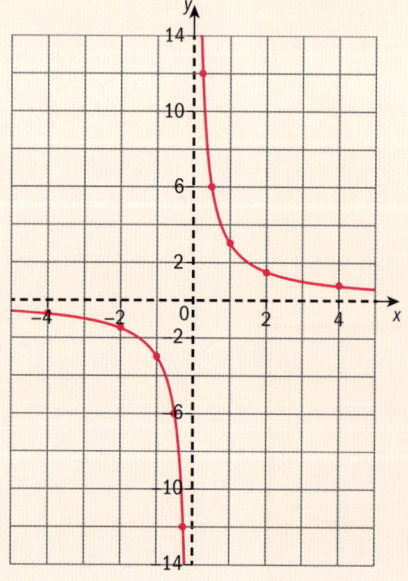

x	y
-4	-0.75
-2	-1.5
-1	-3
$-\frac{1}{2}$	-6
$-\frac{1}{4}$	-12
$\frac{1}{4}$	12
$\frac{1}{2}$	6
1	3
2	1.5
4	0.75

Make a table of values. Draw the graph by plotting several points from the table of values.

▶ Continued on next page

b $f(x) = -\dfrac{2}{x}$

Domain: $x \in \mathbb{R}$, $x \neq 0$; range: $y \in \mathbb{R}$, $y \neq 0$

Horizontal asymptote: $y = 0$

Vertical asymptote: $x = 0$

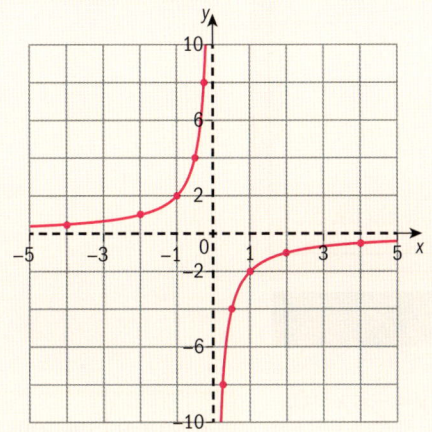

x	y
-4	0.5
-2	1
-1	2
$-\dfrac{1}{2}$	4
$-\dfrac{1}{4}$	8
$\dfrac{1}{4}$	-8
$\dfrac{1}{2}$	-4
1	-2
2	-1
4	-0.5

When $a > 0$, $y = \dfrac{a}{x}$ is always in quadrants 1 and 3. When $a < 0$, the graph is reflected in the x-axis, and is therefore always in quadrants 2 and 4.

For the function $y = \dfrac{1}{x}$:

$y = af(x)$ is a vertical dilation of $f(x)$, scale factor a, parallel to the y-axis.	$y = f(ax)$ is a horizontal dilation of $f(x)$, scale factor $\dfrac{1}{a}$, parallel to the x-axis.
$af(x)$	$f(ax)$
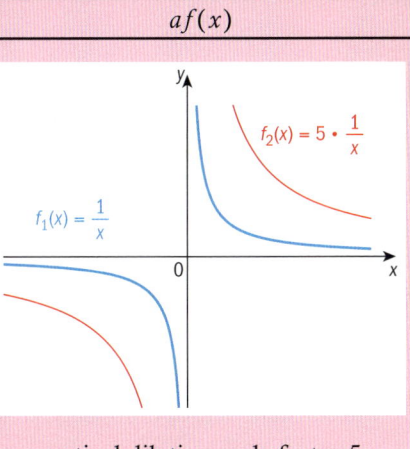	
vertical dilation scale factor 5	horizontal dilation scale factor $\dfrac{1}{5}$

▶ Continued on next page

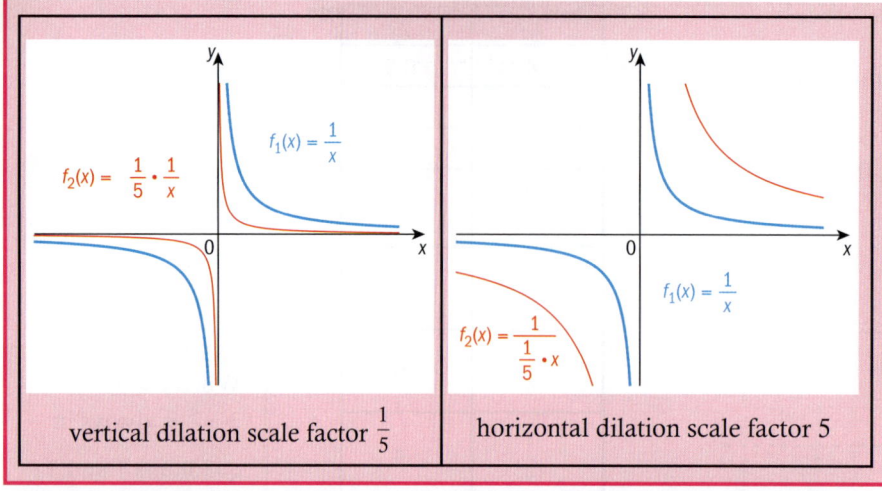

| vertical dilation scale factor $\frac{1}{5}$ | horizontal dilation scale factor 5 |

Reflect and discuss 4

- Explain why it makes sense that the vertical asymptote of $y = \frac{a}{x}$ is $x = 0$.
- Based on your answer above, what do you think the vertical asymptote will be for the function $y = \frac{2}{x-1}$?
- When does a rational function have two vertical asymptotes? Give an example of such a function.

> Rational functions with more than one vertical asymptote are beyond the level of this course.

Example 2

It takes 20 students 14 days to eat all the snacks in a vending machine.

Model this situation with a rational function and sketch its graph.

Determine how many days it would take 8 students to eat all the snacks.

Let x = number of students

Let y = number of days

> Define variables. Decide which variable is dependent on the other.

$y \propto \frac{1}{x} \Rightarrow y = \frac{k}{x}$

When $x = 20$, $y = 14$, so:

> Identify inverse proportion – as the number of students increases, the number of days decreases.

$14 = \frac{k}{20} \Rightarrow k = 280$

$\Rightarrow y = \frac{280}{x}$

> Use the initial condition to calculate the constant of proportionality, k.

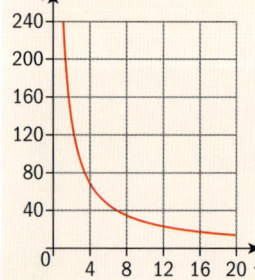

When $x = 8$ (8 students),

$y = \frac{280}{8} = 35$. Therefore, it would take 35 days for 8 students to eat the same number of snacks.

> x cannot take negative values, so the graph is in the first quadrant only.

- In Example 2, what kind of values can x take? Is it possible to have any number of students, including fractions? Does your graph represent this? If not, describe how to change your graph to reflect this limitation.

- In Example 2, do x and y have maximum or minimum values? If so, state them. Explain your reasoning. Would it make sense for either x or y to have a value of 0?

Practice 1

1 For each function:

  - state the domain and range

  - draw a graph of the function

  - draw and label the asymptotes.

  a $y = \dfrac{4}{x}$ **b** $y = -\dfrac{8}{x}$ **c** $y = \dfrac{1}{4x}$ **d** $y = -\dfrac{2}{3x}$

2 The length of time it takes to build a community shelter is inversely proportional to the number of people working on the project. It takes 600 hours for 4 people to build a shelter.

  a Model this situation with a rational function and sketch its graph.

  b Determine how long it would take 12 people to build a shelter.

A 2016 Design of the Year was awarded to a flat-pack shelter kit which included all the tools required for assembling, and could be put together by four people in just four hours.

3 Below is the graph of the resistance in an electric circuit (R) versus the current (I) flowing through it for a constant voltage.

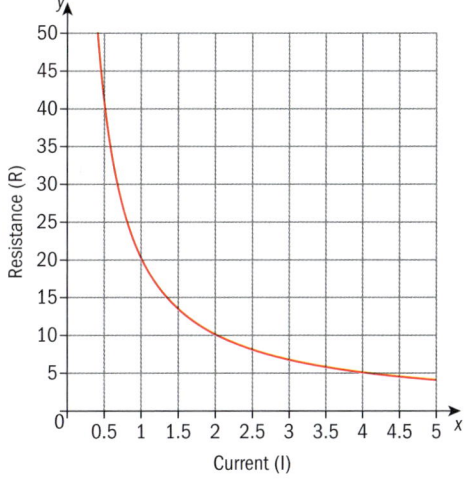

a Describe the relationship between current and resistance.

b Find the constant of proportionality using points from the graph.

c Hence write down the function relating current (I) and resistance (R).

4 The graph models the number of hours (y) it takes for aid workers (x) to build a shelter for refugees.

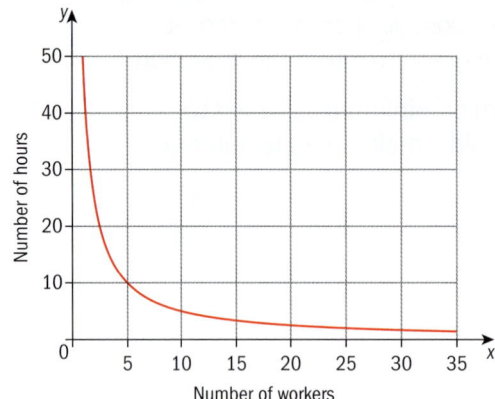

From this graph, determine the rational function and hence explain how long it would take:

a 1 person to build the shelter

b 5 people to build the shelter

c 10 people to build the shelter.

Problem solving

5 Newton's second law of motion, $F = ma$, states the relationship between force, mass and acceleration.

a Describe the proportional relationship between:
  i force and acceleration
  ii acceleration and mass.

b Hence sketch graphs of:
  i force versus acceleration for a fixed mass
  ii acceleration versus mass for a fixed force.

C **Transforming rational functions**

• How can understanding transformations of rational functions help you graph them?

Reflect and discuss 6

• For the function $y = f(x - h) + k$, describe the effects of the parameters h and k on the graph of $y = f(x)$. Use appropriate mathematical terms and demonstrate what you mean with an example.

• Predict what transformation takes the graph of $y = \dfrac{1}{x}$ to the graph of $y = \dfrac{1}{x-2} + 3$. What will be the equations of its asymptotes? Explain your reasoning.

Objective B: Investigating patterns	

Objective B: Investigating patterns
i. select and apply mathematical problem-solving techniques to discover complex patterns

In Exploration 4 you will use graphing and exploration skills to make new findings and draw new conclusions. Explain your findings clearly with labelled sketches and state your conclusions clearly.

Exploration 4

1 Use your GDC to graph the function $y = \dfrac{a}{x-h} + k$ and insert sliders for the parameters a, h and k.

2 Set the values $h = 0$ and $k = 0$. Move the slider to explore what happens to the graph for different values of a (e.g. positive, negative, fraction).

3 Describe the effect of a on the graph of $y = \dfrac{a}{x}$. Include positive, negative and fractional values of a. State the asymptotes, domain and range.

4 Set the value $a = 1$. Move the sliders one at a time to explore what happens for different values of h and k (positive, negative, fraction).

5 Sketch several graphs to demonstrate the effect of h on the graph of $y = \dfrac{1}{x-h} + k$. Include positive, negative and fractional values of h.
   Label the asymptotes and state the domain and range.

6 Sketch several graphs to demonstrate the effect of k on the graph of $y = \dfrac{1}{x-h} + k$. Include positive, negative and fractional values of k.
   Label the asymptotes and state the domain and range.

7 Generalize the effects of the parameters h and k in $y = \dfrac{a}{x-h} + k$ on the graph of $y = \dfrac{1}{x}$.

8 Determine the horizontal and vertical asymptotes of a rational function, $y = \dfrac{a}{x-h} + k$, just by looking at the function.

9 Determine the domain and range of $y = \dfrac{a}{x-h} + k$ just by looking at the function.

Reflect and discuss 7

- In Reflect and discuss 6, you were asked to predict how the graph of $y = \dfrac{1}{x-2} + 3$ might look. How good was your prediction? If you weren't completely correct, what should you have predicted?

The function $f(x) = \dfrac{a}{x-h} + k$, where $a \neq 0$, is a transformation of $f(x) = \dfrac{1}{x}$ (the parent function).

The domain of the rational function $f(x) = \dfrac{a}{x-h} + k$ is $x \in \mathbb{R}, x \neq h$.

The range of the rational function $f(x) = \dfrac{a}{x-h} + k$ is $y \in \mathbb{R}, y \neq k$.

The equation of the horizontal asymptote is $y = k$ and the equation of the vertical asymptote is $x = h$.

Example 3

Sketch the graph of $y = \dfrac{1}{x-1} + 3$.

Horizontal asymptote: $y = 3$

Vertical asymptote: $x = 1$

Find the asymptotes.

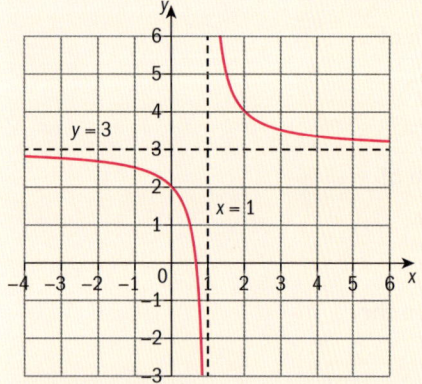

Sketch the asymptotes on the graph using dashed lines.

Sketch the function.

To check where a graph is located, you can substitute into its equation a value of x to the right of the vertical asymptote, and a value to the left.

For the graph in Example 3: when $x = 0$, $y = 2$; when $x = 2$, $y = 4$.

You can then sketch the curves through these points.

Practice 2

1 For each of the functions below:

- find the value of h and k
- write down the equations of the asymptotes
- write down the domain and range.

a $f(x) = \dfrac{1}{x+3} - 7$ b $f(x) = \dfrac{1}{x+2}$ c $f(x) = \dfrac{1}{x-5} + 8$

d $f(x) = \dfrac{1}{x} - 11$ e $f(x) = \dfrac{1}{x-1} + \pi$

2 For each function below:

- draw and label the asymptotes
- sketch the function on a graph
- state the domain and range.

a $y = \dfrac{1}{x} - 4$

b $y = \dfrac{1}{x-4}$

c $y = \dfrac{1}{x} + 3$

d $y = \dfrac{1}{x-2}$

e $y = \dfrac{1}{x+2} + 5$

f $y = \dfrac{1}{x-3} + 1$

3 Each of these functions has an equation of the form $y = \dfrac{1}{x-h} + k$.
Find the equation of each graph.

a
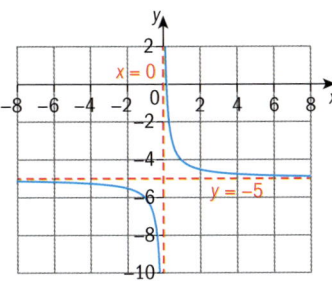

b
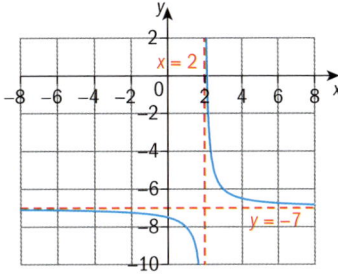

c
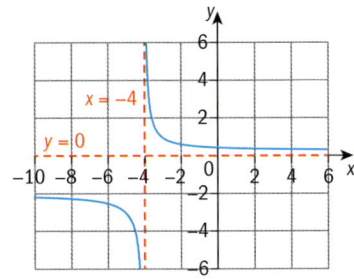

d
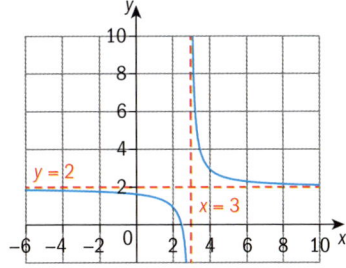

Problem solving

4 Find the equation of a curve $y = \dfrac{1}{x-h} + k$ with asymptotes:

a $y = 4$ and $x = 3$

b $y = 2$ and the y-axis

c $y = -1$ and $x = 2$

d $y = \dfrac{4}{3}$ and $x = -\dfrac{3}{4}$

5 Describe the individual transformations on $f(x) = \dfrac{1}{x}$ to obtain $f(x) = \dfrac{1}{x-h} + k$
for each set of values for h and k.

a i $h > 0, k = 0$

b i $k > 0, h = 0$

ii $h < 0, k = 0$

ii $k < 0, h = 0$

Example 4

For each function below:

- list the individual transformations on $f(x) = \dfrac{1}{x}$
- find the equations of the asymptotes
- hence sketch the graph of the function.

a $f(x) = \dfrac{10}{x-3} + 2$

b $f(x) = \dfrac{4}{3-2x} + 3$

a $f(x) = \dfrac{10}{x-3} + 2$ ———————————————

> Use the values a, h and k from the rational function $f(x) = \dfrac{a}{x-h} + k$.

$h = 3 \Rightarrow$ horizontal translation of 3 units in the positive x-direction

$a = 10 \Rightarrow$ vertical dilation scale factor 10

$k = 2 \Rightarrow$ vertical translation of 2 units in the positive y-direction

Horizontal asymptote: $y = 2$

Vertical asymptote: $x = 3$

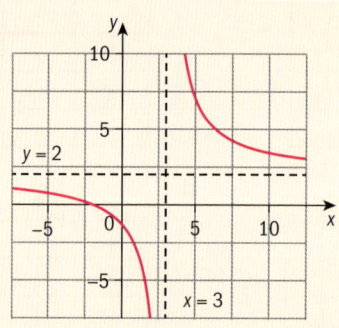

> Draw the asymptotes as dashed lines before sketching the graph.

b $f(x) = \dfrac{4}{3-2x} + 3$

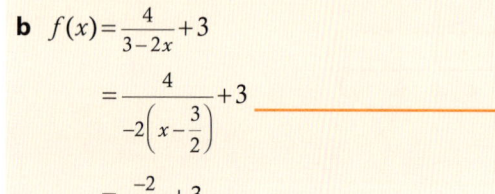

$$= \dfrac{4}{-2\left(x - \dfrac{3}{2}\right)} + 3$$ ———————————————

> Rearrange the equation to look like $f(x) = \dfrac{a}{x-h} + k$ by factorizing out the coefficient of x in the denominator.

$$= \dfrac{-2}{x - \dfrac{3}{2}} + 3$$

$h = \dfrac{3}{2} \Rightarrow$ horizontal translation 1.5 units in the positive x-direction

$a = -2 \Rightarrow$ vertical stretch of factor 2 and horizontal reflection ———

> A negative value of a gives a reflection in the x-axis.

$k = 3 \Rightarrow$ vertical translation 3 units in the positive y-direction

Horizontal asymptote: $y = 3$

Vertical asymptote: $x = 1.5$

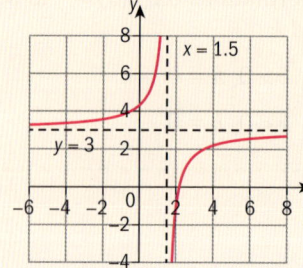

For a rational function $f(x) = \dfrac{a}{x-h} + k$:

- h determines the horizontal translation; the vertical asymptote is $x = h$.
- k determines the vertical translation; the horizontal asymptote is $y = k$.
- a determines
  - either the horizontal dilation of factor $\dfrac{1}{a}$ or the vertical dilation of factor a
  - the reflection in the x-axis (if $a < 0$)

Practice 3

1 Perform these transformations on the rational function $f(x) = \dfrac{1}{x}$, then write down the function obtained as a single algebraic fraction.

a Vertical dilation by scale factor $\dfrac{1}{2}$, vertical translation of 1 unit in the negative y-direction, horizontal translation of 4 units in the positive x-direction.

b Horizontal dilation by scale factor 3, horizontal translation of 3 units, vertical translation of -2 units.

c Vertical dilation by scale factor $\dfrac{1}{4}$, reflection in the x-axis, vertical translation of 8 units.

d Vertical dilation by scale factor $\dfrac{3}{2}$, reflection in the y-axis, vertical translation of 4 units, horizontal translation of -2 units.

2 For each rational function below:

- list the transformations applied to $f(x) = \dfrac{1}{x}$
- find the equations of the asymptotes
- hence sketch the graph of the rational function.

a $f(x) = \dfrac{3}{x+6} - 5$ **b** $f(x) = -\dfrac{5}{2-x} + 3$ **c** $f(x) = \dfrac{9}{3x+1}$

d $f(x) = \dfrac{5}{8-2x} + 2$ **e** $f(x) = -\dfrac{5}{2x-1} - 8$ **f** $f(x) = -\dfrac{13}{x} - 11$

D The inverse of a rational function

- Can a function be its own inverse?
- Does science solve problems or create them?

Exploration 5

1 Using your GDC, draw the graph of $y = \frac{1}{x}$ and the line $y = x$. Reflect the graph of $y = \frac{1}{x}$ in the line $y = x$. Describe what you notice.

2 Repeat step **1** for the graphs of:

   a $y = \frac{2}{x}$ **b** $y = \frac{5}{x}$ **c** $y = \frac{0.5}{x}$ **d** $y = \frac{0.1}{x}$

3 Explain what your results tell you about the inverse relation of a rational function $y = \frac{a}{x}$, $a \neq 0$. Justify why this inverse relation is a function.

4 a Find the inverse function $f^{-1}(x)$ of the function $f(x) = \frac{a}{x}$, $a \neq 0$ algebraically.

   b Determine the domain and range of $f^{-1}(x)$.

   c Summarize your findings about the inverse function of $y = \frac{a}{x}$, $a \neq 0$.

Reflect and discuss 8

You could say that in the reciprocal function $y = \frac{1}{x}$, y is the inverse of x, because y represents the multiplicative inverse (or reciprocal) of x, except when $x = 0$. This means that $xy = 1$. However, the reciprocal function $y = \frac{1}{x}$ is not the inverse function of $y = x$.

- How are the multiplicative inverse (reciprocals) and inverse functions different?
- What is meant by 'inverse function'?
- What is the inverse function of $y = x$?
- What is the inverse function of $y = \frac{1}{x}$?

Example 5

Find the inverse of $f(x) = \frac{-2}{x+8} - 10$.

$y = \frac{-2}{x+8} - 10$ ———————————————— Interchange the x and the y.

$x = \frac{-2}{y+8} - 10$

$x + 10 = \frac{-2}{y+8}$

$y + 8 = \frac{-2}{x+10}$ ———————————————— Isolate the variable y.

$y = \frac{-2}{x+10} - 8$

$f^{-1}(x) = \frac{-2}{x+10} - 8$

Practice 4

1 On your GDC, graph each function and its inverse on the same grid.

a $y=\dfrac{4}{x}$ **b** $y=-\dfrac{2}{x}$ **c** $y=\dfrac{1}{x+4}$

d $y=\dfrac{3}{x}-1$ **e** $y=3+\dfrac{3}{3-x}$ **f** $y=\dfrac{1}{1-x}+1$

2 Find the inverse of each of each function:

a $y=\dfrac{-5}{x+1}$ **b** $y=\dfrac{7}{x-9}+6$ **c** $y=-\dfrac{1}{x-12}-8$

d $y=\dfrac{6}{5-x}-3$ **e** $y=\dfrac{3x-1}{x+3}$ **f** $y=-\dfrac{2x}{x-4}$

Summary

A **rational function** is any function which can be expressed as a quotient $\dfrac{f(x)}{g(x)}$ where $f(x)$ and $g(x)$ are functions of x, and $g(x)\neq 0$.

The function $f(x)=\dfrac{1}{x}$, $x\neq 0$, is a rational function called the reciprocal function. Its domain is the set of real numbers excluding zero and its range is the set of real numbers excluding zero.

For a reciprocal function, the **horizontal asymptote** is the horizontal line that the graph approaches as x approaches positive or negative infinity.

For a reciprocal function, the **vertical asymptote** is the vertical line that $f(x)$ approaches as the denominator approaches 0. (The denominator can never equal 0.)

For the function $f(x)=\dfrac{a}{x-h}+k$, the vertical asymptote is $x=h$ and the horizontal asymptote is $y=k$.

For a rational function $f(x)=\dfrac{a}{x-h}+k$:

- h determines the horizontal translation
- k determines the vertical translation
- a determines
  - either the horizontal dilation of factor $\dfrac{1}{a}$ or the vertical dilation of factor a
  - the horizontal reflection
  - whether the graph is reflected in the x-axis ($a<0$) or not ($a>0$).

The domain of the rational function $f(x)=\dfrac{a}{x-h}+k$ is $x\in\mathbb{R}, x\neq h$.

The range of the rational function $f(x)=\dfrac{a}{x-h}+k$ is $y\in\mathbb{R}, y\neq k$.

The horizontal asymptote is at $y=k$ and the vertical asymptote is at $x=h$.

Mixed practice

1 For each function below:

- **state** the largest possible domain and range
- **write down** the equations of the asymptotes
- **sketch** the graph.

a $y=-\dfrac{5}{x}$ **b** $y=\dfrac{1}{x}+1$

c $y=\dfrac{2}{x-2}-8$ **d** $y=-\dfrac{4}{x+3}+2$

2 Perform these transformations on the rational function $f(x)=\dfrac{1}{x}$ to obtain $g(x)$.
Write down $g(x)$ obtained as a single algebraic fraction.

a The function $f(x)=\dfrac{1}{x}$ is vertically dilated by scale factor 3, translated vertically 5 units in the negative y-direction and horizontally by 5 units in the positive x-direction.

b The function $f(x) = \frac{1}{x}$ is vertically dilated by scale factor $\frac{1}{2}$, translated 1 unit vertically in the positive y-direction and reflected in the y-axis.

c The function $f(x) = \frac{1}{x}$ is reflected in the x-axis, translated vertically by 2 units in the negative y-direction and horizontally by 3 units in the positive x-direction.

d The function $f(x) = \frac{1}{x}$ is dilated horizontally by scale factor 12, reflected in the x-axis, translated 1 unit vertically in the negative y-direction and 4 units horizontally in the positive x-direction.

3 For each rational function:

- **list** the individual transformations applied to $f(x) = \frac{1}{x}$ to obtain the given function

- **find** the equations of the asymptotes

- **sketch** the graph of the rational function

- **find** its inverse.

a $g(x) = -\frac{1}{x-2} + 9$

b $h(x) = \frac{3}{x+1} - 3$

c $k(x) = \frac{10}{5-x}$

d $m(x) = -\frac{4}{3x+2} + 1$

e $n(x) = \frac{5}{8-4x} + 6$

f $p(x) = \frac{1}{4x-5}$

Problem solving

4 Young's dosage calculates drug dosages for children. For a certain pharmaceutical drug the adult dose is 50 mg.

Young's dosage says that the children's dose is $C = 50\left(\frac{x}{x+12}\right)$, where x is the age of the child in years.

a **Calculate** the dosage of the medicine for a 10-year-old child.

b Rewrite the function in the form $C = \frac{a}{x-h} + k$.

c **Explain** the series of transformations.

Review in context

1 Catherine is travelling from New York to Tokyo and then to Sydney.

She starts with 1000 USD and converts this to Yen. She spends 40 000 Yen in Tokyo, and converts her remaining money into AUD when she reaches Sydney. Using your knowledge of reciprocal functions and the currency conversion rates below, **explain** how much money Catherine now has in AUD.

1 USD = 113.4 YEN = 1.32 AUD

2 Two oil pipelines run between Abuja and Lagos in Nigeria. One pipeline can fill an oil reservoir three times faster than a second pipeline. If both pipelines are operational, an oil tanker's reservoir can be filled in 14 hours.

$r = \frac{W}{t}$ where r is the rate, W is the work required (in this case to fill 1 reservoir), t is the time taken in hours.

a Let the hours needed to fill one reservoir from the fast pipe be p. The rate of filling is the reciprocal function $r = \frac{1}{p}$. Find the reciprocal function for the rate of filling by the slow pipe.

b Hence find an expression for the rate of filling one reservoir with both pipes working together.

c As it takes 14 hours to fill the reservoir with both pipelines, find p. Hence find the time taken to fill the reservoir with just the slow pipe.

Reflect and discuss 9

How have you explored the statement of inquiry? Give specific examples.

Statement of inquiry:

Representing patterns and change in a variety of forms has helped humans apply their understanding of scientific principles.

E8.4 Solving linear and quadratic rational equations

Global context: Scientific and technical innovation

Related concept: Equivalence

Objectives

- Solving linear and quadratic rational equations algebraically and graphically
- Using equivalence transformations to solve rational equations
- Using rational equations to model situations and solve problems

Inquiry questions

 F
- What is a rational algebraic equation?
- How do you solve equations with fractions?

 C
- How are the different methods of solving rational algebraic equations related?
- What makes different methods equivalent?

 D
- Is there a 'best method' for solving rational equations?
- Does science solve problems or create them?

FORM

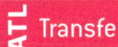
ATL Transfer

Apply skills and knowledge in unfamiliar situations

Statement of inquiry:

Representing patterns and change in a variety of forms has helped humans apply their understanding of scientific principles.

📖 **Launch additional digital resources for this chapter.**

You should already know how to:

• apply equivalence transformations to solve linear equations	**1** Solve using equivalence transformations: **a** $2x + 3 = 5x - 9$ **b** $4(x - 1) = 2x + 7$ **c** $\dfrac{3x}{2} = 10$
• carry out the four arithmetic operations on rational algebraic expressions	**2** Simplify: **a** $\dfrac{x}{3} + \dfrac{3x}{4}$ **b** $\dfrac{7}{x+2} - \dfrac{5}{x}$ **c** $\dfrac{2x-6}{x^2-9} \times \dfrac{x^2+4x+3}{5x+5}$ **d** $\dfrac{16x^2}{4x-12} \div \dfrac{x^2-14x}{x^2-49}$
• factorize quadratic expressions	**3** Factorize: **a** $x^2 - 16$ **b** $3x^2 - 6x$ **c** $x^2 - 5x - 6$ **d** $3x^2 - 5x - 12$
• solve quadratic equations	**4** Solve: **a** $2x^2 - 18 = 0$ **b** $x^2 + 2x = 3$ **c** $2x^2 + 7x + 3 = 0$ **d** $3x^2 - 4x + 1 = 0$

F   Rational algebraic equations

- What is a rational algebraic equation?
- How do you solve equations with fractions?

A rational number is of the form $\dfrac{p}{q}$ where p and q are integers, and $q \neq 0$.

Similarly, a rational algebraic expression is of the form $\dfrac{P(x)}{Q(x)}$ where

$Q(x) \neq 0$. A rational algebraic equation is an equation containing rational algebraic expressions.

The rules and procedures you use with rational numbers also apply to rational algebraic expressions and equations.

Example 1

The total electrical current (16 amps) used by two appliances is given by the equation $\dfrac{x}{10} + \dfrac{x}{30} = 16$, where x volts is the voltage used by each appliance. Find the voltage used by each appliance.

$$\frac{x}{10} + \frac{x}{30} = 16$$

$$30 \times \frac{x}{10} + 30 \times \frac{x}{30} = 30 \times 16$$

$$3x + x = 480$$

$$4x = 480$$

$$x = 120$$

Each appliance uses 120 volts.

$$\frac{120}{10} + \frac{120}{30} = 12 + 4 = 16 \checkmark$$

> There is no standard mains voltage used by all countries. In most countries it is between 200 and 240 volts while in Japan and most of the Americas it is between 100 and 127 volts.

> Use the multiplication principle. Multiply each term by 30 to simplify.

> Check by substitution.

Multiplying each fraction in the equation by the lowest common denominator eliminates one of the denominators so it is no longer a rational equation.

Practice 1

Solve these rational equations, leaving your answers exact, or to 3 s.f.

1 $\dfrac{x}{4} + \dfrac{3x}{5} = 2$ **2** $\dfrac{5x-9}{6} + \dfrac{2x-4}{7} = 1$ **3** $\dfrac{2x}{7} - \dfrac{1}{3} = \dfrac{x}{2}$

4 $\dfrac{x+3}{6} + \dfrac{2x}{5} = \dfrac{5x}{2}$ **5** $\dfrac{2x-1}{4} - \dfrac{x+4}{3} = \dfrac{5x}{6}$ **6** $\dfrac{4x+1}{2} + \dfrac{3x-5}{5} = \dfrac{2x-2}{4}$

7 $\dfrac{x-3}{2} + \dfrac{3x-1}{4} = \dfrac{4x+7}{6} + \dfrac{1-5x}{8}$ **8** $\dfrac{5x}{3} - \dfrac{4x-1}{8} = \dfrac{x+2}{6} - \dfrac{x+1}{12}$

Problem solving

9 $\dfrac{2}{x} - \dfrac{3x}{4} = \dfrac{1}{3}$

- -

Reflect and discuss 1

- How is question **9** in Practice 1 similar to and different from the other questions?

- How did that affect the process you used to solve the equation?

 C ## When different is the same

- How are the different methods of solving rational algebraic equations related?
- What makes different methods equivalent?

Multiplying by the lowest common denominator is a useful method for solving simple rational algebraic equations. The LCM is easy to find when the denominators are rational numbers. What happens when rational expressions or equations have variables in the denominator?

> Finding the lowest common denominator is the same as finding the lowest common multiple, LCM, of two or more numbers or two or more algebraic expressions.

Exploration 1

Look at these pairs of rational expressions and their lowest common denominators.

Rational expressions	Lowest common denominator
$\dfrac{2}{x}, \dfrac{3}{x+2}$	$x(x+2)$
$\dfrac{-1}{x+1}, \dfrac{7}{x-3}$	$(x+1)(x-3)$
$\dfrac{5}{x}, \dfrac{1}{x^2-7x}$	$x(x-7)$

▶ Continued on next page

$\dfrac{10}{x^2-4}, \dfrac{-6}{x-2}$	$(x+2)(x-2)$
$\dfrac{8}{(x+1)(x-5)}, \dfrac{-3}{(x-1)(x+1)}$	$(x+1)(x-5)(x-1)$
$\dfrac{2x-5}{x^2+x-2}, \dfrac{3x}{x^2-1}$	$(x+2)(x+1)(x-1)$
$\dfrac{x+2}{2x^2+x}, \dfrac{3x-1}{2x^2-x-1}$	$x(2x+1)(x-1)$
$\dfrac{x-1}{x^2-9}, \dfrac{4}{x^2+6x+9}$	$(x-3)(x+3)^2$

1 Determine the first step in finding the LCM of two algebraic rational expressions.

2 After that first step, explain how you would find the LCM of two rational algebraic expressions.

3 Find the LCM of these three expressions: $\dfrac{7}{x}, \dfrac{3}{x^2-6x}$ and $\dfrac{x+1}{x^2-7x+6}$.

Practice 2

1 The denominators of two or more algebraic fractions are given. Find the lowest common denominator of the given denominators.

a x, x **b** $2x, 3x$ **c** $x, x^2, 3x^4$

d $x, x-2$ **e** $x, 2, x$ **f** $x-2, x+2$

g $x, x-2, x+2$ **h** x, x^2+1 **i** $x-1, x^2-1$

j $x^2-x, x+1$ **k** $x+4, 1, 2x+8$ **l** $x+1, x-1, x^2-1$

m $x-a, x+1, x^2-1$ **n** $x, x+2, x^2-x-6$ **o** $2x, 2x-3, x+1$

p $3x^2, 2x^2-8, x+2$

Reflect and discuss 2

- Do you see any potential issues with having variables in the denominator? Explain.

- Find any value(s) of x that are not allowed in each expression in Exploration 1.

To solve rational algebraic equations with variables in the denominator, you use the same procedure as for rational equations with numerical denominators.

Example 2

Solve the equation $\frac{3}{x} = \frac{8}{x-2}$ and check your answer algebraically.

$\text{LCM}(x, x-2) = x(x-2)$ ——————————————— Find the lowest common denominator.

$x(x-2) \times \frac{3}{x} = x(x-2) \times \frac{8}{(x-2)}$ ——————————— Rearrange to place each equal algebraic expression in a fraction.

$\frac{\cancel{x}}{\cancel{x}} \times 3(x-2) = \frac{\cancel{(x-2)}}{\cancel{(x-2)}} \times 8x$ ———————— $\frac{x}{x}=1$ for $x \neq 1$, $\frac{x-2}{x-2}=1$ for $x \neq 2$.

$3(x-2) = 8x$

$3x - 6 = 8x$

$-5x = 6$

$x = -\frac{6}{5} = -1.2$ ——————————— This solution is valid since the only excluded values are 0 and 2.

LHS: $\frac{3}{x} = \frac{3}{-1.2} = -2.5$

——————————————————————— Check your answer.

RHS: $\frac{8}{x-2} = \frac{8}{-1.2-2} = -2.5$

LHS = RHS = -2.5 ✓

Reflect and discuss 3

- Why are you allowed to put lines through the factors that are common to both numerator and denominator?

- What number are you really multiplying by when you do this?

In rational equations, you must exclude any values of the variable that make the denominator equal to 0.

For example, in the rational equation $\frac{3}{x} = \frac{8}{x-2}$ you need to exclude the values $x = 0$ and $x = 2$ because they make one of the denominators equal to zero. If the solution to the equation includes either 0 or 2, you need to eliminate that answer.

> An extraneous solution is one that you find algebraically, but does not satisfy the original equation. First, determine any values of x that are not allowed in the equation because they make the denominator zero. When you have the solutions, reject any that are not allowed.

Practice 3

Solve these rational equations using appropriate equivalence transformations, and check your answers algebraically. Make sure you check for extraneous solutions.

1 $\dfrac{4}{x} = \dfrac{9}{x-2}$

2 $\dfrac{10}{x+4} = \dfrac{15}{4(x+1)}$

3 $\dfrac{6}{3x} + \dfrac{5}{4} = \dfrac{3}{x}$

4 $\dfrac{4}{3x} + \dfrac{5}{4} = \dfrac{3}{x}$

5 $\dfrac{10}{x(x-2)} + \dfrac{4}{x} = \dfrac{5}{x-2}$

6 $\dfrac{5}{x-2} = 7 + \dfrac{10}{x-2}$

7 $\dfrac{3}{x-2} + \dfrac{2}{2-x} = 2 - x$

8 $x + 1 = \dfrac{72}{x}$

9 $x + \dfrac{3}{x+1} = 4$

- -

Reflect and discuss 4

For the equation: $\dfrac{7}{x^2-4} + \dfrac{2}{x^2+2x} = \dfrac{3}{x}$

- How easy is it to determine the LCM of the algebraic fractions?
- What could you do first, to make it easier to determine the LCM?
- What is the LCM?
- What values of x are not allowed?

Example 3

Solve $\dfrac{1}{x-6} + \dfrac{x}{x-2} = \dfrac{4}{x^2-8x+12}$ and check your answers algebraically.

$x^2 - 8x + 12 = (x-6)(x-2)$ — Factorize the denominator on the right side.

$\dfrac{1}{x-6} + \dfrac{x}{x-2} = \dfrac{4}{(x-6)(x-2)}$; $x \neq 6, x \neq 2$ — Identify any values of x that are not allowed.

$(x-6)(x-2)\left[\dfrac{1}{x-6} + \dfrac{x}{x-2}\right] = (x-6)(x-2)\left[\dfrac{4}{(x-6)(x-2)}\right]$ — Use the multiplication principle with the LCM of all denominators.

$(x-2) + x(x-6) = 4$

$x^2 - 5x - 2 = 4$

$x^2 - 5x - 6 = 0$ — Set the quadratic equal to 0.

$(x-6)(x+1) = 0 \Rightarrow x = 6, x = -1$ — Factorize and solve.

Since $x \neq 6$, the only possible solution is $x = -1$. — Reject any invalid solutions.

LHS: $\dfrac{1}{-1-6} + \dfrac{-1}{-1-2} = -\dfrac{1}{7} + \dfrac{1}{3} = \dfrac{4}{21}$

RHS: $\dfrac{4}{(-1)^2 - 8(-1) + 12} = \dfrac{4}{1+8+12} = \dfrac{4}{21}$ — Substitute the solution found into the original equation.

LHS = RHS ✓

Practice 4

Solve these equations using appropriate equivalence transformations.

1 $\dfrac{7}{x+2}+\dfrac{5}{x-2}=\dfrac{10x-2}{x^2-4}$

2 $\dfrac{x}{x-2}+\dfrac{1}{x-4}=\dfrac{2}{x^2-6x+8}$

3 $\dfrac{2x-4}{x^2-10x+16}=\dfrac{2}{x+2}$

4 $\dfrac{2}{x^2-x}=\dfrac{1}{x-1}$

5 $\dfrac{2x}{x-3}=\dfrac{3x}{x^2-9}+2$

> Make sure you check for extraneous solutions.

Are there any other methods for solving rational equations?

Exploration 2

1 For the fractions $\dfrac{a}{b}$ and $\dfrac{c}{d}$ to be equal, determine what conditions must hold for a, b, c, and d.

2 If $b=d$, determine what must be true about a and c in order for the fractions to be equal.

3 Select any pair of equivalent fractions, for example $\dfrac{3}{6}=\dfrac{12}{24}$, and multiply diagonally across the equal sign, so 3×24 and 6×12. Suggest what is true about these products. Explain if you think that it is always true.

4 Generalize your result for any pair of equivalent fractions $\dfrac{a}{b}=\dfrac{c}{d}$.

5 Prove your result using equivalence transformations.

6 State in which examples from Practice 3 and Practice 4 this result would be useful.

7 State the condition necessary to use this result in solving rational equations.

Consider again the rational equation in Example 3: $\dfrac{1}{x-6}+\dfrac{x}{x-2}=\dfrac{4}{x^2-8x+12}$.

Instead of multiplying both sides by the LCM, what happens if you write all the terms in the equation with the LCM as denominator? The LCM is $(x-2)(x-6)$, so you get an equivalent equation:

$$\frac{1(x-2)}{(x-6)(x-2)}+\frac{x(x-6)}{(x-2)(x-6)}=\frac{4}{(x-6)(x-2)}$$

which simplifies to:

$$\frac{1(x-2)+x(x-6)}{(x-6)(x-2)}=\frac{4}{(x-6)(x-2)}$$

$$\frac{x^2-5x-2}{(x-6)(x-2)}=\frac{4}{(x-6)(x-2)}$$

> Try using this method in Practice 5, before you decide which method you prefer for solving a rational equation.

Since the denominators are equal, the numerators must be as well, so:

$$x^2-5x-2=4$$

Set the quadratic equal to 0 and solve:

$$x^2 - 5x - 6 = 0$$

$$(x - 6)(x + 1) = 0$$

$$x = 6 \text{ or } x = -1$$

From the original equation $x \neq 2$ and $x \neq 6$, since these values would make denominators equal to zero.

So $x = 6$ is an extraneous solution. The only solution is $x = -1$.

Practice 5

Solve these rational equations by first obtaining equal denominators on both sides of the equation equals sign. Make sure that you check your answers in the original equation to exclude any extraneous answers.

1 $\dfrac{5}{x-2} - \dfrac{4}{x} = \dfrac{10}{x(x-2)}$ **2** $\dfrac{4}{x} = \dfrac{3}{x-2}$ **3** $\dfrac{2x^2-5}{x^2-4} + \dfrac{6}{x+2} = \dfrac{4x-7}{x-2}$

4 $\dfrac{6}{x-1} + \dfrac{2x}{x-2} = 2$ **5** $\dfrac{x}{x^2-8} = \dfrac{2}{x}$

- -

Reflect and discuss 5

What makes different methods equivalent?

D Modelling real-life problems using rational equations

- Is there a 'best method' for solving rational equations?
- Does science solve problems or create them?

Exploration 3

1 Choose two questions from Practice 5 and solve them again, this time multiplying by the LCM.

2 State any differences between the equations from the two methods.

3 Which method do you think is better? Explain your choice.

4 Solve these equations using the method you prefer:

a $\dfrac{1}{a+1} + \dfrac{1}{a-1} = \dfrac{2}{a^2-1}$ **b** $3 - x + \dfrac{1}{x-2} = \dfrac{x-1}{x-2}$ **c** $\dfrac{1}{x+1} = \dfrac{1}{x^2-4x-5}$

5 State what you notice about your answers, and explain whether or not the results would be the same independent of the method you use. Justify your answer.

Practice 6

Problem solving

Translate each situation described below into a rational equation. Make sure that you identify all variables. Select the most efficient method for solving the rational equation and use appropriate equivalence transformations. Interpret your answer in the given context.

1 A motorist makes a 1080-mile journey on brand A of gasoline and averages x miles per gallon. For the return trip, she uses the less expensive brand B. On brand B, she travels 3 miles fewer per gallon, and uses 4 gallons more for the same journey.

  a Determine the number of miles per gallon for the initial journey.

  b Brand A costs 35 cents per gallon, and brand B costs 32 cents per gallon. Calculate the difference in the cost for the 1080-mile journey.

2 The concentration of a medication in a patient's bloodstream C (in mg/l), can be modelled by:

$C(t) = \frac{6t}{t^2 - 4}$, where t is the time (in hours) after taking the medication.

  a Determine how many hours after taking the medication the concentration will be 2 mg/l.

  b How many solutions did you find? Explain whether or not all the solutions you found made sense.

  c One dose equals 5 mg/l and the concentration should never be more than $6\frac{1}{8}$ mg/l. Determine a safe time interval between doses.

> Doctors and nurses need to know the concentration of medication in a patient's bloodstream, so they can decide on a safe time interval between doses.

3 On a mountain trail, a group of hikers walked for 7 miles on a level path, and then hiked 12 miles uphill. They generally walked 3 miles per hour faster than they hiked. The entire excursion lasted 4 hours. Determine the rate at which they hiked uphill.

4 To stay underwater, divers need air that contains enough oxygen. However, oxygen under high pressure can act like poison in the body, so the recommended percentage of oxygen in the air changes as you dive deeper. The percentage of oxygen (P) recommended at depth d meters is calculated using the formula $P = \frac{1980}{d + 99}$.

  a At sea level the percentage of oxygen in the air is approximately 20%. Explain how this compares to the value calculated using the formula.

  b Find the depth at which the recommended amount of oxygen is 10%.

5 Juan drives 20 km/h per hour faster than Maria. Juan drives 100 km in the same time that Maria drives 75 km. Find their driving speeds.

6 Carl's water pump removes 10 000 *l* of water in 15 minutes. His neighbor Sareeta's pump removes the same amount in 20 minutes. Determine how long it would take to remove 10 000 *l* of water using both pumps combined.

7 A scientist studying fish wants to find out how fast a salmon swims in still water. When the river speed is 0.5 m/s she records that a salmon swims 20 m upstream (against the current) and then 45 m downstream (with the current) in a total of 70 seconds. Determine how fast the salmon swims in still water.

Summary

A rational number is of the form $\frac{p}{q}$ where p and q are integers, and $q \neq 0$. Similarly, a rational algebraic expression is of the form $\frac{P(x)}{Q(x)}$, where $Q(x) \neq 0$. A rational algebraic equation is an equation containing rational algebraic expressions.

To solve a rational equation, first find the lowest common denominator (LCM) of all the denominators.

Either: Multiply both sides of the equation by the LCM to eliminate all the fractions.

Or: Rewrite the equation so that all terms have the common denominator. The two numerators are then equal.

An **extraneous solution** to an equation is one that you find algebraically, but does not satisfy the original equation. First determine any values of x that are not allowed in the equation because they make the denominator zero. When you have the solutions, reject any that are not allowed.

Mixed practice

Solve these equations using appropriate equivalence transformations and the most efficient method. Make sure you check for extraneous solutions. Leave all answers exact.

1 $\frac{2x-3}{x+3} = \frac{3x}{x-4}$

2 $\frac{4x-3}{x-4} = \frac{x}{x-3}$

3 $\frac{2}{x(x-2)} + \frac{3}{x} = \frac{4}{x-2}$

4 $\frac{10}{x^2+2x} + \frac{4}{x} = \frac{5}{x+2}$

5 $\frac{2(x+7)}{x-4} - 2 = \frac{2x+20}{2x+8}$

Problem solving

6 a **Determine** if a pair of consecutive integers exists whose reciprocals add up to $\frac{5}{6}$.

b **Determine** if a pair of consecutive integers exists whose reciprocals add up to $\frac{3}{4}$.

c **Determine** if a pair of consecutive even integers exists whose reciprocals add up to $\frac{3}{4}$.

d **Determine** if a pair of consecutive odd integers exists whose reciprocals add up to $\frac{11}{60}$.

Review in context

Scientific and technical innovation

1 The water in the Danube Delta flows at about 2 km/h. On a kayaking trip Max paddles upstream for 15 km, takes a half-hour lunch break, and then returns to his original starting point. His entire trip takes 3.5 hours (including his lunch break).

Let x km/h represent Max's paddling speed in still water. Then the kayak's speed upstream is $(x-2)$ km/h and downstream is $(x+2)$ km/h.

Average speed = $\frac{\text{total distance}}{\text{total time}}$

a **Justify** the expressions for the average speed of the kayak going upstream and downstream.

b **Write** an expression for the time taken for the kayak to travel:

   i upstream

   ii downstream.

c **Use** your expressions from part **b** to write an equation representing the whole journey.

d **Find** the average speed of the kayak in still water.

2 When resistors are connected in parallel, the total resistance R_{tot} is given by:

$$\frac{1}{R_1}+\frac{1}{R_2}+\frac{1}{R_3}+\cdots=\frac{1}{R_{tot}}.$$

Find the resistances of two resistors connected in parallel where:

a One resistance is three times as large as the other. Total resistance is 12 ohms.

b One resistance is 3 ohms greater than the other. Total resistance is 2 ohms.

c **Find** the resistances of three resistors connected in parallel where the resistance of one is 2 ohms greater than the smallest one, and the other has resistance twice as large as the smallest one.

The total resistance is $\frac{10}{7}$ ohms.

d An engineer wants to build a circuit with total resistance of 3 ohms. **Show** how he can do this with two resistors, where the resistance of one is 8 ohms greater than the other.

3 Lucy makes an 8-hour round trip of 45 km upstream and 45 km back downstream on a motorboat traveling at a speed of 12 km/h relative to the river. **Determine** the speed of the current.

4 Lenses are used to look at objects, and to project images on to a screen.

> The focal length of a lens is the distance between the lens and the point where parallel rays of light passing through the lens would converge.

The distance between a lens and the image produced d_i is related to the focal length f and the distance between the lens and the object d_o by the formula $\frac{1}{d_o}+\frac{1}{d_i}=\frac{1}{f}$.

a The focal length of a lens is 15 cm. The image appears to be twice as far away as the original object. **Find** how far the object is from the lens.

b An object is placed in front of a lens, at a distance 2 cm more than the focal length. The image appears to be 4 cm from the lens. **Find** the focal length of the lens.

c The human eye contains a lens that focuses an image on the retina for it to be seen clearly.

An object is at a distance from the eye that is 20 cm longer than the focal length. The distance from the eye to the retina is −20 mm (on the other side of the lens from the object). **Find** the focal length of this eye.

5 An airplane travels 910 miles with a tailwind in the same time that it travels 660 miles with headwind. The speed of the airplane is 305 m/h in still air. **Determine** the wind's speed.

> 'speed of 12 km/h relative to the river' means the speed traveling upstream is $12 - x$, where x is the speed of the current.

Reflect and discuss 6

How have you explored the statement of inquiry? Give specific examples.

Statement of inquiry:

Representing patterns and change in a variety of forms has helped humans apply their understanding of scientific principles.

9 So, what do you think?

Statement of inquiry:

Generalizing and representing relationships can help to clarify trends amongst individuals.

Key concept:

Relationships are the connections and associations between properties, objects, people and ideas.

F Can relationships always be generalized?

In mathematics we talk about two different types of generalization. The first involves looking at specific information and trying to find out about something less specific that might underlie it. The other is to tackle specific problems by looking at more general ones.

> 'All generalizations are dangerous, even this one.'
>
> Alexandre Dumas

C How can relationships be best represented?

Representation is the manner in which something is presented.

Biological relationships

To reproduce and survive, living organisms must coexist and interact with each other. Ecological relationships between living organisms are either oppositional or symbiotic.

In oppositional relationships, one organism eats others (predation) or organisms compete for the same resources (competition).

In symbiotic relationships, one organism lives in or on another. Sometimes this relationship is beneficial to both (mutualism), such as the clownfish and anemone (top pair of photographs on opposite page). The anemone protects the clownfish (which is immune to its toxin) and the clownfish's waste provides food for the anemone.

▶

The suckerfish (bottom left) attaches itself to a host like this turtle and eats its parasites.

A symbiotic relationship may benefit one organism but have no effect on the other (commensalism). Corals and anemones provide camouflage for commensal shrimps and pygmy seahorses but do not benefit from them (bottom right).

D **To what extent do generalized representations provide a true picture of trends within individuals?**

Global context: Identities and relationships

Exploration: Explore trends and characteristics amongst individuals

Launch additional digital resources for this unit.

E9.1 Covariance and correlation

Global context: Identities and relationships

Related concept: Generalization

RELATIONSHIPS

Objectives

- Calculating measures of dispersion
- Calculating covariance
- Calculating correlation coefficients

Inquiry questions

F
- Can you measure the relationships between two variables quantitatively?

C
- How does the way the data is represented affect our ability to make generalizations and predictions?

D
- Which formula is better?

ATL Communication

Make inferences and draw conclusions

Statement of inquiry:

Generalizing and representing relationships can help to clarify trends among individuals.

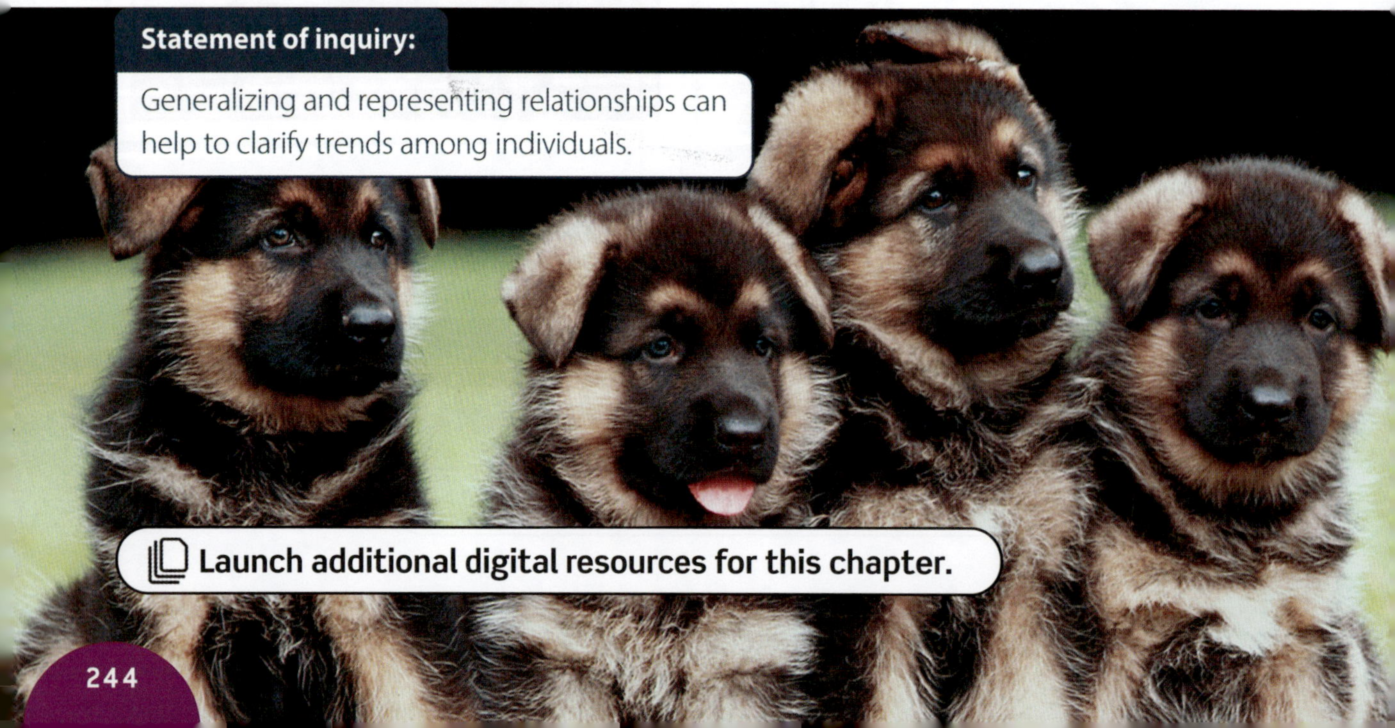

Launch additional digital resources for this chapter.

You should already know how to:

• calculate the mean and standard deviation of a data set	**1** Calculate the mean and standard deviation for these data: 6, 3, 8, 5, 2, 9, 11, 21, 15, 8 **2** Calculate the standard deviation for these data:

Price of main course in euros	Frequency
18	6
19	4
20	5
21	8
22	3
23	2
24	5
25	4

• calculate the range and interquartile range of a data set	**3** An experiment was performed 50 times. The scores from the experiment were recorded in the table.
	  a Write down the range.
	  b Find the interquartile range.
	  c Find the mean and standard deviation.

Score	Frequency
1	4
2	12
3	11
4	15
5	6
6	2

 F   ## Understanding covariance

• Can you measure the relationship between two variables quantitatively?

In a data set, the mean and variance are very important characteristics of the distribution. The mean is a measure of the central tendency and the variance (and standard deviation) is a measure of the dispersion. The variance of a set of data measures how far the observations deviate from the mean. The variance is calculated by finding out how far each data point lies from the mean. These individual deviations could be either positive or negative, so their values are squared to ensure that positive and negative values do not simply cancel each other out when all the deviations are added together.

Recall the formula for the variance is:

$$\sigma^2 = \frac{\sum(x-\bar{x})^2}{n}$$

and for standard deviation is:

$$\sigma = \sqrt{\frac{\sum(x-\bar{x})^2}{n}}$$

where $\bar{x}$ is the mean, n is the number of values in the data set, and x represents each data value in the set in turn.

Recall that $\sum x$ means add up all the values of x. Similarly, $\sum(x-\bar{x})^2$ means subtract the mean from each data value, square this difference, and finally add up the resulting values.

The variance is always a positive number.

Observing where the majority of the data points lie relative to the mean point gives an indication of the relationship between the two variables.

One way of measuring this relationship is called the **covariance**.

Just as the variance measures the dispersion of a set of univariate data points, the covariance measures the dispersion in a set of bivariate data points away from the two separate means.

$$s_{xy} = \frac{\sum(x-\bar{x})(y-\bar{y})}{n}$$

The covariance is denoted as s_{xy} and can be used to answer the question 'do higher values of x tend to occur with higher values of y?'

The points in the top right quadrant (TRQ) have x and y values greater than $\bar{x}$ and $\bar{y}$ respectively, so $x-\bar{x}$ and $y-\bar{y}$ are both positive and so is their product $(x-\bar{x})(y-\bar{y})$.

Those in the BLQ have values less than $\bar{x}$ and $\bar{y}$ so $x-\bar{x}$ and $y-\bar{y}$ are both negative and so their product $(x-\bar{x})(y-\bar{y})$ is positive.

Data points in the TLQ have an x-value less than $\bar{x}$ and a y-value greater than $\bar{y}$, hence the product $(x-\bar{x})(y-\bar{y})$ is negative and similarly data points in the BRQ have an x-value greater than $\bar{x}$ and a y-value less than $\bar{y}$, hence the product $(x-\bar{x})(y-\bar{y})$ is negative.

Summing the product $(x-\bar{x})(y-\bar{y})$ will therefore give a positive number if most of the data points lie in the TRQ and BLQ, and a negative value if most of the points lie in the BRQ and TLQ.

For that reason, if the majority of the data points fall in TRQ and BLQ the value of the covariance will be positive and if the majority of the data points fall in TLQ and BRQ the value of the covariance will be negative. And so if $s_{xy} > 0$ then the points follow a trend with a positive slope.

The value of the covariance conveys little information as it can easily be altered by a change of scale.

Exploration 1

The following data was collected from 10 patients after they were admitted to hospital showing symptoms of a virus.

Their blood marker score is marked out of 30 and their taste perceptor score was marked out of 40.

The data is recorded in the table below.

Patient	A	B	C	D	E	F	G	H	I	J
Blood x	8	11	11	14	17	17	20	20	23	29
Taste y	21	22	26	33	33	36	30	31	35	33

1 Draw a scatter diagram to represent the data.

2 Find the mean of x and the mean of y $(\bar{x}, \bar{y})$ and plot on the scatter diagram.

3 Draw horizontal and vertical lines which pass through the point $(\bar{x}, \bar{y})$.

4 Describe, using quadrants, where the distribution of data points lie. BLQ represents Bottom Left Quadrant, TLQ represents Top Left Quadrant, BRQ represents Bottom Right Quadrant and TRQ represents Top Right Quadrant.

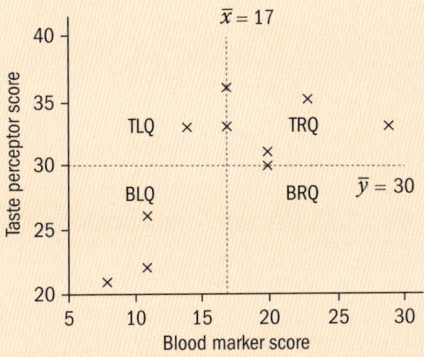

5 Use the formula $s_{xy} = \dfrac{\sum (x - \bar{x})(y - \bar{y})}{n}$ to calculate the covariance for this data set

6 An alternative formula for covariance is $s_{xy} = \dfrac{1}{n} \sum (xy) - \bar{x}\,\bar{y}$.

   Verify that this formula gives you the same value for the covariance.

7 What does the value of the covariance tell you about the relationship between blood marker score and taste perceptor score?

Reflect and discuss 1

What does the sign of the covariance tell you about a set of bivariate data?

Which formula do you think is more convenient when calculating the variance?

ATL

Example 1

The following data table shows the heights of nine students and the number of baskets they threw in a five-minute period.

	A	B	C	D	E	F	G	H	I
Height (cm)	168	149	173	166	185	159	195	144	176
Basketballs shot in a five-minute period	77	45	65	59	79	87	94	53	65

Calculate the covariance from the data set.

$$\bar{x} = \frac{\sum x}{n}$$

$$\bar{x} = \frac{1515}{9}$$

Calculate the mean of the x-values and the y-values.

$$\bar{y} = \frac{\sum y}{n}$$

$$\bar{y} = \frac{624}{9}$$

$$\sum xy = \sum((168 \times 77)) + (149 \times 176) + \cdots (45 \times 65)$$
$$= 106\,530$$

Calculate $\sum xy$

$$s_{xy} = \frac{1}{9}(106530) - \left(\frac{1515}{9}\right)\left(\frac{624}{9}\right)$$

Use the covariance formula
$$S_{xy} = \frac{1}{n}\sum(xy) - \bar{x}\bar{y}$$

$$s_{xy} = 166 \ (3\,\text{s.f})$$

State a final answer for the covariance and a conclusion.

As the value of the covariance is a positive number, there is a tendency of the data to lie in the bottom left and top right quadrants.

From this we can interpret that as the height of a student increases the number of basketball shots they can make in a five-minute period also increases.

Moving between the different forms of the formula is in the debatable section.

C How can we scale the covariance to make it meaningful?

- How does the way the data is represented affect our ability to make predictions?

Exploration 2

The following two tables both show the mass and length for a litter of eight Cavapoo puppies.

Table 1 shows the mass and length in metric measure and Table 2 shows the same puppies' masses and heights in imperial measure.

Table 1

	A	B	C	D	E	F	G	H
Mass (grams) *u*	75	78	82	83	87	90	91	95
Length (cm) *v*	10.0	10.1	11.1	10.9	11.3	12.0	12.7	12.5

Table 2

	A	B	C	D	E	F	G	H
Mass (ounces) *x*	2.65	2.75	2.89	2.93	3.06	3.17	3.21	3.35
Length (inches) *y*	3.94	3.98	4.37	4.29	4.45	4.72	5.00	4.92

1   Calculate the s_{uv} and s_{xy}, the covariance for each data set.

2   Comment on the values you have obtained. What similarities and differences are there?

3   Calculate σ_u, σ_v, σ_x and σ_y, the standard deviations of u, v, x and y.

4   Calculate $\dfrac{s_{uv}}{\sigma_u \sigma_v}$ and $\dfrac{s_{xy}}{\sigma_x \sigma_y}$.

5   Comment on the values you have obtained. What do you notice?

Reflect and discuss 2

Which is a better measure of the relationship between the two variables, s_{xy} or $\dfrac{s_{xy}}{\sigma_x \sigma_y}$?

Dividing $(x - \bar{x})$ by the standard deviation σ_x gives the distance of each x-value above or below the mean as a proportion of the standard deviation. For this reason, $\dfrac{s_{xy}}{\sigma_x \sigma_y}$ has the same value regardless of the units in which the data has been measured. It is a more meaningful way to describe the strength of the correlation and is known as a **correlation coefficient**.

Dividing by the standard deviation means that the formula

$$S_{xy} = \frac{\sum(x - \bar{x})(y - \bar{y})}{n}$$

or

$$S_{xy} = \frac{1}{n}\sum(x - \bar{x})(y - \bar{y})$$

becomes

$$\frac{1}{n}\sum\left(\frac{(x - \bar{x})}{\sigma_x}\right)\left(\frac{(y - \bar{y})}{\sigma_y}\right)$$

a more user-friendly version of the formula is

$$\text{correlation coefficient} = \frac{\frac{1}{n}\sum xy - \bar{x}\,\bar{y}}{\sigma_x\sigma_y}$$

This is commonly known as Pearson's product-moment correlation coefficient and produces a value with more meaning than the covariance.

On the calculator it is generally found under the linear regression menu and is often represented by r.

The value of r gives a measure of how close the points are to lying on a straight line.

It is always true that $-1 \leq r \leq 1$

- if the r value = 1, the points lie exactly on a straight line with positive gradient
- if the r value = -1, the points lie exactly on a straight line with negative gradient
- if $r = 0$, there is no relationship at all between the two sets of data.

Practice 1

1 The following table shows bivariate data.

x	12	14	15	17	19
y	19	20	22	23	25

Use your calculator to calculate the following statistics.

a $\sum x$ **b** $\sum y$ **c** n

d $\sum xy$ **e** $\bar{x}$ **f** $\bar{y}$

g $\bar{x}\bar{y}$ **h** σ_x **i** σ_y

j hence using the formula $\dfrac{\frac{1}{n}\sum xy - \bar{x}\,\bar{y}}{\sigma_x\sigma_y}$, calculate the PMCC.

k Verify that your calculator gives the same value of r.

2 Referring to the virus question in Exploration 1.

Patient	A	B	C	D	E	F	G	H	I	J
Blood x	8	11	11	14	17	17	20	20	23	29
Taste y	21	22	26	33	33	36	30	31	35	33

Calculate by hand and by your calculator the correlation coefficient.

3 Ten students were asked a set of questions to measure their attitude to social media as a news medium, and a further set of questions to measure their attitude to television as a news medium. A higher score shows a higher satisfaction. The scores are shown in the following table.

> From the standard book you have seen that if there is a strong enough correlation, a line of best fit can be drawn by eye. It is also possible to construct a line of best fit using technology.

  a Draw a scatter diagram to represent the data.

  b Calculate the correlation coefficient.

  c Comment on your findings.

Student	1	2	3	4	5	6	7	8	9	10
Social media score x	5	0	3	1	2	2	5	3	5	4
Television score y	1	2	1	3	3	4	3	1	0	2

ATL

D # Moving between different forms of representation

- Which formula is better?

An alternative formula

There is another form for the expression for covariance which is often easier to use in calculations.

Follow the steps below to move between different representations of the formula

$$s_{xy} = \frac{\sum (x - \bar{x})(y - \bar{y})}{n}$$

1 Expand $(x - \bar{x})(y - \bar{y})$

$$s_{xy} = \frac{\sum (xy - \bar{x}y - x\bar{y} + \bar{x}\,\bar{y})}{n}$$

2 Distribute the sigma sign.

$$s_{xy} = \frac{\left(\sum xy - \sum \bar{x}y - \sum x\bar{y} + \sum \bar{x}\,\bar{y} \right)}{n}$$

As $\bar{x}$ and $\bar{y}$ are independent of the sigma sign they can be removed from inside the sign:

$$s_{xy} = \frac{\left(\sum xy - \bar{x}\sum y - \bar{y}\sum x + n\bar{x}\,\bar{y} \right)}{n}$$

> Summing up n lots of $\overline{xy}$ gives $n\overline{xy}$.

As

$$\bar{x} = \frac{\sum x}{n} \text{ and } \bar{y} = \frac{\sum y}{n}$$

then

$$S_{xy} = \frac{\left(\sum xy - \bar{x}n\bar{y} - \bar{y}n\bar{x} + n\bar{x}\,\bar{y}\right)}{n}$$

$$S_{xy} = \frac{\left(\sum xy - n\bar{x}\,\bar{y}\right)}{n}$$

$$S_{xy} = \frac{1}{n}\sum xy - \bar{x}\,\bar{y}$$

which is a preferred formula for the calculation of the covariance of a data set.

Use this formula to calculate the covariance for this table.

Table 1

	A	B	C	D	E	F	G	H
Mass (grams) x	75	78	82	83	87	90	91	95
Length (cm) y	10.0	10.1	11.1	10.9	11.3	12.0	12.7	12.5

Example 2

Yara collected data for her statistics project on the weight and length of an acorn to determine whether there was a relationship between the two variables.

Calculate the correlation coefficient.

In order to calculate the correlation coefficient she first calculated the covariance

x (g)	66	68	69	75	78	82	101	114	128	135
y (cm)	119	112	116	123	122	123	135	151	141	141

▶ Continued on next page

Method 1: calculating the covariance using the formula

$$S_{xy} = \frac{\sum(x-\bar{x})(y-\bar{y})}{n}$$

Draw a table to see all the results clearly.

x	$x-\bar{x}$	y	$y-\bar{y}$	$(x-\bar{x})(y-\bar{y})$
66	−25.6	119	−9.3	238.08
68	−23.6	112	−16.3	384.68
69	−22.6	116	−12.3	277.98
75	−16.6	123	−5.3	87.98
78	−13.6	122	−6.3	85.68
82	-9.6	123	-5.3	50.88
101	9.4	135	6.7	62.98
114	22.4	151	22.7	508.48
128	36.4	141	12.7	462.28
135	43.4	141	12.7	551.18
91.6		128.3		2710.2

Find the sum.

$$S_{xy} = \frac{\sum(x-\bar{x})(y-\bar{y})}{n}$$

$\bar{x} = 91.6 \qquad \bar{y} = 128.3$

Calculate the mean of x and y.

$$S_{xy} = \frac{\sum(x-\bar{x})(y-\bar{y})}{n}$$

$$= \frac{2710.2}{10}$$

$$= 271.02$$

Method 2

$$S_{xy} = \frac{1}{n}\sum xy - \overline{xy}$$

x	y	xy
66	119	7854
68	112	7616
69	116	8004
75	123	9225
78	122	9516
82	123	10 086
101	135	13 635
114	151	17 214
128	141	18 048
135	141	19 035
		120 233

Find the sum.

▶ Continued on next page

$$S_{xy} = \frac{1}{n}\sum xy - \bar{x}\,\bar{y}$$

$$= \frac{1}{10}(120\,233) - (91.6)(128.3)$$

$$= 271.02$$

The correlation coefficient can then be calculated by the formula:

$$r = \frac{S_{xy}}{\sigma_x \sigma_y}$$

Recall there are two methods for calculating the standard deviation.

Method 1

$$\sigma_x = \sqrt{\frac{\sum(x - \bar{x})^2}{n}}$$

$$= \sqrt{\frac{6074.4}{10}}$$

$$= 24.646$$

$$\sigma_y = \sqrt{\frac{\sum(y - \bar{y})^2}{n}}$$

$$= \sqrt{\frac{1482.1}{10}}$$

$$= 12.174$$

$$r = \frac{271.02}{(24.646)(12.174)}$$

$$= 0.903 \ (3 \text{ s.f.})$$

Method 2

$$\sigma_x = \sqrt{\frac{\sum x^2}{n} - \left(\frac{\sum x}{n}\right)^2}$$

$$= \sqrt{\frac{89\,980}{10} - \left(\frac{839\,056}{100}\right)}$$

$$= \sqrt{607.44}$$

$$= 24.646$$

$$\sigma_y = \sqrt{\frac{\sum y^2}{n} - \left(\frac{\sum y}{n}\right)^2}$$

$$= \sqrt{\frac{166\,091}{10} - \frac{1\,646\,089}{100}}$$

$$= \sqrt{148.21}$$

$$= 12.174$$

$$r = \frac{271.02}{(24.646)(12.174)}$$

$$= 0.903 \ (3 \text{ s.f.})$$

Reflect and discuss 3

Which method for calculating the both the standard deviation and the covariance do you prefer?

Under which circumstances might one be better than the other?

Mixed review

1 Eight students were asked to record the number of hours of screen time (x) per week and the number of hours of sleep they had (y) in the same week. The results are given below in the table.

x	23	25	25	26	27	29	32	33
y	45	51	49	54	52	60	58	58

a Complete the following table.

x	y	x^2	y^2	xy
23	45			
25	51			
25	49			
26	54			
27	52			
29	60			
32	58			
33	58			
Totals				

b Calculate the covariance.

c Calculate the standard deviation for x and y.

d By calculating the correlation coefficient, draw conclusions about the relationship between the amount of screen and sleep time of these eight students.

2 The table below shows the number of items of jewellery produced at a craft fair and the average price each piece of jewellery sold for.

x	14	23	17	32	16	19	17	25	27	31	17	18	26	24	22
y ($)	6.2	7.3	4.9	7.1	5.2	5.7	5.9	6.4	7.3	6.1	5.4	5.7	6.9	7.2	4.8

From the data calculate the following:

a $\bar{x}$

b $\bar{y}$

c Use both methods to calculate the covariance, the standard deviation and hence the correlation coefficient.

Decide whether there is a relationship between the number of items produced and the cost of each item.

Reflect and discuss 4

How have you explored the statement of inquiry? Give specific examples.

Statement of inquiry:

Generalizing and representing relationships can help to clarify trends among individuals.

Statement of inquiry:

Generalizing changes helps establish relationships that can model duration, frequency and variability.

Key concept:

Relationships are the connections and associations between properties, objects, people and ideas.

F **What does it mean to validate?**

Change is a variation in size, amount or behaviour.

Climate change

From ice core sample data we know that the Earth's climate has changed over millions of years, between ice ages with warmer interglacial periods of about 10 000 years between them. Scientists debate the exact causes of glacial and interglacial periods, but almost all agree that the amount of carbon present in the Earth's atmosphere from burning fossil fuels – oil, coal and gas – is increasing global temperatures at a faster rate than ever before.

- Scientists analyze data to observe and predict change. How can predicting change also help us to make changes?

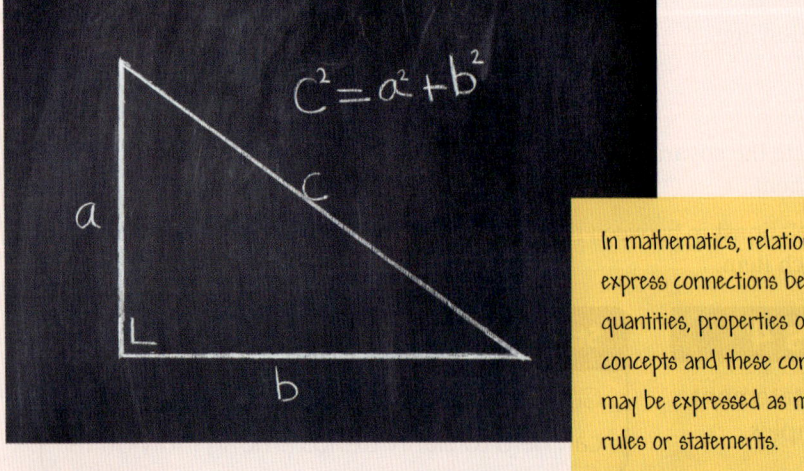

$$c^2 = a^2 + b^2$$

In mathematics, relationships express connections between quantities, properties or concepts and these connections may be expressed as models, rules or statements.

C Can all changes be generalized? Can all relationships be validated?

Models are depictions of real life events using expressions, equations or graphs.

When you do an internet search for a particular topic, you will normally get pages of websites related to the topic. Which sites appear earlier or later in your search depends on how they are ranked. The model used to rank them is a logarithmic scale.

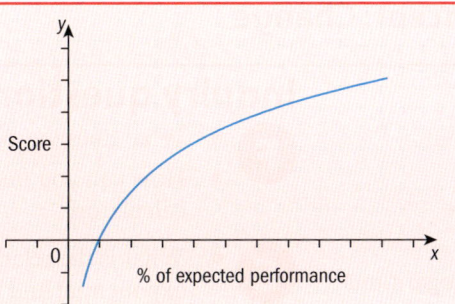

D At what point is a discovery valid?

Validity is the use of well-founded, logical mathematics to come to a true and accurate conclusion or a reasonable interpretation of results.

Ammonites became extinct at the same time as the dinosaurs. They were sea creatures, closely related to squid, and lived in a shell. When studying their properties, mathematicians discovered that their chambers form a logarithmic spiral.

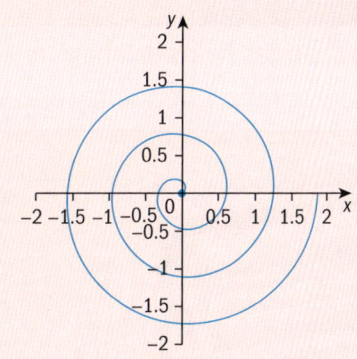

Global context: Orientation in space and time

Exploration: Explore scales and model duration, frequency and variability

📑 **Launch additional digital resources for this unit.**

E10.1 Logarithms

Global context: Orientation in space and time

Related concept: Change

Objectives

- Evaluating logarithms with and without a calculator
- Writing an exponential statement as a logarithmic statement
- Solving exponential equations using logarithms
- Writing and solving logarithmic equations from real-life situations
- Using natural logarithms

Inquiry questions

F
- What does $\log_a b$ mean?
- How can you find logarithms using a calculator?

C
- What is the relationship between exponential and logarithmic statements?
- How do logarithms make problems easier to solve?

D
- Does e deserve to be called the natural number?
- Is change measurable and predictable?

RELATIONSHIPS

ATL Critical-thinking

Consider ideas from multiple perspectives

Statement of inquiry:

Generalizing changes helps establish relationships that can model duration, frequency and variability.

Launch additional digital resources for this chapter.

You should already know how to:

• use index laws	**1** Simplify $x^2 \times x^5$. **2** Evaluate: **a** 5^3 **b** 2^{-1} **c** $16^{\frac{1}{2}}$
• rewrite surds and roots as quantities with exponents	**3** Write with an exponent: **a** $\sqrt{6}$ **b** $\sqrt[3]{9}$ **c** $\sqrt{5^3}$
• model a real-life problem with an exponential equation	**4** In 2007, the Zika virus was growing at a rate of 18% per week on Yap Island. Two people were infected initially. Use an exponential model to determine the number of people infected after 52 weeks.

 F **Introduction to logarithms**

- What does $\log_a b$ mean?
- How can you find logarithms using a calculator?

An exponential equation is in the form $a^x = b$.

- a is the base
- x is the exponent or power

Exploration 1

Write each statement as an exponential equation, and solve to find x.
The first one is done for you.

1 Find the exponent of 10 that gives the answer:

100	$10^x = 100$	$x = 2$
1000		
10 000		
0.1		
0.0001		

2 Find the exponent of 2 that gives the answer:

4		
8		
16		
128		
$\frac{1}{2}$		

▶ Continued on next page

3 Find the exponent of 6 that gives the answer:

36		
216		
$\frac{1}{216}$		

4 What patterns do you notice?

Determine what would happen to the answer if you add 1 to the exponent.

Determine what would happen to the answer if you subtract 1 from the exponent.

In steps **1** to **3** the exponents are all integers. When you can't spot the answer, you can use trial and improvement.

5 To solve $10^x = 150$, estimate the value of x and try it. Improve your estimate to find x correct to 2 decimal places.

6 Solve $2^x = 45$. Give your answer to 2 decimal places.

7 Solve $5^x = 77$. Give your answer to 2 significant figures.

8 You can also use graphing software to solve exponential equations graphically.

For example, to solve $10^x = 60$, draw the graph of the exponential function $y = 10^x$ and the graph of $y = 60$.

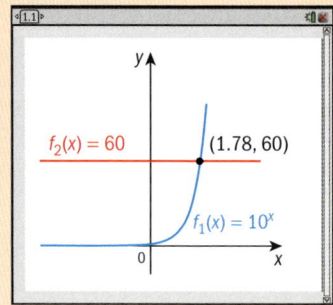

Read the value of x at the intersection to 2 decimal places.

a Solve $2^x = 6$ graphically. Give your answer to 2 decimal places.

b Solve $7^x = 14$ graphically. Give your answer to 2 significant figures.

The three methods for solving exponential equations in Exploration 1 are:

- the inspection method
- trial and improvement
- graphical.

Reflect and discuss 1

- Would you use the trial and improvement method or the graphical method to solve the equation $9^x = 85$? Explain your choice.

- What are the advantages and disadvantages of the three methods?

The trial and improvement method and the graphical method give two different perspectives on solving exponential equations.

Here is another method. In the exponential equation $10^x = 500$, the quantity x is defined as 'the logarithm to base 10 of 500'.

You can write $\log_{10} 500 = x$.

Using a calculator: $\log_{10} 500 = 2.69897\ldots$

$$x = 2.70 \text{ (2 d.p.)}$$

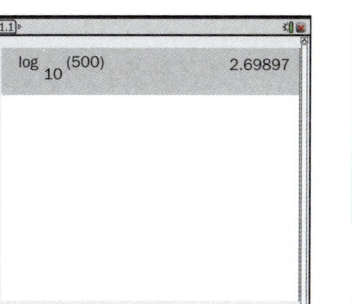

You can use the equivalent statements $10^x = 500$ and $\log_{10} 500 = x$ to find the unknown exponent.

Rewriting exponential statements as logarithmic statements changes the unknown variable from an exponent to a regular variable. Whenever you see an exponential or logarithmic statement you can use the equivalence concept to consider it from another perspective.

> For any two positive numbers a and b, there exists a third number c so that you can write:
>
> the exponential statement $a^c = b$
>
> or   the equivalent logarithmic statement $\log_a b = c$; $a, b > 0$.
>
> We say that c is 'the logarithm to base a of b', or 'the exponent of a that gives the answer b'. In the logarithmic statement $\log_a b = c$, a is called the **base** of the logarithm and b is called the **argument** of the logarithm.

The log button on your calculator is for '$\log_{10}$'. You do not need to enter the number 10.

Before calculators, logarithms of different values were published in log tables. Modern calculators calculate logarithms at the touch of a button.

When solving equations involving exponents or logarithms, it can be helpful to rewrite the equation using the other form. This allows you to see the equation from a new perspective.

Example 1

Solve $\log_7 x = 2$.

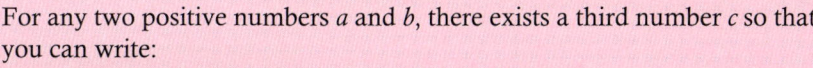

$7^2 = x$

$x = 49$

Rewrite as an exponential statement.
$\log_a b = c$ means $a^c = b$.

Logarithms with base 10 are often called 'common' logs and written $\log x$, without a base.

When you see 'log' written without a base, you can assume the base is 10.

On most calculators you can choose the base of the logarithm. If your calculator does not allow this, you will need to use the **change of base formula**.

> Change of base formula: $\log_a b = \dfrac{\log_c b}{\log_c a}$, where c is any new base.

Example 2

Solve $2^x = 50$ using a calculator and the change of base formula.

$2^x = 50$ ——— Rewrite as a logarithmic statement.

$\log_2 50 = x$

$\log_2 50 = \dfrac{\log_{10} 50}{\log_{10} 2}$ ——— Use the change of base formula with $c = 10$.

$= 5.64385619$ ——— Work out $\dfrac{\log 50}{\log 2}$ on your calculator.

$= 5.64$ (3 s.f.)

Example 3

$\log_7 7\sqrt{7} = x$. Find the value of x.

$\log_7 (7 \times 7^{\frac{1}{2}}) = x$ ——— Write surds as exponents.

$\log_7 (7^{\frac{3}{2}}) = x$

$7^x = 7^{\frac{3}{2}}$ ——— Rewrite as an exponential statement.

$x = \dfrac{3}{2}$ ——— The bases are equal, so the exponents are equal.

Practice 1

1 Write down the equivalent logarithmic statement for:

   a $10^x = 500$ **b** $10^x = 150$ **c** $10^x = 60$ **d** $2^x = 45$ **e** $2^x = 6$

   Hence, using your calculator, find the value of x in each case.
   Give your answers to 3 s.f.

2 Write down an equivalent exponential statement for:

   a $\log_8 64 = 2$ **b** $\log_8 4 = \dfrac{2}{3}$ **c** $\log 0.1 = -1$

   d $\log_5 x = 5$ **e** $\log_b b = 4$ **f** $\log_x y = 0$

3 Write down an equivalent logarithmic statement for:

   a $3^2 = 9$ **b** $4^{-\frac{2}{3}} = 0.125$ **c** $1000^{\frac{1}{3}} = 10$

Use this table to help you answer questions **4–5**.

Powers of 2		Powers of 3		Powers of 4		Powers of 5	
2^{-3}	0.125	3^{-3}	$0.0\dot{3}\dot{7}$	4^{-3}	0.015625	5^{-3}	0.008
2^{-2}	0.25	3^{-2}	$0.\dot{1}$	4^{-2}	0.0625	5^{-2}	0.04
2^{-1}	0.5	3^{-1}	$0.\dot{3}$	4^{-1}	0.25	5^{-1}	0.2
2^{0}	1	3^{0}	1	4^{0}	1	5^{0}	1
2^{1}	2	3^{1}	3	4^{1}	4	5^{1}	5
2^{2}	4	3^{2}	9	4^{2}	16	5^{2}	25
2^{3}	8	3^{3}	27	4^{3}	64	5^{3}	125
2^{4}	16	3^{4}	81	4^{4}	256	5^{4}	625
2^{5}	32	3^{5}	243	4^{5}	1024	5^{5}	3125

Learn these results to help you solve logarithmic and exponential equations without a calculator.

4 Without using a calculator, find the value of x.

   a $\log_5 625 = x$ **b** $\log_3 243 = x$ **c** $\log_4 0.0625 = x$ **d** $\log_4 1024 = x$

   e $\log 0.00001 = x$ **f** $\log_2 0.125 = x$ **g** $\log_3 1 = x$ **h** $\log_5 0.04 = x$

5 Without using a calculator, find the value of x.

   a $\log_5 \sqrt{5} = x$ **b** $\log_3 3\sqrt{3} = x$ **c** $\log_4 \sqrt{256} = x$ **d** $\log_2 \sqrt{256} = x$

6 Find the value of x to the nearest hundredth.

   a $\log_2 17 = x$ **b** $\log_6 121 = x$ **c** $\log_3 31 = x$ **d** $\log_8 5 = x$

7 Solve, using a calculator:

   a $3^x = 40$ **b** $5^x = 100$ **c** $4^x = 85$ **d** $2^x = 90$

Logarithms are used in astronomy to measure the apparent magnitude of stars; in geology to measure the intensity of earthquakes; in music, to measure semitones; and perhaps most beautifully, in nature, as seen in the inside of nautilus shells whose chambers form a logarithmic spiral.

Problem solving

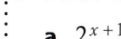

8 Solve these exponential equations.

   a $2^{x+1} = 4^{2x}$ **b** $3^{x+2} = 9^{2x-2}$ **c** $2^{x+1} = \left(\dfrac{1}{2}\right)^{2x}$

   d $\left(\dfrac{1}{3}\right)^{x+2} = 3^{2x-2}$ **e** $\left(\dfrac{1}{3}\right)^{x+2} = 9^{2x-2}$

In **8**, write them with the same base and use the laws of exponents.

C Using logarithms to solve equations

- What is the relationship between exponential and logarithmic statements?
- How do logarithms make problems easier to solve?

You can use logarithms to solve complex exponential equations. Rewriting an exponential statement as an equivalent logarithmic statement changes the equation into one you can solve.

Example 4

Solve $6^{2x+1} = 20$, accurate to 2 decimal places.

$\log_6 20 = 2x + 1$ —————————————— Rewrite as a logarithmic statement.

$1.67195... = 2x + 1$ —————————————— Use a calculator to find $\log_6 20 = \dfrac{\log_{10} 20}{\log_{10} 6}$.

$x = 0.33567 = 0.34$ (2 d.p.) —————————————— Solve for x.

Practice 2

Solve each equation, giving your answer to the degree of accuracy stated.

1 $2^x = 5$ (2 d.p.)   **2** $2^{2x+1} = 5$ (3 d.p.)

3 $5^{x-1} = 3$ (2 s.f.)   **4** $3^{2x+1} = 5$ (3 s.f.)

5 $4 \times 2^x = 6$ (2 d.p.)   **6** $2 \times 2^{x-1} = 6$ (2 d.p.)

7 $\dfrac{2^x}{3} = 6$ (2 s.f.)   **8** $\dfrac{2^{2x-3}}{3} = 16$ (2 s.f.)

- -

You can also use logarithms to solve equations that result from real-life growth and decay problems.

Objective D: Applying mathematics in real-life contexts
ii. select appropriate mathematical strategies when solving authentic real-life situations

In Exploration 2, you will write an equation to describe a real-life situation and then use an appropriate strategy to solve it.

Exploration 2

An amoeba is a single-celled organism that reproduces by cell division. A certain amoeba splits into two separate amoebas every hour. There is one amoeba on a microscope slide at the beginning of an experiment. Determine how long it will take for there to be 1000 amoebas on the slide.

1 The number of amoebas depends on time t. Copy and complete the table:

Time (hours)	$t = 0$	$t = 1$	$t = 2$	$t = 3$	$t = 4$
Number of amoebas	$A(0) =$	$A(1) =$	$A(2) =$	$A(3) =$	$A(4) =$

2 Write the number of amoebas as powers of 2.

3 Write $A(t)$ as an exponential function.

4 Write and solve an exponential equation to find t when $A(t) = 100$.

Reflect and discuss 2

- How do you know when to use logarithms to solve an equation?

- How could you verify that your answer makes sense?

Example 5

The number of drosophila (fruit flies) in a laboratory at the beginning of an experiment is 200. The population increases by 8.5% each day.

a Find the population at the end of the first and second days.

b Write an exponential function for the number of drosophila after x days.

c Find the number of days until the population reached 100 000 drosophila.

a

Number of days (x)	Number of drosophila (D)
0	200
1	200×1.085
2	200×1.085^2

Growth factor $b = 1 + r = 1 + 0.085 = 1.085$

b $a = 200, r = 1.085$

$D = 200 \times 1.085^x$

Exponential growth is modelled by $y = a(1 + r)^x$ where x is the number of days.

c $100\,000 = 200 \times 1.085^x$

$\dfrac{100\,000}{200} = 1.085^x$

Rearrange to isolate the term in x.

$500 = 1.085^x$

$\log_{1.085} 500 = x$

Rewrite as a logarithmic statement.

$x = 76.18$

After 77 days there would be more than 100 000 drosophila.

Practice 3

1 At the end of the year 2000 the population of a city was 300 000. The population then increased by 1.3% per year.

    a Find the population at the end of 2001 and 2002.

    b Write an exponential function for $P(t)$, the population after t years.

    c Predict the year in which the population should exceed 350 000.

2 A group of 15 snow foxes are introduced into a nature reserve. The number of snow foxes N can be modelled by the exponential equation $N = 15 \times 3^{0.4t}$ where t is the number of years since their introduction.

Find how many years after their introduction there should be at least 100 snow foxes.

3 The half-life of caffeine in the human body is approximately 5 hours.

Copy and complete the table for a student who consumes 120 mg of caffeine at 08:00 one morning.

> Half-life means the time taken to fall to half of its original amount.

Time	Time period (in 5-hour intervals) (t hours)	Amount of caffeine (C mg)
08:00	$t = 0$	120
13:00	$t = 1$	60
18:00	$t = 2$	
23:00		

    a Find the common ratio for the geometric sequence.

    b Find the exponential equation for the half-life of caffeine in terms of t.

    c Calculate the amount of caffeine in the student's body after 35 hours.

    d The effect of caffeine is negligible below 0.02 mg. Determine the number of hours after which there is only a negligible effect from the caffeine.

Problem solving

4 Coco is training for a race and records her 10 km times each week. Before she starts training, she can run 10 km in 72 minutes.

Week (w)	Time (t, min) to run 10 km
1	70.560
2	69.149
3	67.766
4	66.411
5	65.082

> The times form a geometric sequence. Use $w = 0$ and $w = 1$ to find the rate of decrease.

Assuming her time continues to decrease at the same rate, calculate how many weeks it will be before Coco can run 10 km in less than one hour.

5 A large lake has a population of 100 000 perch. The number of perch is decreasing at a rate of 10% per year due to pollution.

   a Make a table to show the number of perch P after 1, 2 and 3 years.

   b Write an exponential model for the number of perch P after t years.

   c When the population of perch falls below 25 000 it is at a 'critical level'. Calculate how long it will take for this lake to be at a critical level.

D   Natural logarithms

- Does e deserve to be called the natural number?
- Is change measurable and predictable?

Exploration 3

In this exploration you will investigate how much $1 can grow at an interest rate of 100%, when the interest is compounded at different intervals.

1 Find the amount $1 is worth at the end of one year at 100% interest.

2 Find the amount $1 is worth at the end of one year at 100% interest compounded half-yearly. In the function $y = a(1 + r)^x$, the initial investment is $1, the growth rate is $\frac{100}{2} = 50\% = 0.5$, and $x = 2$, as interest is now compounded two times per year. Therefore, $y = (1 + 0.5)^2$ or $y = 1.5^2$.

3 Find the amount $1 is worth at the end of one year at 100% interest compounded quarterly (every 3 months). In this case, $y = (1 + 0.25)^4$ or $y = 1.25^4$.

4 Write down an exponential function representing the investment of $1 at 100% interest compounded x times per year.

5 Use your function to find the amount your investment of $1 is worth at the end of one year at 100% interest if it is compounded:

   a monthly   **b** weekly   **c** daily

   d hourly   **e** each minute   **f** each second.

6 Graph your function. Determine if there is a limit to the amount the $1 investment can grow in one year if it is compounded an infinite number of times at 100% interest. Justify your answer.

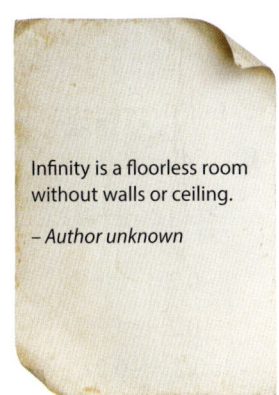

Infinity is a floorless room without walls or ceiling.

– Author unknown

The number of times the interest is compounded is n. As n approaches infinity, the total investment approaches $2.71828…

The number 2.71828… is called **e** and it is the base rate for growth/decay of all continually growing processes.

In general, all populations that grow continually are modelled by the population growth equation $P = P_0 e^{rt}$, where:

   P is the final population

   P_0 is the original population when $t = 0$

   r is the growth rate

   t is the time period.

Reflect and discuss 3

How could the formula $P = P_0 e^{rt}$ be used for problems involving a quantity that is decreasing or decaying exponentially?

To calculate the growth rate or the time you can use logarithms with base e.

If $y = e^x$ then the equivalent logarithmic statement is $\log_e y = x$, $y > 0$.

The natural logarithm $\log_e y$ is written as: $\ln y$.

Your calculator should have an ln button, and an e^x button.

The first mention of e, the natural logarithm, was noted in 1618 as an appendix to Napier's work on logarithms, but it wasn't officially named 'e' until Leonhard Euler, a Swiss mathematician, completed his work in 1748.

Example 6

A skydiver jumps off a cliff. Sensibly, the skydiver has remembered to wear a parachute. As he falls, his speed of descent is modelled by the equation $v(t) = 50(1 - e^{-0.2t})$, where his speed, $v(t)$, is in m/s and time t is in seconds.

Find:

a his initial speed

b the time it takes for him to reach a speed of 40 m/s.

a $v(0) = 50(1 - e^{-0.2 \times 0})$ — Initial speed occurs when $t = 0$.

$= 50(1 - 1) = 0$

Initial speed is 0 m/s.

b $40 = 50(1 - e^{-0.2t})$ — Substitute 40 for the speed and solve for t.

$\dfrac{40}{50} - 1 = -e^{-0.2t}$

$-0.2 = -e^{-0.2t}$

$0.2 = e^{-0.2t}$

$\ln 0.2 = -0.2t$ — Write the equivalent logarithmic statement.

$t = 8.05$ seconds (2 d.p.)

Example 7

In the year 2000, an island in the Caribbean had a population of 2600 people.

Assuming that the population was continually increasing at a rate of 1.68% per year, calculate:

a the predicted population in the year 2020

b the time taken for the population to double

c the time taken for the population in part **b** to return to 2600 if it began to decrease at a rate of 2% per year.

a $P = P_0 e^{rt}$ ——————————————————— Standard population equation.

$P = 2600 e^{0.0168 \times 20}$

$= 3638.3$ ——————————————————— Use your calculator.

The population in 2020 will be 3638 people.

b $P = P_0 e^{rt}$

$5200 = 2600 e^{0.0168t}$ ——————————————— Double the population is 5200.

$2 = e^{0.0168t}$

$\ln 2 = 0.0168t$ ——————————————— Rewrite as a logarithmic statement.

$t = \dfrac{\ln 2}{0.0168} = 41.258\ldots$

The population will double in 42 years.

c $P = P_0 e^{rt}$

$2600 = 5200 e^{-0.02t}$ ——————————————— For exponential decay, the rate is negative.

$0.5 = e^{-0.02t}$

$\ln 0.5 = -0.02t$ ——————————————— Rewrite as a logarithmic statement.

$t = \dfrac{\ln 0.5}{-0.02} = 34.657\ldots\ldots$

The population will return to 2600 people in 35 years.

Practice 4

ATL

1 Carbon-14 dating is a common method used to determine the age of fossils and bones.

One formula used to calculate the age t (in years) of an item is $P = e^{-0.000121t}$, where P is the percentage of carbon-14 left in the item (written as a decimal).

A femur bone found in an Australian aboriginal burial site contains 11% of the carbon-14 found in a normal femur. Determine the femur's age.

2 Radioactive substances decay over time and are often described by their half-life (the time taken for half of the substance to decay/disappear). The formula used to describe this decay is $A = A_0 e^{bt}$, where A is the amount left after time t, A_0 is the original amount of the radioactive substance, and b is the decay constant.

Iodine-131 has a half-life of 8 days. It is a common substance used in diagnosing issues with the thyroid gland.

a Find the decay constant, b, for iodine-131 if you begin with 3 grams.

b Hence write down the formula for the exponential decay of iodine-131.

c Find how many grams of iodine-131 will be present after 28 days if you start with 3 grams.

3 A biologist monitoring a fire ant infestation notices that the area infected by the ants can be modelled by $A = 1000e^{0.7n}$, where A is the area in hectares, and n is the number of weeks after the initial observation.

a Find the initial population size.

b Find the population after one week.

c Calculate how long it will take the population to cover 50 000 hectares.

4 A group of 20 rabbits is introduced to a rabbit farm. After t years the number of rabbits, N, is modelled by the exponential equation $N = 20e^{0.6t}$.

a Predict the number of rabbits after 3 years.

b Determine how long it will take for the number of rabbits to reach 400.

Give your answers to an appropriate degree of accuracy.

5 The model for the population, P, of wombats in a nature reserve is $P = 50e^{0.8t}$, where t is measured in years.

a Write down how many wombats were introduced to the reserve.

b Calculate how long it will take for the original population to quadruple.

Problem solving

6 The population of a small Dutch town was obtained for two consecutive years:

Year	2010	2011
Population	5101	5204

Assume that the population is modelled by the standard equation, and that $t = 0$ in 2010.

a Calculate the rate of growth, r.

b Calculate the predicted population in 2020.

c Calculate the number of years until the population exceeds 10 000.

Reflect and discuss 4

- What do you think are the limitations of continuous growth and decay models?

- Why do you think ln is called a 'natural' logarithm?

Summary

An exponential equation has the form $a^x = b$:

- a is the base

- x is the exponent or power

For any two positive numbers a and b, there exists a third number c so that you can write

the exponential statement $a^c = b$

or the equivalent logarithmic statement $\log_a b = c$; $a, b > 0$.

We say that c is 'the logarithm to base a of b', or 'the exponent of a that gives the answer b'.

In the logarithmic statement $\log_a b = c$, a is called the **base** of the logarithm and b is called the **argument** of the logarithm.

Change of base formula: $\log_a b = \dfrac{\log_c b}{\log_c a}$

Generally, all populations that grow continually are modelled by the population growth equation $P = P_0 e^{rt}$, where:

P is the final population

P_0 is the original population when $t = 0$

r is the growth rate

t is the time period.

If $y = e^x$ then the equivalent logarithmic statement is $\ln y = x$, $y > 0$.

The natural logarithm $\log_e y$ is written as $\ln y$.

The common logarithm $\log_{10} y$ is written as $\log y$.

Mixed practice

1 **Write down** the equivalent logarithmic statement for:

a $7^x = 23$ b $10^x = 95$

c $8^x = 6$ d $4^x = 47$

e $12^x = 1200$

2 **Write down** an equivalent exponential statement for:

a $\log_5 125 = 3$ b $\log_3\left(\dfrac{1}{9}\right) = -2$

c $\log 1000 = 3$ d $\log_7 2401 = 4$

e $\log_a m = n$

 3 **Find** the value of x without a calculator:

a $\log_2 16 = x$ b $\log_3 9 = x$

c $\log_7\left(\dfrac{1}{7}\right) = x$ d $\log_6 1 = x$

e $\log_3 3 = x$ f $\log_8 \sqrt{8} = x$

g $\log_6 6\sqrt{6} = x$

4 **Find** the value of x to the nearest hundredth.

a $\log_2 7 = x$ b $\log_4 12 = x$

c $\log_5 312 = x$ d $\log_9 21 = x$

e $\log 650 = x$ f $\ln 5 = x$

5 **Find** the value of x to 2 d.p.

a $3^x = 20$ b $5^x = 20$

c $e^x = 20$ d $3 \times 3^x = 15$

e $2 \times 3^{2x+1} = 45$ f $3 \times e^{2x+1} = 30$

6 **Find** the value of x without using a calculator.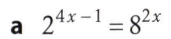

a $2^{4x-1} = 8^{2x}$ b $5^{x+4} = 125^{3x-1}$

c $3^{2x+3} = \left(\dfrac{1}{9}\right)^{2x-1}$

7 The table below shows the average movie ticket price in Canada from 1990 to 1994.

Year	Price of a movie ticket ($)
1990	4.00
1991	4.22
1992	4.45
1993	4.70
1994	4.96

a **Find** the exponential model for the average movie ticket price as a function of t, the number of years since 1990.

b **Calculate** the average price of a movie ticket in the year 2016.

c **Find** when the average price will reach $20.

8 A kettle of water is heated and then allowed to cool. The temperature can be modelled by the exponential equation $T = 100e^{-0.2t}$, where T is the temperature (in °C) and t is the time in minutes.

a **Find** the initial temperature.

b **Determine** the temperature after 3 minutes.

c Elizabeth can drink the water when the temperature is 40 °C. **Find** how long she must leave it to cool.

Review in context

Orientation in time and space

Charles Francis Richter was an American seismologist and physicist who created the Richter magnitude scale, which quantifies the size of earthquakes by measuring their intensity. It is a logarithmic scale, and since 1935 it has been the standard measure of earthquake intensity.

1 One formula for modelling the magnitude of an earthquake using the Richter scale is:

$$M = \log_{10} \frac{I_c}{I_n}$$

where M is the magnitude, I_c is the intensity of the 'movement' of the earth from the earthquake in microns, and I_n is the intensity of the 'movement' of the earth on a normal day-to-day basis in microns.

a The intensity of the movement on a normal day in Oklahoma is 100 microns. Last December, the intensity of the movement of the earth from the earthquake was recorded as 250 000 microns. **Determine** the size of this earthquake on the Richter scale.

b **Find** the measurement of each earthquake on the Richter scale:

Earthquake	I_c	I_n
i Southeast Indian ridge	3 767 829 647	150
ii Near coast of Northern Chile	25 896 531	140
iii Admiralty Island, Papua New Guinea	45 487 563	160
iv Chiapas, Mexico	123 568 544	140
v Cuba region	86 532 658	110

c An earthquake in northern Peru was recorded as 4.8 on the Richter Scale.

Usual movement in that area is 1450 microns. Using this information, **calculate** the intensity of the movement of the earth from the earthquake.

d An earthquake in Bermuda was recorded as 2.7 on the Richter Scale. The movement of the earth from the earthquake was calculated to be 2 145 000 microns. Using this information, **calculate** the usual movement.

2 To calculate the pH of a liquid you need to know the concentration of hydrogen ions (H^+) in moles per liter of the liquid.

The pH is then calculated using the logarithmic formula: $pH = -\log_{10}(H^+)$.

a HCl is a strong acid with a hydrogen ion concentration of 0.0015 moles per liter. **Find** the pH of the HCl solution.

b **Find** the hydrogen ion concentration of a liquid which has a pH of 9.4.

c A solution is said to be neutral (neither an acid nor a base) if its pH is 7. **Find** the concentration of hydrogen ions which would be considered to be neutral.

3 The pOH of an aqueous solution measures the number of hydroxide ions (OH^-) in a solution, using the formula: $pOH = -\log_{10}(OH^-)$.

a **Find** the pOH of an aqueous solution that has a hydroxide ion concentration of 6.1×10^{-5} moles per liter.

b **Find** the hydroxide ion concentration in an aqueous solution that has a pOH of 2.3.

4 The decibel scale measures the intensity of sound D using the equation $D = 10 \log I$, where I is the intensity ratio of a sound. On the decibel scale, the purr of a cat measures $D = 10 \log 330 = 25.2$ (3 s.f.) decibels.

Sound intensity is measured on a traffic light system:

Green: no ear protection needed. 1 – 75 DB

Orange: ear protection recommended. 80 – 120 DB

Red: ear protection necessary. 120 + DB

Calculate the sound intensity of these noises and **determine** whether or not ear protection equipment is recommended or necessary.

a A chainsaw has an intensity ratio of 1.04×10^{11}.

b A flowing river has an intensity ratio of 3100 000.

c A rocket launching has an intensity ratio of 8.2×10^{16}.

Reflect and discuss 5

How have you explored the statement of inquiry? Give specific examples.

Statement of inquiry:

Generalizing changes helps establish relationships that can model duration, frequency and variability.

E10.2 Laws of logarithms

Global context: Orientation in space and time

Related concept: Validity

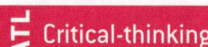
RELATIONSHIPS

Objectives

- Developing the laws of logarithms
- Using the laws of logarithms to simplify expressions and solve equations
- Proving the laws of logarithms
- Proving the change of base formula

Inquiry questions

F
- What are the laws of logarithms?

C
- How can you validate generalizations?

D
- Are all methods of solving logarithmic equations equivalent?

ATL Critical-thinking

Draw reasonable conclusions and generalizations

Statement of inquiry:

Generalizing changes helps establish relationships that can model duration, frequency and variability.

📖 Launch additional digital resources for this chapter.

274

You should already know how to:

• evaluate logarithms using a calculator	**1** Evaluate: **a** $\log 5$ **b** $\ln 3$ **c** $\log_2 6$
• changing exponential equations to logs in order to solve	**2** Solve the equation $3^x = 20$ by changing it to $\log_3 20 = x$.
• solve equations involving logs	**3** Solve the equation $\log_7\left(\frac{1}{7}\right) = x$.
• confirm algebraically and graphically that two functions are inverses of each other	**4** Show algebraically and graphically that $f(x) = 3x - 4$ and $g(x) = \frac{x+4}{3}$ are inverses of each other.
• find the inverse of a logarithmic function	**5** Find the inverse of the function $y = 2\log_5(x+3) - 11$.

F Creating generalizations

- What are the laws of logarithms?

ATL

Exploration 1

1 Choose any positive value of a for the base, and use your calculator to evaluate each logarithm in this table to 3 decimal places.

$\log_a 2 + \log_a 3$	$\log_a 6$
$\log_a 8 + \log_a 4$	$\log_a 32$
$\log_a 10 + \log_a 100$	$\log_a 1000$
$\log_a\left(\frac{1}{3}\right) + \log_a 81$	$\log_a 9$

Examine the patterns and write down a generalized rule:

The **product rule**: $\log_a xy =$

2 Do the same for the expressions in this table.

$\log_a 3 - \log_a 2$	$\log_a\left(\frac{3}{2}\right)$
$\log_a 8 - \log_a 4$	$\log_a 2$
$\log_a 100 - \log_a 10$	$\log_a 10$
$\log_a 81 - \log_a\left(\frac{1}{3}\right)$	$\log_a 243$

Examine the patterns and write down a generalized rule:

The **quotient rule**: $\log_a\left(\frac{x}{y}\right) =$

▶ Continued on next page

3 Compare the values in each column to discover a pattern.

$\log_a 3^4$	$\log_a 3$
$\log_a 7^2$	$\log_a 7$
$\log_a 75^{\frac{1}{2}}$	$\log_a 75$
$\log_a 81^{-\frac{1}{3}}$	$\log_a 81$

Examine the patterns and write down a generalized rule:

The **power rule**: $\log_a (x^n) =$

4 Evaluate $\log_a 1$ for different values of a.

Write down a generalized rule:

The **zero rule**: $\log_a 1 =$

5 Evaluate $\log_a a$ for different values of a.

Write down a generalized rule:

The **unitary rule**: $\log_a a =$

6 Rewrite $b^{\log_b x} = y$ as a logarithmic statement.

Hence solve for y in terms of x.

Write this as a generalized rule.

Scottish mathematician and astronomer John Napier (1550–1617), most famous for discovering logarithms, is also credited for introducing the decimal notation for fractions.

Reflect and discuss 1

- How are the rules you discovered similar to the laws of exponents? Give two specific examples.

- Explain why the zero rule and the unitary rule are true.

- How can you simplify $e^{\ln x}$?

Laws of logarithms

For **all** logarithm rules: $x, y, a \in \mathbb{R}^+$

The **product rule**: $\log_a xy = \log_a x + \log_a y$

The **quotient rule**: $\log_a \left(\dfrac{x}{y}\right) = \log_a x - \log_a y$

The **power rule**: $\log_a (x^n) = n \log_a x$

The **zero rule**: $\log_a 1 = 0$

The **unitary rule**: $\log_a a = 1$

$a^{\log_a m} = m$

Example 1

Rewrite $6 \ln x - 3 \ln 3 + 2 \ln x$ as a single logarithm.

$$6 \ln x - 3 \ln 3 + 2 \ln x = \ln x^6 - \ln 3^3 + \ln x^2 \quad\text{—— The power rule: } \log_a x^n = n \log_a x$$

$$= \ln(x^6 \times x^2) - \ln 3^3 \quad\text{—— The product rule: } \log_a xy = \log_a x + \log_a y$$

$$= \ln x^8 - \ln 3^3$$

$$= \ln\left(\frac{x^8}{27}\right) \quad\text{—— The quotient rule: } \log_a x - \log_a y = \log_a\left(\frac{x}{y}\right)$$

Example 2

Express $\ln\left(\frac{1}{\sqrt{ab}}\right)$ in terms of x and y, where $x = \ln a$ and $y = \ln b$.

$$\ln\left(\frac{1}{\sqrt{ab}}\right) = \ln 1 - \ln\sqrt{ab} \quad\text{—— The quotient rule.}$$

$$= \ln 1 - \frac{1}{2}\ln(ab) \quad\text{—— The power rule.}$$

$$= 0 - \frac{1}{2}\ln(ab) \quad\text{—— The zero rule: } \log_a 1 = 0.$$

$$= -\frac{1}{2}(\ln a + \ln b) \quad\text{—— The product rule.}$$

$$= -\frac{1}{2}(x + y)$$

Practice 1

1 Rewrite each expression as a single logarithm.

a $\log 4 + \log 3$

b $\log 5 - \log 2 + \log 6$

c $2\log 5 + 3\log 2 + \log 1$

d $3\log x - \log y + \frac{1}{2}\log z$

e $5\ln x - 3\ln 2 + 4\ln x$

f $\log y + 4\log x - (5\log 2y + \log 3x)$

2 Express in terms of $\ln a$ and $\ln b$:

a $\ln ab$

b $\ln\left(\frac{a}{b}\right)$

c $\ln(a^2 b)$

d $\ln\sqrt{a}$

e $\ln\left(\frac{1}{a^2}\right)$

f $\ln(a\sqrt{b})$

g $\ln\left(\frac{a^3}{b}\right)$

h $\ln\left(\frac{a^3}{b^2}\right)$

i $\ln\sqrt{\frac{a}{b}}$

Problem solving

3 Write each expression in terms of x and y, where $\log_a 3 = x$ and $\log_a 6 = y$.

a $\log_a 18$

b $\log_a 2$

c $\log_a 0.5$

d $\log_a 9$

e $\log_a 36$

f $\log_a 27$

g $\log_a 162$

4 Express in terms of x and y, where and $x = \log a$ and $y = \log b$:

a $\log(100a^2b^3)$

b $\log\left(\dfrac{a^5}{100b^4}\right)$

c $\log\sqrt[3]{1000a^6b^8}$

d $\log\left(\dfrac{1}{10a\sqrt{b}}\right)$

Example 3

Find the inverse of the function $g(x) = \ln x - \ln(x-3)$ and confirm it algebraically using the laws of logarithms. State the domain and range of the function and its inverse.

$$y = \ln x - \ln(x-3) = \ln\left(\frac{x}{x-3}\right)$$

Use the quotient rule.

$$x = \ln\left(\frac{y}{y-3}\right)$$

Interchange x and y.

$$e^x = \frac{y}{y-3}$$

Solve for y, and simplify.

$$(y-3)e^x = y$$
$$ye^x - 3e^x = y$$
$$ye^x - y = 3e^x$$
$$y = \frac{3e^x}{e^x - 1}$$
$$g^{-1}(x) = \frac{3e^x}{e^x - 1}$$

$$g(g^{-1}(x)) = \ln\left(\frac{3e^x}{e^x-1}\right) - \ln\left(\frac{3e^x}{e^x-1} - 3\right)$$

Show that $g(g^{-1}(x)) = x = g^{-1}(g(x))$.

$$= \ln\left(\frac{3e^x}{e^x-1}\right) - \ln\left(\frac{3e^x}{e^x-1} - \frac{3(e^x-1)}{e^x-1}\right)$$

$$= \ln\left(\frac{3e^x}{e^x-1}\right) - \ln\left(\frac{3}{e^x-1}\right)$$

$$= \ln\left(\frac{3e^x}{e^x-1} \div \frac{3}{e^x-1}\right)$$

$$= \ln e^x = x$$

$$g^{-1}(g(x)) = \frac{3e^{\ln\left(\frac{x}{x-3}\right)}}{e^{\ln\left(\frac{x}{x-3}\right)} - 1} = \frac{3\left(\frac{x}{x-3}\right)}{\frac{x}{x-3} - 1} = x$$

Since $g(g^{-1}(x)) = x = g^{-1}(g(x))$, they are inverses.

Domain of g is $x > 3$; range of g is $y > 0$.

Domain of g^{-1} is $x > 0$; range of g^{-1} is $y > 3$.

Exploration 2

1 Describe the transformations on the graph of $f(x) = \log_3 x$ that give the graph of $g(x) = \log_3(9x)$.

2 Describe the transformations on the graph of $f(x) = \log_3 x$ that give the graph of $h(x) = 2 + \log_3 x$.

3 Graph the functions f, g and h on the same coordinate axes, and write down what you notice. Explain, using laws of logarithms.

4 a Describe the **horizontal dilations** that transform the graph of f into the graph of:

    i $y = \log_3\left(\dfrac{x}{9}\right)$ **ii** $y = \log_3(27x)$

  b By using the laws of logarithms, describe the **horizontal translations** that transform the graph of f into the graph of:

    i $y = \log_3\left(\dfrac{x}{9}\right)$ **ii** $y = \log_3(27x)$

5 Summarize what you have learned in this Exploration about the transformations of dilations and translations with logarithmic functions.

Practice 2

1 Find the inverse of each function and prove that it is an inverse, both graphically and algebraically. State the domain and range of the function and its inverse.

  a $f(x) = 2^{x-3}$ **b** $g(x) = \sqrt{\ln(2x)}$

  c $h(x) = 4\log(1+2x)$ **d** $j(x) = \ln(x+2) - \ln(x-1)$

2 Use the laws of logarithms to explain why the graph of $g(x) = \log x^n$ is a vertical dilation of the graph of $f(x) = \log x$ for any positive n.

3 Given $f(x) = \log_3\left(\dfrac{9}{x}\right)$, use properties of logs to find an equivalent function.

Describe the transformations on the graph of $y = \log_3 x$ that give the graph of the equivalent function.

Problem solving

4 a Use properties of logs to find an equivalent expression for each function:

    i $g(x) = \log_2\left(\dfrac{8}{x}\right)$ **ii** $h(x) = \log_2(x+3)^2$

  b Then describe the sequence of transformations on the graph of $y = \log_2 x$ that give the graphs of g and h.

C Proving the generalizations

- How can you validate generalizations?

If a and b are positive real numbers, then the exponential statement $a^c = b$ is equivalent to $\log_a b = c$. Does this mean that the exponent rules are also related to the logarithm rules?

ATL

Exploration 3

1 Proving the product rule

Let $\log_a x = p$ and $\log_a y = q$.

a Write both these expressions as exponential statements.

b Multiply the two expressions together to obtain an expression for xy.

c Write this expression in logarithmic form.

d Substitute $p = \log_a x$ and $q = \log_a y$.

You should have the product rule.

2 Proving the quotient rule

Let $\log_a x = p$ and $\log_a y = q$.

a Write both these expressions as exponential statements.

b Divide to obtain an expression for $\frac{x}{y}$.

c Write this expression in logarithmic form.

d Substitute $p = \log_a x$ and $q = \log_a y$.

You should have the quotient rule.

3 Proving the power rule

Let $\log_a x = p$.

1 Write this expression as an exponential statement.

2 Raise this expression to the power n.

3 Write this expression in logarithmic form.

4 Substitute $p = \log_a x$.

You should have the power rule.

Internet search engines rank every website to determine an approximate measure of how important the site is. The algorithms which rank pages use a logarithmic scale, so a site with a rank of 5 is 100 times more popular than a site with a rank of 3. The difference of $5 - 3 = 2$ signifies two orders of magnitude on the logarithmic scale, where an order of magnitude is a power of 10.

Reflect and discuss 2

- How could you use a graphing tool with a slider to demonstrate the power rule for $f(x) = \log(x^2)$?

- What transformation takes the graph of $f(x) = \log x$ to the graph of $f(x) = \log(x^2)$? Explain.

Example 4

Express $3\ln x + 2\ln(2x+1)$ as a single logarithm.

$3\ln x + 2\ln(2x+1) = \ln x^3 + \ln(2x+1)^2$ ———— The power rule.

$= \ln\left[x^3(2x+1)^2\right]$ ———— The product rule.

$= \ln\left[x^3(4x^2+4x+1)\right]$ ———— Expand.

$= \ln(4x^5+4x^4+x^3)$

Practice 3

1 Express as a single logarithm:

   a $4\log p + 2\log q$ **b** $n\log p - 3\log q$

   c $3\ln(x-2) - \dfrac{1}{2}\ln x$ **d** $\ln x - 2\ln(x-2)$

   e $1 - \ln x$ **f** $4\ln x + 2\ln(x-1)$

2 Let $a = \ln x$, $b = \ln(x-1)$ and $c = \ln 3$. Express in terms of a, b and c:

   a $\ln\left(\dfrac{x}{x-1}\right)$ **b** $\ln(x^2-x)$

   c $\ln(3x^2)$ **d** $\ln\sqrt{\dfrac{x+1}{x}}$

   e $\ln\sqrt{3x^2-6x+3}$

Problem solving

3 Express as a sum and/or difference of linear logarithms:

   a $\ln(x^2-9)$ **b** $\ln(x^2+5x+6)$ **c** $\ln\left(\dfrac{x-3}{x+4}\right)$

   d $\ln\left(\dfrac{x+1}{x^2-4}\right)$ **e** $\ln\left(\dfrac{x^2-5x-6}{x^2-4}\right)$ **f** $\ln\left(\dfrac{x^4-3x^3-10x^2}{5x-20}\right)$

You can use a calculator to find the logarithms of any number with any base. Until quite recently, calculators could not do this. Books of log tables gave logarithms to base 10, and mathematicians used the change of base formula to calculate logs to other bases.

> You may have used the change of base formula in E10.1.

> Any positive value can be the base of a logarithm, but the two bases that are the most useful for practical applications arc the 'common' logarithm (base 10) and the 'natural' logarithm (base e).
>
> Logarithms date back to 1614, when John Napier took an interest in simplifying astronomical calculations which often involved multiplying very large numbers together.

Exploration 4

How to calculate $\log_2 5$ using logs to base 10

To find $\log_a b$ when you know $\log_c b$ and $\log_c a$:

Let $\log_a b = x$, $\log_c b = y$, and $\log_c a = z$.

1 Write all three expressions in exponential form.

2 Equate the two expressions for b to get an identity involving a, c, x and y.

3 Substitute for a to get an identity involving z, c, x and y.

4 Equate the exponents to find an identity linking x, y and z.

5 Rearrange to make x the subject.

6 Substitute the logarithmic expressions for x, y and z. You should have the change of base formula.

7 Use values from the log table to the right to find the value of $\log_2 5$.

In step **3**, use the exponential form of statement $\log_c a = z$.

x	$\log_{10}x$
1	0
2	0.301029996
3	0.477121255
4	0.602059991
5	0.698970004
6	0.778151250
7	0.845098040
8	0.903089987
9	0.954242509
10	1

Practice 4

1 Use the log table to find each value to 3 s.f.

a $\log_2 7$ **b** $\log_5 8$

c $\log_3 10$ **d** $\log_9 5$

e $\log_2 2$ **f** $\log_4 5$

Verify your results with a calculator.

Example 5

Given that $\ln a = 4$:

a express $\log_a(x^2)$ as a simple natural logarithm

b express $\ln(x^2) + 5\log_a x$ as a single logarithm.

a $\log_a(x^2) = 2\log_a x$ — The power rule.

$= 2\dfrac{\log_e x}{\log_e a}$ — Change of base.

$= 2\dfrac{\ln x}{\ln a}$ — $\ln a = 4$ is given.

$= 2\dfrac{\ln x}{4} = \dfrac{1}{2}\ln x$

▶ Continued on next page

b $\ln(x^2) + 5\log_a x = \ln(x^2) + 5\dfrac{\log_e x}{\log_e a}$

$$= \ln(x^2) + 5\dfrac{\ln x}{\ln a}$$

$$= \ln(x^2) + \dfrac{5}{4}\ln x$$

$$= \ln(x^2) + \ln(x^{1.25}) = \ln(x^2 \times x^{1.25}) = \ln(x^{3.25})$$

Practice 5

1 Given that $\ln a = 5$, express as a simple natural logarithm:

  a $\log_a(x^3)$ **b** $\log_a(x^2)$

  c $\dfrac{1}{2}\log_a x$ **d** $\log_a\left(\dfrac{x}{3}\right)$

2 Given that $\ln a = 1$, express as a single logarithm:

  a $\ln(x^3) + 2\log_a x$ **b** $2\ln x - 3\log_a x$

  c $3\log_a x + \dfrac{1}{2}\log_a x$ **d** $2\ln\dfrac{x}{3} - \dfrac{3}{2}\log_a x$

- -

D   Solving equations

    •   Are all methods for solving logarithmic equations equivalent?

A useful technique for solving equations involving exponents is to take logarithms of both sides.

Example 6

Solve $4^x = 25$ by taking logarithms of both sides.

$\log 4^x = \log 25$

$x\log 4 = \log 25$ ——————————————— The power rule.

$x = \dfrac{\log 25}{\log 4}$ ——————————————— Isolate x.

$x = 2.32$ (3 s.f.) ——————————————— Use a calculator to evaluate.

Reflect and discuss 3

Show that you can obtain the same result in Example 6 by first rewriting the original equation as a logarithmic statement. Which method do you prefer? Explain.

Example 7

A mathematician has determined that the number of people P in a city who have been exposed to a news story after t days is given by the function $P = P_0(1 - e^{-0.03t})$, where P_0 is the city population. A lawyer knows that it is very difficult to appoint an unbiased jury to determine guilt in a crime after 25% of the population has read the news.

Find the maximum number of days available to select a jury.

$$P = P_0(1 - e^{-0.03t})$$ — 25% of the population implies $\frac{P}{P_0} = 0.25$

$$0.25 = 1 - e^{-0.03t}$$

$$e^{-0.03t} = 1 - 0.25$$

$$e^{-0.03t} = 0.75$$ — Take natural logs of both sides.

$$\ln e^{-0.03t} = \ln 0.75$$

$$-0.03t = \ln 0.75$$

$$t = \frac{\ln 0.75}{-0.03}$$

$$t = 9.56$$

There is a maximum of 9 days available to select a jury.

To solve equations that contain logarithms, you often need to use the laws of logarithms first.

Each logarithm has three parts: the base, the argument and the answer.

Example 8

Find the value of x in each equation.

a $\log_2 x + \log_2 3 = \log_2 9$

b $\log_4 (x + 1) + \log_4 (x - 2) = 1$

a $\log_2 x + \log_2 3 = \log_2 9$

$$\log_2 (3x) = \log_2 9$$ — The product rule.

$$3x = 9$$

$$x = 3$$ — The arguments of the logarithms must be equal to each other.

b $\log_4 (x + 1) + \log_4 (x - 2) = 1$

$$\log_4 [(x + 1)(x - 2)] = 1$$ — The product rule.

$$x^2 - x - 2 = 4^1$$

$$x^2 - x - 6 = 0$$

$$(x - 3)(x + 2) = 0$$

$$x = 3 \text{ or } -2$$

$x \neq -2$ since the logarithm $\log_4 (-2 - 2) = \log_4 (-4)$ doesn't exist.

Therefore, $x = 3$

Practice 6

1 Solve these equations by taking logs of both sides:

   a $3^x = 25$ **b** $7^x = 41$ **c** $12^x = 25$

2 Solve:

   a $3^{5x} = 45$ **b** $4^{2x} = 9$ **c** $3^{5x+1} = 60$

3 Solve these equations for x:

   a $3 \times 4^{2x} = 9$ **b** $7 \times 4^{2x+1} = 89$ **c** $5 \times 3^{3x-1} = 52$

4 Solve these exponential equations:

   a $2^{2x} - 7 \times 2^x + 6 = 0$ **b** $4^{2x} - 10 \times 4^x + 24 = 0$

> Look for quadratic equations.

5 Find the value of x in each equation:

   a $\log_5 x + \log_5 10 = \log_5 12$

   b $\log_7 (3x) + \log_7 12 = \log_7 (2x + 5)$

   c $\log_3 (x + 1) - \log_3 (x + 4) = -2$

   d $\log_2 (x - 1) + \log_2 (x + 6) = 3$

   e $\log_{20} x = 1 - \log_{20} (x - 1)$

Objective A: Knowing and understanding
iii. solve problems correctly in a variety of contexts

You can use the rules you have found to solve these context problems involving exponential equations.

---

6 A state surveys school traffic. At the end of 2010, there were 25 000 cars per day taking children to school.

After t years the number of cars, C, was modelled by the exponential equation $C = 25\,000 \times e^{0.07t}$.

   a Show that by the end of 2015, there were 35 477 cars per day taking children to school.

   b By taking logs of both sides, calculate the time until the number of cars taking children to school reaches 50 000.

7 The time taken for an online video to go viral can be modelled by an exponential function, $H = 15e^{0.5t}$, where H is the number of times the video is watched and t is the number of hours since the first people shared the video.

   a Describe what the value 15 represents in this model.

   b By taking logs of both sides, calculate the number of hours before the video is watched 500 000 times.

   c By rewriting the exponential statement as a logarithmic statement, calculate the number of hours before the video is watched 1 000 000 times.

   d Determine which method (**b** or **c**) is most efficient.

Problem solving

8 Solve:

   a $2^{5x-2} = 5^x$ **b** $3^{2x-1} = 4^x$

   c $2^{x+1} = 4^{2x}$ **d** $3^{x+2} = 9^{2x-2}$

9 If $\log_a x = p$, show that rewriting it as a logarithmic statement and solving the resulting equation proves the power rule for logarithms.

> Rearrange to get all the x terms on one side, then factorize to isolate x.

Summary

Laws of logarithms

For **all** logarithm rules: $x, y, a \in \mathbb{R}^+$

The **product rule**: $\log_a xy = \log_a x + \log_a y$

The **quotient rule**: $\log_a\left(\dfrac{x}{y}\right) = \log_a x - \log_a y$

The **power rule**: $\log_a(x^n) = n \log_a x$

The **zero rule**: $\log_a 1 = 0$

The **unitary rule**: $\log_a a = 1$

$a^{\log_a m} = m$

Change of base formula:

$$\log_a b = \frac{\log_c b}{\log_c a}$$

Mixed practice

1 Rewrite in terms of $\log a$, $\log b$ and $\log c$:

   a $\log(abc)$ **b** $\log\left(\dfrac{ac}{b}\right)$

   c $\log(a^3 b^2 c^4)$ **d** $\log\left(a\sqrt{b}\right)$

   e $\log\left(a\sqrt{\dfrac{b}{c^2}}\right)$

2 Express as a single logarithm:

   a $2\log 5 + \log 4 - \log 8$

   b $3\ln 5 - \ln 4 + \ln 8$

   c $3\log_4 5 - 2\log_4 5 + \log_4 8$

   d $2\log_a\left(\dfrac{1}{2}\right) + \log_a 4 - \log_a\left(\dfrac{1}{4}\right)$

   e $6\ln x - 2\ln(x+1) - 3\ln(2x+6)$

   f $\log_4 2 + 3\log_4 3$

   g $\dfrac{1}{2}\log_7 16 + \dfrac{1}{3}\log_7 x - 2\log_7 y$

3 Given that $\log_a 3 = x$ and $\log_a 4 = y$, **write down** each expression in terms of x and y.

   a $\log_a 0.25$ **b** $\log_a 48$

   c $\log_a\left(\dfrac{1}{12}\right)$ **d** $\log_a 144$

   e $\log_a\left(\dfrac{27}{16}\right)$

4 Express in terms of x and y, given that $x = \log a$ and $y = \log b$.

   a $\log(a^5 b)$

   b $\log(10\sqrt[4]{ab^3})$

   c $\log(0.01a^3 b^4)^2$

   d $\log\left(\dfrac{50a^7}{5\sqrt{b}}\right)$

5 **Find** the inverse of each function and **state** the domain and range of both the function and its inverse. **Prove** they are inverses both graphically and algebraically.

   a $f(x) = 6(5^{2x+1})$

   b $g(x) = \sqrt[3]{\log x} - 2$

   c $h(x) = -\dfrac{2}{3}\ln(3x-1)$

   d $k(x) = \log_4(7x) - \log_4(x+5)$

6 **Use** properties of logarithms to **find** an equivalent expression for each function. Then **describe** the sequence of transformations on the graph of $y = \log_3 x$ that give the graphs of the equivalent expressions for f and g.

   a $f(x) = \log_3(27x)$

   b $g(x) = \log_3(x-9)^4$

7 Let $a = \ln x$, $b = \ln(x+2)$ and $c = \ln 4$.

Express in terms of a, b and c:

a $\ln\left(\dfrac{4}{x+2}\right)$ **b** $\ln(4x^2 + 8x)$

c $\ln\left(\dfrac{x^3}{16}\right)$ **d** $\ln\sqrt{\dfrac{x^2 + 4x + 4}{4x}}$

e $\ln\sqrt{x^4 + 2x^3}$

Problem solving

8 Express as a sum and/or difference of logarithms:

a $\ln(x^2 - 25)$ **b** $\ln(x^2 - 3x - 28)$

c $\ln\left(\dfrac{x+1}{x-8}\right)$ **d** $\ln\left(\dfrac{x^2 - 4x - 5}{x^2 + 6x + 8}\right)$

e $\ln\left(\dfrac{x^2 - 10x - 24}{x^3 - 4x}\right)$

9 **Solve** these exponential equations:

a $3^{2x+1} + 3 = 10 \times 3^x$

b $2^{2x} - 3 \times 2^x - 4 = 0$

10 **Solve** these logarithmic equations:

a $\log_a x + \log_a 4 - \log_a 5 = \log_a 12$

b $\log_4 x - \log_4 7 = 2$

c $\log_9 x + \log_9(x^2) + \log_9(x^3) + \log_9(x^4) = 5$

d $1 - \log(x+3) = \log x$

e $\log(x-5) - \log(x+4) = -1$

11 Let $\log_a 2 = x$ and $\log_a 5 = y$. **Find**, in terms of x and y, expressions for:

a $\log_5 2$ **b** $\log_a 40$

c $\log_a 400$ **d** $\log_a 2.5$

e $\log_a 0.4$

12 **Solve** by taking logs of both sides:

a $19^x = 2$ **b** $\left(\dfrac{1}{2}\right)^x = 25$

c $2^{5x-2} = 80$ **d** $3^{5x-6} = 111$

13 Let $\log_a 3 = x$ and $\log_a 7 = y$.

Find expressions, in terms of x and y, for:

a $\log_3 7$ **b** $\log_7 3$ **c** $\log_3 49$

14 Given that $\ln a = 8$:

a express $\log_a(x^3)$ as a simple natural logarithm

b express $3\log_a x - \ln(a^2)$ as a single logarithm.

15 Reproduction in a colony of sea urchins can be modelled by the equation $N = 100e^{0.03x}$ where N is the number of sea urchins and x is the number of days since the original 100 were introduced to the reef.

a **Find** the number of days it takes for the population to double.

b **Find** the increase in population of sea urchins on day 19.

Problem solving

16 A mathematician calculated that the number of people infected after the first case of a disease was identified followed the model $P = P_0(1 - e^{-0.001t})$ where P is the number of infected people, P_0 is the population of the city, and t is the number of days after the first case was identified.

a **Calculate** how long it would take for 5% of the population to be infected.

b In a city, 58 187 people are infected after 21 days. **Calculate** the population of the city.

17 A game park in Swaziland recorded 15 rhinoceros in 2000, and 26 rhinoceros in 2011. Assuming the number of rhinoceros in the game park follows an exponential function, **find** the function.

Review in context

Orientation in time and space

In E10.1 you used this formula for modelling the magnitude, M, of an earthquake using the Richter scale:

$$M = \log_{10} \frac{I_c}{I_n}$$

where I_c is the intensity of the 'movement' of the earth from the earthquake, and I_n is the intensity of the 'movement' on a normal day-to-day basis.

You can also write this as:

$$M = \log_{10} I$$

where I is the intensity ratio $\frac{I_c}{I_n}$.

1 a The San Francisco earthquake of 1906 measured magnitude 8.3 on the Richter scale. Shortly afterward, an earthquake in South America had an intensity ratio four times greater than the San Francisco earthquake. **Find** the magnitude on the Richter scale of the earthquake in South America.

b A recent earthquake in Afghanistan measured 7.5 on the Richter scale. **Find** how many times more intense the San Francisco earthquake was.

c **Find** how much larger an earthquake's magnitude is, if it is 20 times as intense on the Richter scale as another earthquake.

d **Determine** how much more intense is an earthquake whose magnitude is 7.8 on the Richter scale than an earthquake whose magnitude is 6.2.

e **Compare** the intensities of two earthquakes: Nevada in 2008 with magnitude 6.0 and Eastern Sichuan in 2008 with magnitude 7.6.

2 The pH value of a solution is used to determine whether a solution is basic (alkaline) or acidic. A pH value of 7 is neutral, less than 7 is acidic, and more than 7 is basic. To calculate the pH of a liquid you need to know the concentration of hydrogen ions (H^+) in moles per liter (mol/l) of the liquid.

The pH is then calculated using the logarithmic formula:

$$pH = -\log_{10}(H^+)$$

a Milk has $H^+ = 1.58 \times 10^{-7}$ mol/l. **Determine** whether milk is acidic or basic.

b **Find** the pH of vinegar with concentration: $H^+ = 1.58 \times 10^{-3}$ mol/l.

c A sample of pool water has concentration: $H^+ = 6.3 \times 10^{-7}$ mol/l. **Determine** the pH of the sample of pool water.

d Some chemicals are added to the water because the answer in **c** indicates that the pH level of the water is not optimal. A sample of water is taken after adding the chemicals, and now the concentration is $H^+ = 7.94 \times 10^{-8}$ mol/l.

Determine if the water is now within optimum levels: $7.0 < pH < 7.4$.

e **Find** the values for H^+ that give a pH in the range $7.0 < pH < 7.4$.

3 The volume of sound D is measured in decibels (db) and I is the intensity of the sound measured in Watts/m^2, using the formula $D = 10\log_{10} I$.

a An anti-theft car alarm has an intensity of 5.8×10^{13} W/m^2. **Find** the volume of the alarm in decibels.

b Jill's scream measured 56 db, and Jack's was 48 db. **Find** how much more intense Jill's scream was than Jack's.

Reflect and discuss 4

How have you explored the statement of inquiry? Give specific examples.

Statement of inquiry:

Generalizing changes helps establish relationships that can model duration, frequency and variability.

Non-linear inequalities

Global context: Orientation in space and time

Related concept: Models

Objectives

- Solving quadratic and rational inequalities both algebraically and graphically
- Solving other non-linear inequalities graphically
- Using mathematical models containing non-linear inequalities to solve real-life problems

Inquiry questions

F
- What is a non-linear inequality?
- How do you solve non-linear inequalities graphically?

C
- How does a model lead to a solution?

D
- Are graphical and algebraic solutions equivalent?
- Which is more efficient: a graphical solution or an algebraic one?

ATL Critical-thinking

Use models and simulations to explore complex systems and issues

Statement of inquiry:

Generalizing changes helps establish relationships that can model duration, frequency and variability.

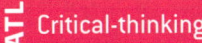 **Launch additional digital resources for this chapter.**

You should already know how to:

• solve linear inequalities	**1** Solve $-3x - 2 < 5 - 4x$.
• sketch graphs of linear, quadratic, rational, radical, exponential and logarithmic functions	**2** Sketch the graphs of: **a** $y = x^2 + 3x - 4$ **b** $y = 2e^x - 3$ **c** $y = 4\log 2x$ **d** $y = \dfrac{-2}{x-4}$ **e** $y = \dfrac{2x-3}{3x+6}$ **f** $y = \sqrt{x-5}$
• solve quadratic equations by completing the square	**3** Solve $x^2 + 6x + 3 = 0$.

F   Non-linear inequalities in one variable

- What is a non-linear inequality?
- How do you solve non-linear inequalities graphically?

Objective D: Applying mathematics in real-life contexts
iii. apply the selected mathematical strategies successfully to reach a solution

In Exploration 1, when you have selected your solution to the quadratic inequality, determine graphically if the range of the hip angle guarantees a lift area of at least 0.5 m².

ATL

Exploration 1

In ski jumping, athletes descend a take-off ramp, jump off the end of it and 'fly' as far as possible. The angle of the skier's hip α determines the 'lift area' A (in m²) which determines how far the skier jumps. The relationship between hip angle and lift area can be modelled by the function:

$$A(\alpha) = -\frac{0.3}{400}(\alpha - 140)^2 + 0.8$$

1 Use this function to write a mathematical model (inequality) of the range of the hip angle that would ensure a lift area of at least 0.5 m².

2 Use a GDC to graph both sides of this inequality and find:

   a the point where both graphs intersect

   b the region of the graph that models the set of points where $A(\alpha) > 0.5$

   c the region of the graph that models the set of points where $A(\alpha) < 0.5$.

3 From your graph, write down:

   a the range of the skier's hip angle to ensure a lift area of 0.5 m² or more

   b the range of the skier's hip angle that gives a lift area less than 0.5 m².

4 Explain how you can test whether or not you have selected the correct ranges in step **2**.

5 Rearrange the inequality in step **1** to the form $A(\alpha) \geq 0$.

6 Graph $A(\alpha)$, and explain how you would use the inequality to answer step **2**.

7 Explain how you could use this graph to check your answer.

Reflect and discuss 1

- How do you know whether or not to include x-values where the two graphs intersect (or the x-intercepts, as in step **6**) in your solution set?

- Which method did you prefer: the one where you graph each side of the original inequality and compare, or the one where you rewrite the inequality? Explain.

To solve a quadratic inequality graphically:

- Graph both sides of the inequality, or rearrange into the form $f(x) > 0$ or $f(x) < 0$ and graph.

- Determine the points of intersection of both functions, or find the zeros of the function.

To check your solution algebraically:

- Choose a point in the region you think satisfies the inequality, and test this point in the inequality. If it satisfies the inequality, then the x-values in this region satisfy the inequality. If your test point does not satisfy the inequality, then test the x-values in the other region(s).

Example 1

Solve the inequality $28 - x \leq 16 + 12x - x^2$. Check your solution algebraically.

Method 1

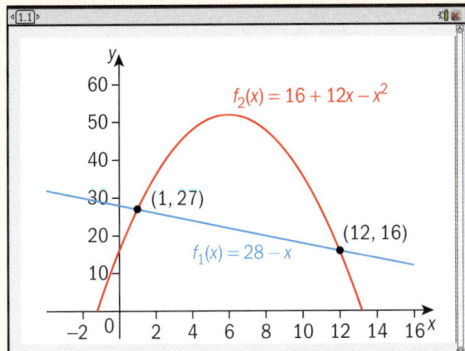

Graph both sides of the inequality and determine the points of intersection.

The x-values of points on the line (LHS) are lower than those on the quadratic (RHS) for $1 < x < 12$.

Test a point with x-value between 1 and 12:

When $x = 2$: $28 - 2 = 26$

$$16 + 12 \times 2 - 2^2 = 36$$

$26 \leq 36$ ✓

The solution is $1 \leq x \leq 12$.

Select an x-value in the solution interval, and check that it satisfies the inequality. Because the original inequality was 'less than or equal to', the endpoints ($x = 1$ and $x = 12$) are included.

▶ Continued on next page

Method 2

$$28 - x \leq 16 + 12x - x^2$$

$$\Rightarrow 0 \leq -12 + 13x - x^2$$

Rearrange to $f(x) \geq 0$.

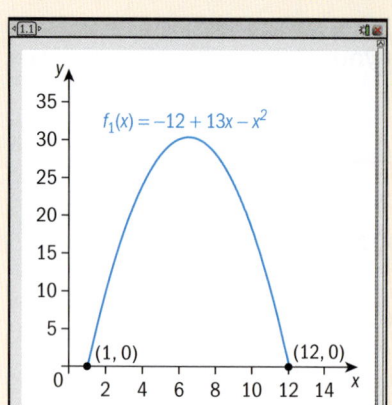

Graph the quadratic function.

The solution is $1 \leq x \leq 12$.

The zeros of the quadratic are $x = 1$ and $x = 12$.
$f(x) \geq 0$ for the x-values between these zeros.

Check: When $x = 2$: $-12 + 13 \times 2 - 2^2 = 10 \geq 0$.

Select an x-value in the solution interval, and check that the inequality is satisfied.

Example 2

Solve the inequality $-2x^2 + 4x < x^2 - x - 6$. Check your solution algebraically.

Method 1

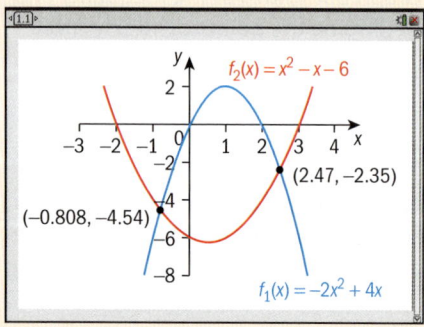

Graph both sides of the inequality and determine the points of intersection of the graphs.

$x < -0.808$ or $x > 2.47$

The blue curve, for $-2x^2 + 4x$ lies below the red curve in the regions $x < -0.808$, $x > 2.47$.

Check:

When $x = -1$: LHS $= -6$, RHS $= -4$

$-6 < -4$

When $x = 3$: LHS $= -6$, RHS $= 0$

$-6 < 0$

▶ Continued on next page

Method 2

$$-2x^2 + 4x < x^2 - x - 6$$

Rearrange to $f(x) > 0$.

$$\Rightarrow 3x^2 - 5x - 6 > 0$$

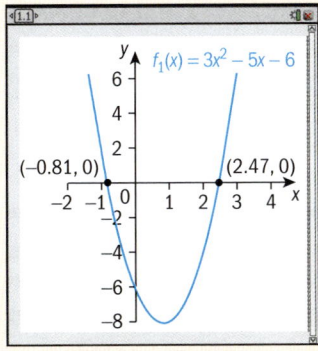

Graph the quadratic function.

$x < -0.808$ or $x > 2.47$

The quadratic is greater than 0 above the x-axis.

Practice 1

ATL

1 Solve each inequality graphically, and check your answers algebraically.

> Use whichever method you prefer.

a $x^2 - 2x - 9 > 2x + 3$ **b** $2x^2 - 5 \leq x + 1$ **c** $5x^2 - 10 \geq 23x$

d $x^2 + 3x - 8 < 4 - 2x - x^2$ **e** $2x^2 - 7x + 7 > 8x^2 - 2x + 1$

2 For astronaut training, weightlessness is simulated in a reduced gravity aircraft that flies in a parabolic arc. The function $h(t) = -3t^2 + 191t + 6950$ models the relationship between the flight time t in seconds, and the height h of the aircraft in meters. The astronauts experience weightlessness when the aircraft's height is above 9600 m.

a Write an inequality that describes this situation.

b Determine how long the astronauts experience weightlessness when the aircraft flies in a parabolic arc.

3 A rectangle is 6 cm longer than it is wide. Its area is greater than 216 cm². Write and solve an inequality to find its possible dimensions.

4 A gardener has 24 meters of fencing to build a rectangular enclosure. The enclosure's area should be less than 24 m². Write and solve an inequality to find possible lengths of the enclosure.

5 For drivers aged between 16 and 70, the reaction time y (in milliseconds) to a visual stimulus (such as a traffic light) can be modelled by the function $y = 0.005x^2 - 0.23x + 22$, where x is the driver's age in years. Write an inequality to determine the ages for which a driver's reaction time is more than 25 milliseconds, and solve.

Problem solving

6 A baseball is thrown from a height of 1.5 m. The relationship between the time t (in seconds) and the height h (in meters) of the baseball while in the air is modelled by the function $h(t) = -4.9t^2 + 17t + 1.5$.

a Write an inequality that describes how long the baseball is in the air.

b Determine how long the baseball is in the air.

7 In a right-angled triangle, one of the perpendicular sides is 2 cm longer than the other. The hypotenuse is more than twice the length of the shortest side. Determine the possible lengths for the shortest side.

8 A 2 cm square is cut from each corner of a square piece of card, and the sides are then folded up to form an open box. Pia needs a box with maximum volume 40 cm³. Find the largest possible dimensions of the box.

Example 3

Find the set of values such that $\frac{1}{x} > \sqrt{x}$ in the domain $\mathbb{R}^+$ and check your answer.

The solutions to Examples 3 and 4 can also be found using the same **Method 2** approach as described in Examples 1 and 2.

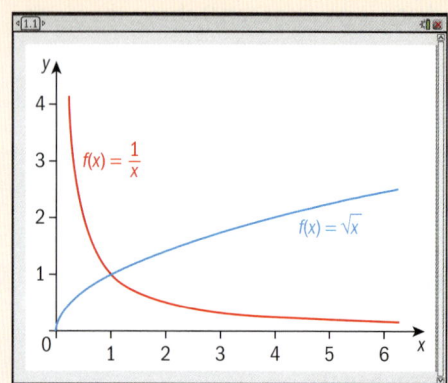

Graph both sides of the inequality, and find the point of intersection.

$\frac{1}{x} > \sqrt{x}$ in the interval $0 < x < 1$.

Select an x-value in the solution interval and test it in the inequality.

Check: When $x = 0.5$, $\frac{1}{0.5} = 2$ and $\sqrt{0.5} \approx 0.707 < 2$

Example 4

Solve $\frac{2x-7}{x-5} \leq 3$, $x \neq 5$, and check your answer.

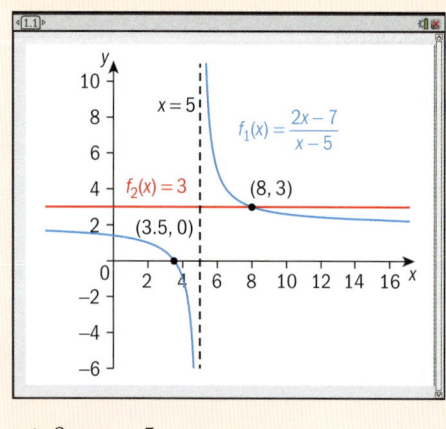

Locate where the LHS function (blue) $\leq$ RHS function (red).

$x \geq 8$ or $x < 5$

▶ Continued on next page

Check:

When $x = 10$, $\frac{2x-7}{x-5} = \frac{13}{5}$ and $\frac{13}{5} \leq 3$.

When $x = 0$, $\frac{2x-7}{x-5} = \frac{7}{5}$, and $\frac{7}{5} \leq 3$.

> Select an x-value in each region, and check in the original inequality.

Practice 2

1 Find the set of values that satisfy each non-linear inequality:

a $\frac{1}{x} - x < 0$

b $\frac{1}{x} - 4 \geq 0$

c $\frac{x+6}{x+1} > 2$

d $\ln x < \log_2(x-2)$

e $x^2 > \sqrt{2x+3}$

f $\frac{4}{x+5} < \frac{1}{2x+3}$

g $\frac{1}{x} < \frac{1}{x+3}$

h $\frac{3x}{x-1} \geq 3 + \frac{x}{x+4}$

Problem solving

2 When two resistors, R_1 and R_2 are connected as shown, the total resistance R is modelled by the equation $\frac{1}{R} = \frac{1}{R_1} + \frac{1}{R_2}$.

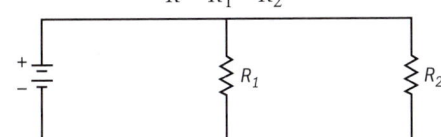

a $R_2 = 2$ ohms and R must be at least 1 ohm. Find the range of possible values for R_1.

b $R_1 = 2.2$ ohms and R must be at least 1.7 ohms. Find the range of possible values for R_2.

- -

C Non-linear inequalities in two variables

- How does a model lead to a solution?

When you solve an inequality in one variable, the solution is a set of x-values. When you solve an inequality in two variables, the solution is a set of points.

For this graph of $y = x^2 - 2x - 3$, the blue shaded area represents the set of points that satisfy $y < x^2 - 2x - 3$. You can test that you have the correct region by substituting the coordinates of a point in this region into the original inequality. For example, for the point $(0, -4)$: $x^2 - 2x - 3 = -3 > -4$, so the correct region is shaded.

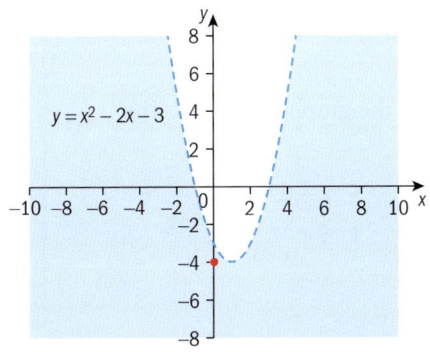

The unshaded region of the graph on the previous page represents the set of points that satisfy the inequality $y > x^2 - 2x - 3$. The quadratic graph is drawn with a dashed line, to show that values on the line are not included in the solution set.

To solve non-linear inequalities in two variables:

- Graph the region defined by the equality.

- Select a point that is not on the curve and substitute the values into the original inequality. If the inequality is true, shade the region where the point is (e.g. inside the curve). If the inequality is not true, shade the region where the point is not (e.g. outside the curve).

Example 5

By sketching a suitable graph, solve the inequality $y < -x^2 + 7x - 10$. Shade the region containing the possible solutions on your graph.

$-x^2 + 7x - 10 = (-x + 2)(x - 5)$ —— Factorize to find the roots of $f(x) = 0$.

$(-x + 2) = 0 \Rightarrow x = 2$

$(x - 5) = 0 \Rightarrow x = 5$

x-coordinate of vertex $= \dfrac{-7}{-2} = 3.5$ —— Use the formula $x = \dfrac{-b}{2a}$ to find the coordinates of the vertex.

Vertex $= (3.5, 2.25)$

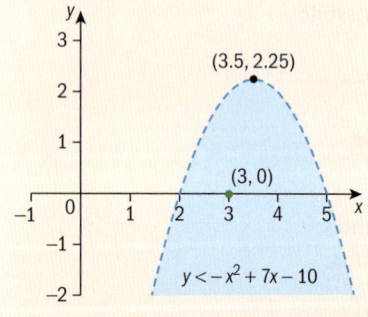

$y < -x^2 + 7x - 10$

Draw the parabola with a dashed line, as it represents a true inequality.

Check:

For $(3, 0)$: $-x^2 + 7x - 10 = 2 > 0$, hence the region shaded is correct.

Test a point in the original inequality, then shade the correct region.

Practice 3

1 Sketch a suitable graph and shade the region on the graph that shows the solution of the inequality.

    a $y > x^2 + 3x - 1$ **b** $y \le -x^2 + 3x - 2$ **c** $y \ge 4 - 3x - 2x^2$

    d $y > \ln(x - 2) + 3$ **e** $y \le e^{(x+1)} - 3$ **f** $y < \dfrac{x+3}{x-3}$

In the case of a strict inequality, the line is dotted as in the graph above. In the case of $\ge$ or $\le$, the graph of the quadratic would be a solid line.

2 Write an inequality to describe the shaded region in each graph.

a

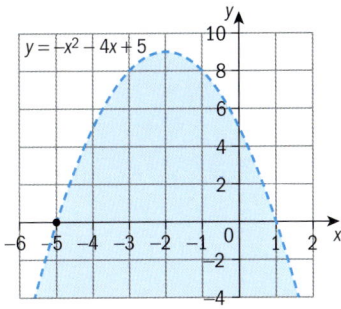

$y = -x^2 - 4x + 5$

b

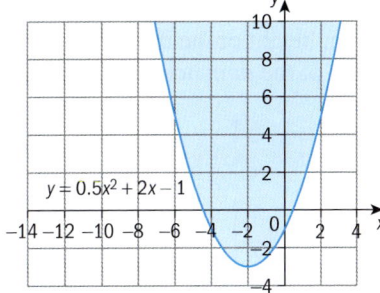

$y = 0.5x^2 + 2x - 1$

c

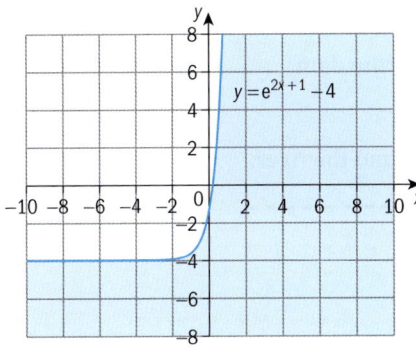

$y = e^{2x+1} - 4$

d

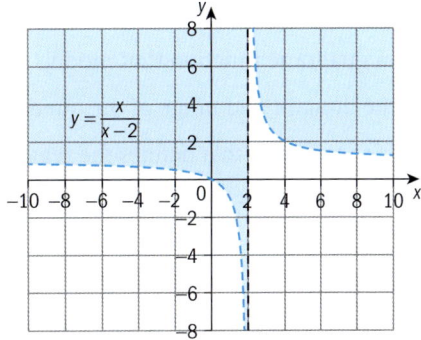

$y = \dfrac{x}{x-2}$

Problem solving

3 For each graph:

   i find the quadratic function for the parabola

   ii write an inequality that describes the shaded region.

a

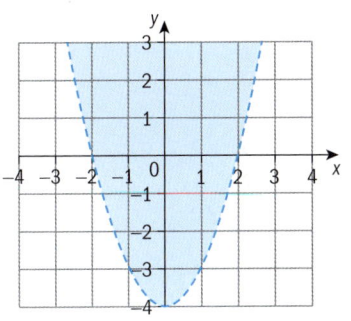

b

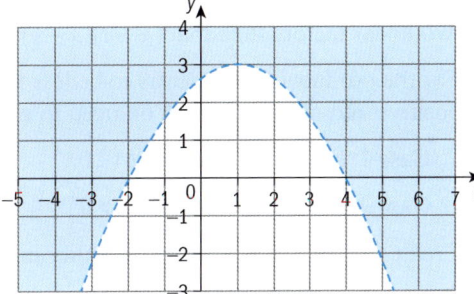

c

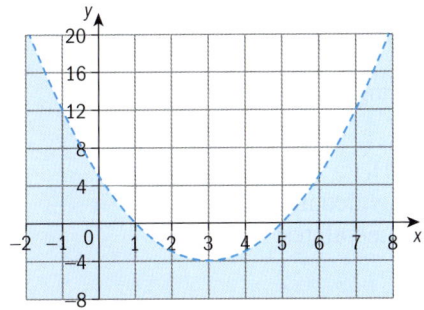

4 A parabolic dam is built across a river, as shown in the graph. The maximum height of the dam above the water level is 3 m, and the length of the dam across the river is 90 m.

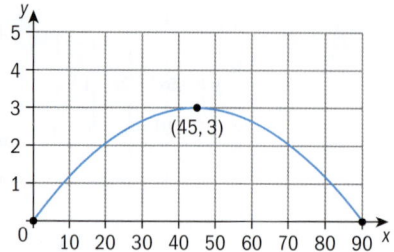

a Write a quadratic function that models the parabolic arch of the dam.

b State the domain and range of the quadratic function.

c Write an inequality that defines the region between the dam and the river.

D Algebraic solutions to non-linear inequalities

• Which is more efficient: a graphical solution or an algebraic one?

• Can good decisions be calculated?

Exploration 2

1 Factorize the quadratic function in the inequality $x^2 - 3x - 4 < 0$ into two linear factors such that $(x + a)(x + b) < 0$.

2 For the product of two factors to be less than zero, one factor must be positive and one negative. You need to solve the two cases separately.

Case 1: $(x + a) > 0$ and $(x + b) < 0$

Case 2: $(x + a) < 0$ and $(x + b) > 0$

3 Create the two cases for the inequality in step **1** and solve each one.

4 Determine which case is the solution to the original inequality. Check your answer graphically.

You can also solve a quadratic inequality algebraically by first finding the zeros of the quadratic function.

The quadratic function in Exploration 2 factorizes into $(x - 4)(x + 1)$, hence the zeros of the function are $x = 4$ and $x = -1$. The x-axis is divided into intervals by the roots of the equation. Choose an x-value in each interval, test it in the inequality to determine if it satisfies the inequality.

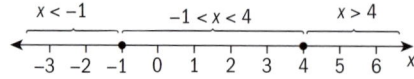

Interval	$x < -1$	$-1 < x < 4$	$x > 4$
Test point	-2	0	7
Substitution in $x^2 - 3x - 4$	$(-2)^2 - 3 \times -2 - 4 = 6$ $6 > 0$	$0^2 - 3 \times 0 - 4 = -4$ $-4 < 0$	$7^2 - 3 \times 7 - 4 = 24$ $24 > 0$
Is $x^2 - 3x - 4 < 0$?	No	Yes	No

The values satisfying the quadratic inequality $x^2 - 3x - 4 < 0$ are $-1 < x < 4$. Written in set notation, the solution set is $\{x : -1 < x < 4\}$.

Reflect and discuss 2

- How would you solve the inequality in Exploration 2 graphically?

- Do you prefer the algebraic or the graphical approach for this question?

- Which two cases would you need to consider to solve $x^2 - 3x - 4 > 0$ algebraically? What is the solution set of this inequality?

To solve a quadratic inequality algebraically:

- Rearrange the inequality so that either $f(x) < 0$ or $f(x) > 0$.

- Factorize the quadratic and find its zeros.

- Place these two x-values on a number line, dividing it into intervals.

- Select an x-value in one of the intervals and substitute it into the original inequality. If the inequality is true, then that interval is part of the solution. If the inequality is false, then it is not.

- Repeat for all intervals.

To check your solution algebraically:

- Choose a point in the region you think satisfies the inequality, and test this point in the inequality. If it satisfies the inequality, then the x-values in this region satisfy the inequality.

Example 6

Solve the quadratic inequality $x^2 - x > 12$ and check your answer graphically.

$$x^2 - x > 12$$
$$x^2 - x - 12 > 0$$
$$(x - 4)(x + 3) > 0$$

▶ Continued on next page

Method 1

Case 1: $x - 4 < 0$ and $x + 3 < 0$
$\Rightarrow x < 4$ and $x < -3$,
$\Rightarrow x < -3$

Case 2: $x - 4 > 0$ and $x + 3 > 0$
$\Rightarrow x > 4$ and $x > -3$,
$\Rightarrow x > 4$

> For a product to be positive, the factors must have the same signs.

> Because the value of x needs to be both less than 4 and less than −3, using $x < -3$ covers all possibilities.

> As before, using $x > 4$ covers both of the inequalities, $x > 4$ and $x > -3$.

Check your solutions by sketching a graph.

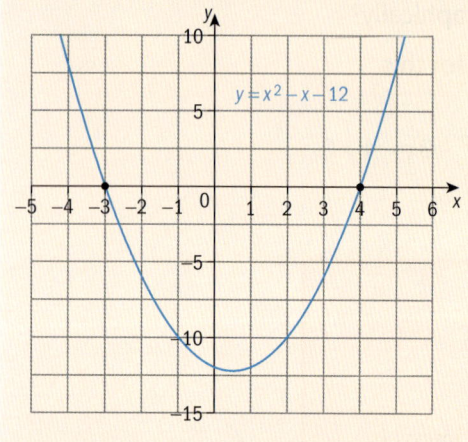

> From the graph, you can see that both cases solve the original inequality since $x^2 - x - 12 > 0$ when $x < -3$ or when $x > 4$.

The solution is $x < -3$ or $x > 4$.

Method 2

The zeros of $x^2 - x - 12$ are $x = -3$ and $x = 4$.

Interval	$x < -3$	$-3 < x < 4$	$x > 4$
Test point	−4	0	5
Substitution in $x^2 - x - 12$	$(-4)^2 - (-4) - 12 = 8$	$0^2 - 0 - 12 = -12$	$5^2 - 5 - 12 = 8$
	$8 > 0$	$-12 < 0$	$8 > 0$
Is $x^2 - x - 12 > 0$?	Yes	No	Yes

From the table, the solution is $x < -3$ or $x > 4$.

Hence, $f(x) > 0$ for $x < -3$ or $x > 4$.

Reflect and discuss 3

Which algebraic method for solving quadratic inequalities is more efficient? Explain your reasons.

Practice 4

1 Solve these quadratic inequalities algebraically and confirm graphically.

a $x^2 - 2x - 3 \leq 0$

b $x^2 - 10x + 16 > 0$

c $12 + x - x^2 \geq 0$

d $x^2 + 6x \leq 40$

e $2x^2 + 5x < 3$

f $3x^2 - 1 > 2x$

g $6x^2 + 4x + 1 < 5x + 3$

2 One of the perpendicular sides of a right-angled triangle is 3 cm longer than the other. Determine the possible lengths of the shorter side that give a triangle with area less than 4cm^2.

Problem solving

3 Each inequality is the solution set of a quadratic inequality. Find a possible quadratic inequality.

a $-1 < x < 1$

b $x < -1$ or $x > 2$

c $x \leq 2$ or $x \geq 10$

d $x > \frac{1}{2}$ or $x < -\frac{2}{3}$

e $\frac{1}{3} \leq x \leq 6$

Exploration 3

1 By using the quadratic formula or the method of 'completing the square', solve the equation $x^2 + 3x - 7 = 0$.

2 From the roots of the equation in step **1**, explain how you would obtain the solution to the inequality **a** $x^2 + 3x - 7 > 0$ and **b** $x^2 + 3x - 7 < 0$.

3 Confirm your solutions graphically.

4 Write out the steps to solve a non-factorizable quadratic inequality.

5 Check that your steps work when solving:

a $x^2 + x - 4 < 0$

b $2x^2 + 4x - 1 > 0$

Practice 5

Solve each inequality algebraically, accurate to 3 s.f.

1 a $x^2 - 5x + 1 > 0$

b $x^2 + 6x - 2 < 0$

c $2x^2 + 3x - 3 \leq 0$

d $3x^2 - 7x + 2 > 0$

e $-x^2 - x + 5 \geq 0$

f $-2x^2 + 4x + 2 \leq 0$

g $5x^2 - 2x - 1 < 0$

h $x^2 + 10x \geq -8$

i $-3x^2 - 2x + 1 < x^2 + x - 1$

j $x^2 - 5x \leq -1$

Problem solving

2 Solve each inequality. Explain your result by considering the discriminant Δ of the quadratic function.

a $x^2 + 2x + 1 \le 0$

b $x^2 - 4x + 4 \ge 0$

c $x^2 + 2x + 4 > 0$

d $-(x-1)^2 - 3 < 0$

$\Delta = b^2 - 4ac$

Reflect and discuss 4

How can the discriminant help you solve quadratic inequalities?

Example 7

Solve $\dfrac{2-x}{x+1} < 1$, $x \ne -1$, and confirm your answer graphically.

$\dfrac{2-x}{x+1} < 1$ —— Rearrange and simplify.

$\dfrac{2-x}{x+1} - 1 < 0$

$\dfrac{2-x-(x+1)}{x+1} < 0$

$\dfrac{1-2x}{x+1} < 0$ —— A fraction is negative when the numerator and denominator have opposite signs.

Method 1

Case 1: $1-2x < 0$ and $x+1 > 0$

Then $x > \dfrac{1}{2}$ and $x > -1$, hence $x > \dfrac{1}{2}$.

Case 2: $1-2x >$ and $x+1 < 0$

Then $x < \dfrac{1}{2}$ and $x < -1$, hence $x < -1$.

Solution $x > \dfrac{1}{2}$ or $x < -1$.

Method 2

$1-2x = 0$; $x = \dfrac{1}{2}$ —— Find the x-intercept by setting the numerator equal to 0, and the asymptote by setting the denominator equal to 0.

$x+1 = 0$; $x = -1$

Interval	$x < -1$	$-1 < x < \dfrac{1}{2}$	$x > \dfrac{1}{2}$
Test point	-2	0	1
Substitution into $\dfrac{2-x}{x+1}$	$\dfrac{2-(-2)}{-2+1} = -4$	$\dfrac{2-0}{0+1} = 2$	$\dfrac{2-1}{1+1} = \dfrac{1}{2}$
Is $\dfrac{2-x}{x+1} < 1$?	Yes	No	Yes

Consider the intervals to the left, right, and between these values.

Solution: $x < -1$ or $x > \dfrac{1}{2}$

▶ Continued on next page

Check:

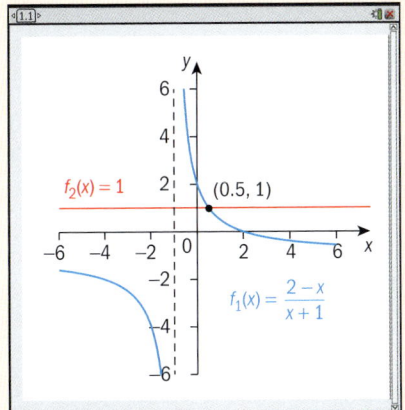

From the graph, $f_1(x)$ is below $f_2(x)$ for x-values greater than 0.5 or less than -1.

Reflect and discuss 5

- Decide which algebraic method for solving rational inequalities you feel is more efficient, and explain your reasons why.

- Does the type of inequality (quadratic, rational, etc.) affect your choice of which algebraic method to use?

Practice 6

1 Solve each inequality algebraically and check your solution graphically.

a $\dfrac{1+x}{1-x} < 0,\ x \neq 1$

b $\dfrac{x+6}{x+1} \geq 2,\ x \neq -1$

c $\dfrac{x+1}{x-4} > 0,\ x \neq 4$

d $\dfrac{8-x}{x-2} \leq 5,\ x \neq 2$

e $\dfrac{3x-1}{x} + 1 < 0,\ x \neq 0$

f $\dfrac{5x-8}{x-5} \geq 2,\ x \neq 5$

Problem solving

2 Determine the range of values that a variable x can take such that adding x to the numerator and denominator of the fraction $\dfrac{2}{3}$ results in a fraction that is less than $\dfrac{1}{2}$.

3 Gretchen would like to improve her free throw average in basketball. She has scored 9 free throws in her first 20 trials. Determine how many more consecutive free throws she would need to successfully make in order to bring her average up to 70%.

Summary

To solve a quadratic inequality graphically:

- Graph both sides of the inequality, or rearrange into the form $f(x) > 0$ or $f(x) < 0$ and graph.

- Determine the points of intersection of both functions, or find the zeros of the function.

Remember to check your solution algebraically:

- Choose a point in the region you think satisfies the inequality, and test this point in the inequality. If it satisfies the inequality, then the x-values in this region satisfy the inequality.

To solve non-linear inequalities in two variables:

- Graph the region defined by the equality.

- Select a point that is not on the curve and substitute the values into the original inequality. If the inequality is true, shade the region where the point is (e.g. inside the curve). If the inequality is not true, shade the region where the point is not (e.g. outside the curve).

To solve a quadratic inequality algebraically:

- Rearrange the inequality so that either $f(x) < 0$ or $f(x) > 0$.

- Factorize the quadratic and find its zeros.

- Place these two x-values on a number line, dividing it into several intervals.

- Select an x-value in one of the intervals and substitute it into the original inequality. If the inequality is true, then that interval is part of the solution. If the inequality is false, then it is not.

- Repeat for all intervals.

To check your solution algebraically:

- Choose a point in the region you think satisfies the inequality, and test this point in the inequality. If it satisfies the inequality, then the x-values in this region satisfy the inequality.

Mixed practice

1 **Solve** each inequality graphically, giving exact answers or accurate to 3 s.f.

   a $(x+2)^2 > 1$ **b** $x^2 - 3x - 1 \geq -11x + 4$

   c $-2x^2 + 15 < 3x$ **d** $2x^2 - 3x + 1 < 3x^2 + 1$

   e $\frac{2}{x} - 3 > 4,\ x \neq 0$ **f** $\frac{5-2x}{5-x} < -1,\ x \neq 5$

2 **Shade** the region representing the graph of each inequality. Check you have shaded the correct region using a test point.

   a $y > x^2 - 4x + 2$ **b** $y \geq -2x^2 + 6x$

   c $y < 2x^2 - 8x - 3$ **d** $y < \log(x+1)$

   e $y \geq e^{(x-2)} + 5$ **f** $y > \frac{x-2}{x+4}$

3 **Solve** algebraically and confirm graphically.

   a $x^2 + 5x - 6 < 0$ **b** $x^2 - 10x - 24 > 0$

   c $2x + x^2 \leq 35$ **d** $(x+3)^2 < 25$

   e $2x^2 - 4x < 7x$ **f** $5x^2 - 13x \geq -6$

   g $\frac{x-3}{x+5} > 0,\ x \neq -5$ **h** $\frac{3x-5}{x-1} > 4,\ x \neq 1$

4 A rectangular playing field with a perimeter of 100 m is to have an area of no less than 500 m². **Determine** the maximum possible length of the playing field.

5 A travel agency's profits P (in dollars) can be modelled by the function

$P(x) = -25x^2 + 1000x - 3000$, where x is the number of tourists. **Determine** the range of the number of tourists needed for the agency's profit to be at least \$5000.

Problem solving

6 Orange juice is to be sold in 2-liter cylindrical cans. To keep costs down, the surface area of a can must be less than 1000 cm². **Determine** possible values for the radius and height of the cans, accurate to 1 d.p. (A liter is 1000 cm³)

7 A packing company designs boxes with a volume of at least 600 cubic inches. Squares are cut from the corners of a 20 inch by 25 inch rectangle of cardboard, and the flaps are folded up to make an open box. **Determine** the size of the squares that should be cut from the cardboard, accurate to 3 s.f.

Review in context

Orientation in time and space

1 A small satellite dish has a parabolic cross-section. Its diameter is 30 cm and it is 15 cm deep.

   a **Sketch** the parabola on the coordinate axes.

   b When designing the satellite dish, engineers decide where to place a receiver so that it receives a maximum number of signals. **Determine** the inequality that represents the region inside the cross section, which is where the signals are likely to be the strongest. **State** its domain.

2 A parabolic microphone uses a parabolic reflector to collect and then focus sound waves onto a receiver. Its cross-section has a maximum width of 50 cm and a maximum depth of 20 cm.

   a **Draw** a graph to represent this information.

   b The microphone needs to be placed in the interior of the parabola's cross-section. **Determine** the mathematical model (inequality) that describes this region and **state** its domain.

   c On your graph from **a**, shade the region in **b**, and check your solution.

Reflect and discuss 6

How have you explored the statement of inquiry? Give specific examples.

Statement of inquiry:

Generalizing changes helps establish relationships that can model duration, frequency and variability.

Statement of inquiry:

Using logic to develop patterns and understanding the properties of space can help design models to use resources responsibly and efficiently.

Key concept:

Logic is used as a process in making decisions about numbers, shapes and variables.

F **What is space? Can space always be represented using patterns?**

Space is the frame of geometrical dimensions describing an entity.

Animation

Have you ever wondered how animated characters can look so fluid and real? An understanding of the three-dimensional space that we live and move in is essential to achieve this effect. Therefore, a large part of the success of modern animations is due to the use of mathematics in creating the different animated figures. To create your favorite animations, mathematicians use harmonic coordinates, which are a form of barycentric coordinates, or coordinates using a triple set of numbers. The advantage of this method is that it greatly simplifies the process of animating a character, and reduces the time and effort required to complete the animation.

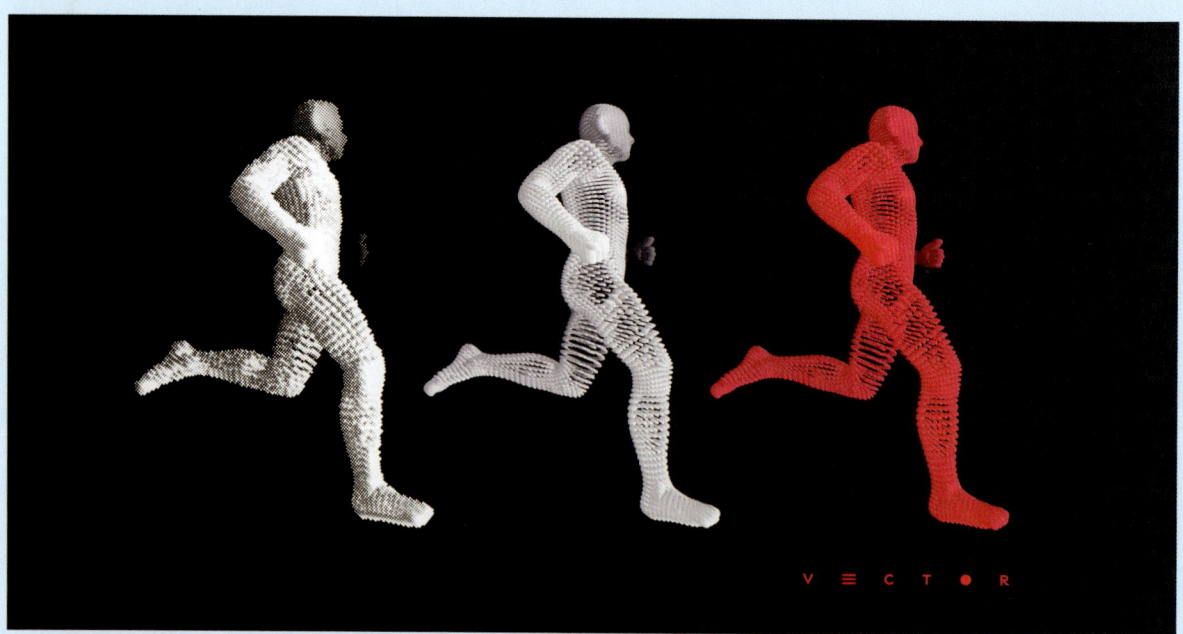

How can patterns in space help identify 'best' solutions to problems?

Patterns are sets of numbers or objects that follow a specific order or rule.

This picture might look like a beautiful fern frond, but in fact, it's mathematically generated. This is an illustration of The Barnsley Set, a fractal which mimics the behaviour of real plants. Plants have evolved to form 'best' solutions to environmental constraints. By understanding the patterns that govern their growth, we can solve other mathematical problems.

Lots of computer illustrations use fractal behaviour and fractal-like patterns to generate intricate images such as animated hair, foliage or landscapes.

D **Is there a specific model to optimize the use of space and resources?**

Solving problems with soap bubbles?

You may have blown bubbles using soapy water before, but did you know that soap bubbles behave in highly mathematical ways? The physics of surface tension means that soap bubbles naturally optimize themselves to create a soap bubble with the lowest possible surface area. That's why soap bubbles on their own are spherical, because a sphere has the lowest surface area for any given volume.

When soap bubbles interact with a frame, they don't form spheres but they do still find optimal solutions. Understanding the shapes that soap bubbles might form has helped mathematicians and physicists to optimize other real-life problems.

Global context: Fairness and development

Exploration: Explore using models to use resources responsibly and efficiently

🗔 **Launch additional digital resources for this unit.**

E11.1 Graph theory: Networks

Global context: Fairness and development

Related context: Pattern

LOGIC

Objectives

- Understanding network terminology
- Representing real-life problems with networks
- Applying simple algorithms to solve problems involving networks

Inquiry questions

- What is a vertex?
- What is an edge?
- What are graphs and directed graphs?
- What does it mean for a graph to be connected?
- What is a network?

- How does investigating patterns, like the Chinese Postman Problem, help us better understand and utilize the spaces we live and work in?
- How can a methodical pattern, or algorithm, help solve real-world problems?
- What real-life problems can be modelled by networks?

- Does the Traveling Salesman Problem facilitate or complicate the optimization of living and working structures?
- What is meant by an exhaustive search?
- What matters more: a quick solution or a perfect solution?

ATL Communication

Use prioritization and structure in problem solving.

Statement of inquiry:

Using logic to develop patterns and understanding the properties of space can help design models to use resources responsibly and efficiently.

📖 **Launch additional digital resources for this chapter.**

F ## What is a network?

- What is a vertex?
- What is an edge?
- What are graphs and directed graphs?
- What does it mean for a graph to be connected?
- What is a network?

You may have heard it said that the world is now more connected than ever before. But what does this mean? How can mathematics help you understand the way in which the world is connected? A branch of maths known as *Graph Theory* is used to model connections between objects.

A **graph** is a collection of points, known as **vertices**.

Those vertices may be joined to each other. The connections are known as **edges**.

The **order** of a vertex is the number of edges connected to it.

A graph is **complete** if every vertex is connected directly to every other vertex by an edge.

A graph is **connected** if every point on the graph may be reached from any other point on the graph, traveling along several edges if needed. If not, it is **disconnected**.

> You are used to using the word 'graph' to describe a line or a curve drawn on axes, or maybe a statistical graph like a scatter diagram or a histogram. Graph Theory uses the term 'graph' to describe something completely different, so be careful not to get confused.

Exploration 1

1 These diagrams each illustrate connected graphs, using dots to represent the vertices and lines or curves to represent the edges. In each case determine the number of vertices and the number of edges.

a 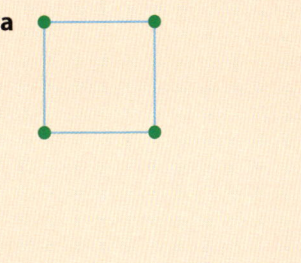   **b**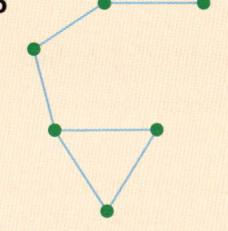

c    **d**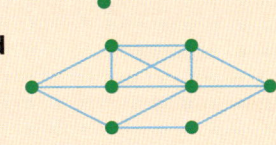

> Vertices are sometimes also known as *nodes*, and edges are sometimes also known as *arcs*.

2 Determine which of the graphs below are connected and which are disconnected.

a 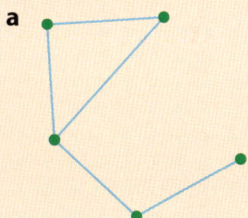   **b** 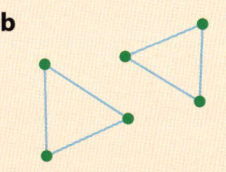   **c**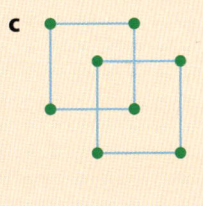

▶ Continued on next page

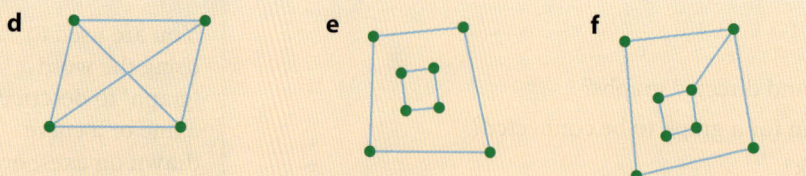

d **e** **f**

3 The graph below shows the rail connections between six British cities. Each edge joins a pair of cities which are connected directly by train, i.e. where you may move from one to another without having to change.

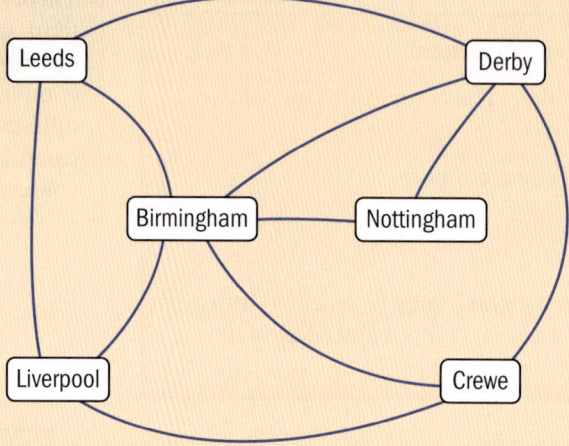

a Write down:

   i the city that is connected directly to all others

   ii the city that is connected to the smallest number of other cities

   iii the order of the vertex representing Liverpool

   iv a pair of cities which are not connected directly to each other.

b For your pair of cities in **a iv**, in how many different ways could you get from one city to another using only one change?

4 The graph below shows six people and the languages that they speak. If a person can speak a language, they are joined to that language by an edge.

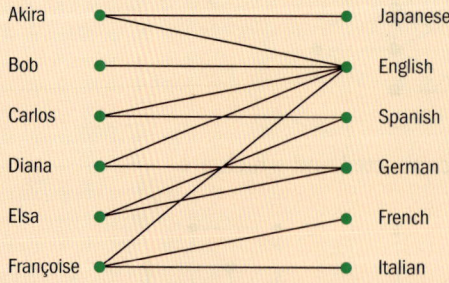

a Explain what is represented by the order of the vertices in this graph.

b Determine which person speaks the most languages.

▶ Continued on next page

c Determine which language is spoken by the most people.

d Elsa and Carlos want to talk to each other. Write down the language they have in common.

e Explain why there will be no conversations in French amongst this group.

f Bob wishes to get a message to Elsa, but they have no language in common. Find a person that could act as a translator for them, and the languages that would be spoken by each person.

g Diana has found some sci-fi comics containing some text written in Italian but can't read it. Suggest a way in which she could find out what it says.

h Create a new graph which just shows the six people and where the edges join people that have languages in common.

5 The maps of metro networks in major cities are often represented as graphs, with vertices for the stations and edges indicating the connections between adjacent stations. You might want to look online for the New York Subway map, the Beijing Metro map or the London Underground map.

a Suggest additional information that the metro maps need to communicate that a graph does not.

b Look at this extract from the New York Subway map. Explain why this section does not meet the usual requirements for the presentation of a graph if stations are interpreted as vertices with the tracks being interpreted as edges.

c Most metro networks would be best represented by a connected graph. Explain what it would mean if the graph of a metro network was disconnected and suggest reasons why such a metro might exist.

Reflect and discuss 1

- what ways is your graph in question 4h in Exploration 1 more useful than the original?
- What information is lost?
- In what ways is your graph less useful?

Consider again the graph from question **3** in Exploration 1. There are two ways of getting from Derby to Liverpool with one change – either via Birmingham or via Crewe. Which one would you choose? You would probably want to make a decision based on either time, cost, or total distance – but the graph doesn't contain this information. Knowing that two places are connected is useful, but without knowing more details about the connection itself, it can be difficult to use the graph to make decisions.

A **network** is a **weighted graph**. In a weighted graph, every edge has a number associated with it. That number could represent many different things, for example time, cost or distance.

> Every edge on a **weighted graph** has a value, or **weight**, associated with it.
>
> Weighted graphs are also known as **networks**.
>
> The **total weight** of the network is the sum of all the weights of the individual edges.

Exploration 2

1 The network below shows the cost, in euros, for a shipping company to transport a particular parcel between warehouses in different French cities.

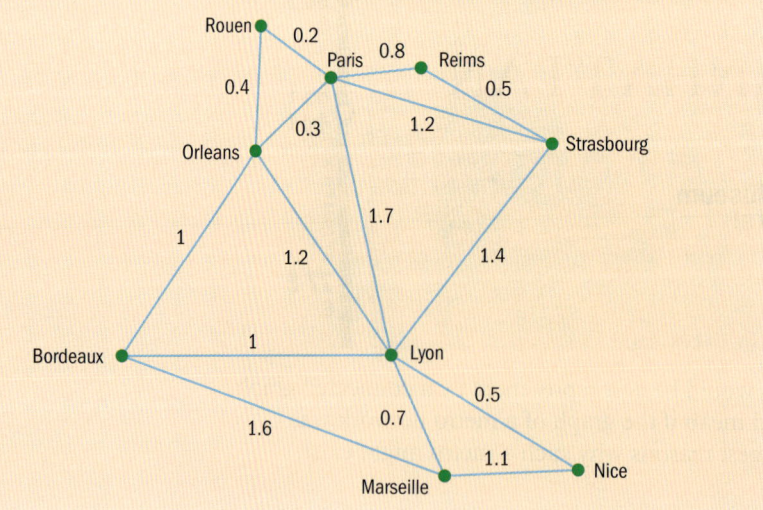

▶ Continued on next page

a Write down the cost of shipping the parcel directly from Orleans to Lyon.

b Write down the cost of the cheapest connection in the network, and the places it joins.

c Find the cost of transporting the parcel from Bordeaux to Nice via Lyon, and the cost of transporting the parcel from Bordeaux to Nice via Marseille. Determine which is more expensive.

d The company needs to move a parcel from Paris to Lyon. Find the cheapest way of doing so. Suggest reasons why someone might choose to transport the parcel other than by the cheapest route.

2 The California Zephyr is a long-distance train service that travels over 3900 km in a journey taking more than two days from Chicago, Illinois, to Emeryville, California. The network below shows the distances (in km) between major stopping points on the route.

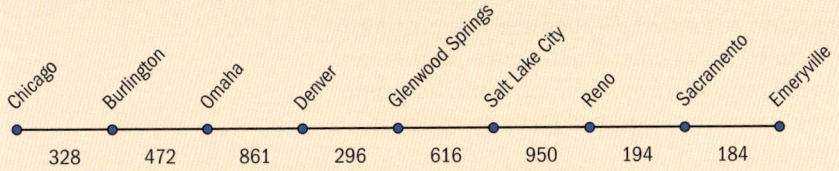

a Find the distance from Salt Lake City to Reno by train.

b Determine which journey is longer, Omaha to Denver or Salt Lake City to Sacramento.

c Find the total weight of this network. What does it represent?

d The whole journey takes approximately 2 days and 4 hours. Find the average speed of the train in km per hour.

3 A parking warden is checking that cars are displaying valid permits. The network below shows the time it takes to travel along each road while checking each car.

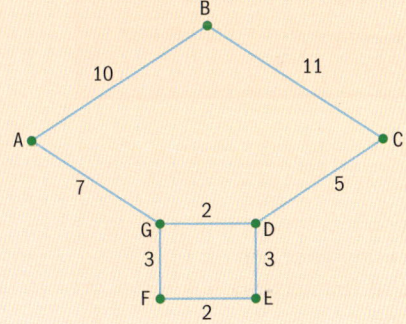

▶ Continued on next page

a The warden checks all the cars along the route A–G–D–C. Find the time taken.

b Determine the total weight of the network. Explain what it represents in this context.

c Show that there is a route starting at G and ending at D which allows the warden to check every street exactly once.

Reflect and discuss 2

In Exploration 2, question **3c**, the parking warden starts at G and is able to visit every street on the network without retracing her steps. Would this have been possible if she had started at A?

The graph in Exploration 2, question **3** is *traversable*, because it is possible to create a single route which includes every edge exactly once. In this case, it was necessary to start either at D or G to traverse the network, but some graphs can be traversed from any start point. You will learn more about traversable graphs in the next exploration.

A graph which is disconnected cannot be traversable, because there would be vertices in the graph which could not be reached from other vertices.

A **walk** is any route through a graph.

A **trail** is a walk which repeats no edges.

A **circuit** is a trail which starts and ends at the same vertex.

A **path** is a route through a graph from one vertex to another which does not pass through a vertex more than once.

A **cycle** is a path which starts and ends at the same vertex, but does not pass through any vertex more than once.

A graph is **traversable** if you can draw it without taking your pen off the paper or retracing your steps.

Exploration 3

1 One way of understanding whether or not a graph is traversable is to consider whether it could be drawn without taking your pen off the paper and without going along an edge twice, as the network below can.

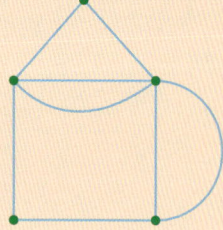 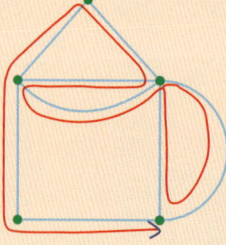

▶ Continued on next page

All of the following graphs are traversable. Find routes which traverse the graph.

a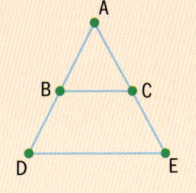

b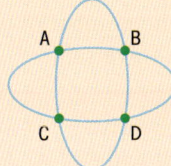

c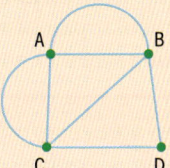

d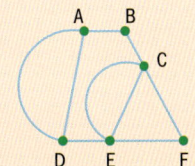

e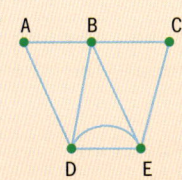

f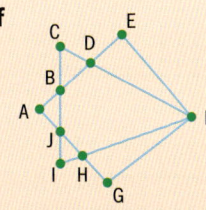

Some of the following graphs are traversable. By looking for suitable routes, determine which ones are traversable.

g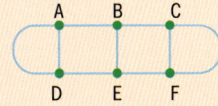

h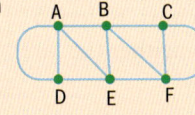

i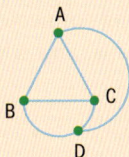

j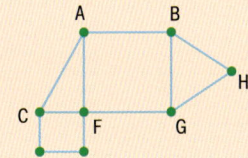

k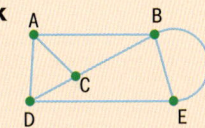

l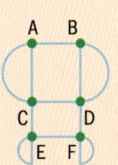

2 Copy and complete this table, describing whether each graph is traversable or not and recording the end points of the path that you found. For each graph, also write down the number of odd vertices (i.e. whose order is an odd number) and the number of even vertices (i.e. whose order is an even number).

Graph	Traversable?	End vertices	End vertices are the only option?	Odd vertices	Even vertices
a	Yes	B, C	Yes	2	3
b	Yes		No		
c	...				
...					

3 Compare the answers in your table to the answers obtained by other students. For the traversable graphs, under what circumstances did you have the same endpoints as others? Which paths could have started in different places? Describe the relationship between the number of odd or even vertices and the traversability of the graph.

In Exploration 3, you will have seen that traversable graphs fall into two categories – those where you can start from anywhere, or those where the route has to start and finish at a particular pair of vertices. The number of odd vertices provides a way of determining whether a network is traversable.

A connected graph with only even vertices is traversable. It may be traversed starting from any point on the graph and the trail will end where it started. It therefore has an **Eulerian circuit**.

A connected graph with exactly two odd vertices is traversable. Any trail which traverses the graph will start at one odd vertex and end at the other. It therefore has an **Eulerian trail**.

A connected graph with more than two odd vertices has neither an Eulerian circuit nor an Eulerian trail and so is non-traversable.

Practice 1

1   Determine which of the following connected graphs have Eulerian circuits, which have Eulerian trails, and which have neither (i.e. are non-traversable).

a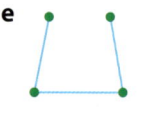

b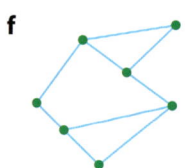

c

d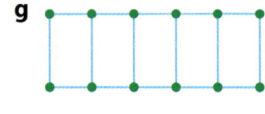

e

f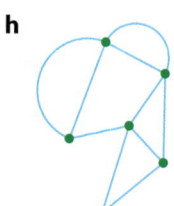

g

h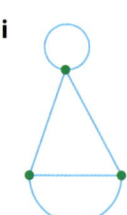

i

2 The following graphs all have Eulerian trails. They may be modified to have a Eulerian circuit by the addition of a single edge. In each case, determine where the edge should be drawn.

a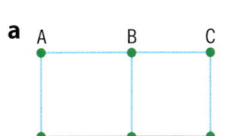

b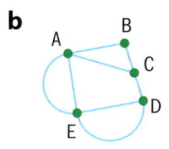

c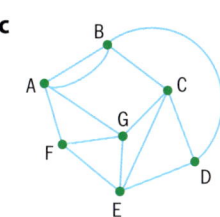

d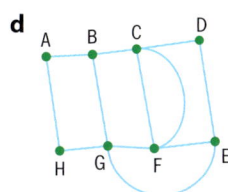

e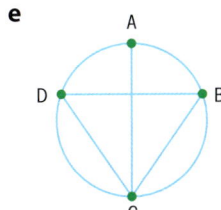

f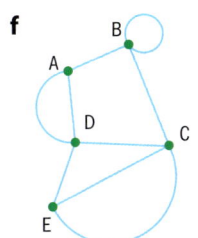

3 For the following graphs, identify whether the graph is traversable, or not. For the traversable graphs, identify a trail which traverses the network.

a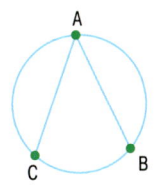

b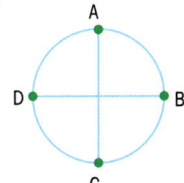

c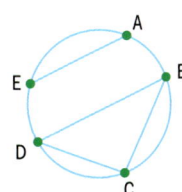

d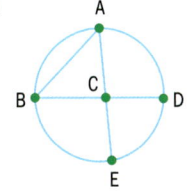

e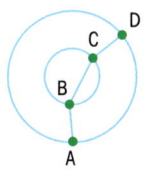

f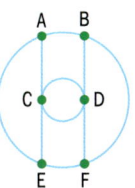

4 Carmela has a part-time job delivering newspapers in her local area, where the streets are arranged in a grid pattern. Every day, her manager gives her a highlighted map of the area showing which streets need deliveries on that day. The diagram below shows the maps for three such days.

Monday

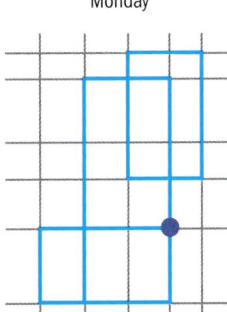

Tuesday

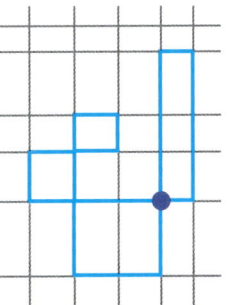

Wednesday

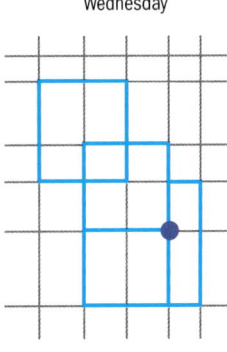

If possible, Carmela likes to deliver all the newspapers and return to the shop without having to walk down the same street twice. If she can't manage this, then she likes to deliver all the newspapers before having to walk along unnecessary roads. Her least favorite option is when she has to walk down roads that either don't need newspapers, or retrace her steps before she has given all of the newspapers out.

Determine which of the given days relates to which of the described scenarios. The newspaper shop is at the location marked with a blue dot.

C How can we solve problems using networks?

- How does investigating patterns, like the Chinese Postman Problem, help us better understand and utilize the spaces we live and work in?
- How can a methodical pattern, or algorithm, help solve real-world problems?
- What real-life problems can be modelled by networks?

Exploration 4

In 1960, Chinese mathematician Meigu Guan published work studying a problem in graph theory which has since become known as the Chinese Postman Problem. It is also known as the Route Inspection Problem, because you might consider the task of inspecting a network of roads thoroughly – every road must be visited individually, but ideally, you don't want to retrace your steps.

Consider a network of streets:

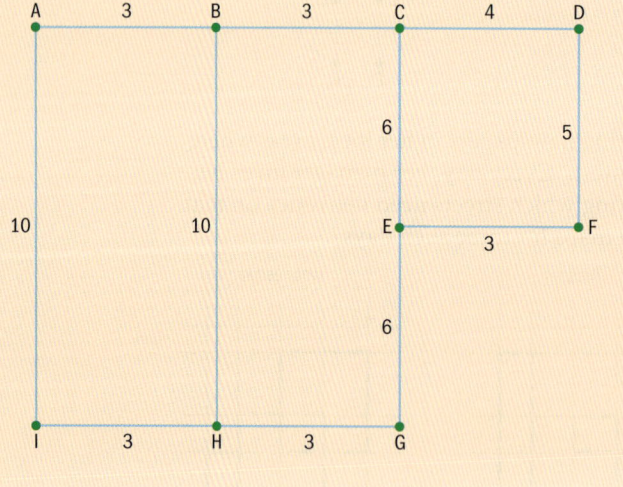

▶ Continued on next page

The weights on each edge represent the time taken to journey down that street (in minutes). A postman wishes to travel down every street and return to his starting point, traveling for the least amount of time possible.

1 Write down the order of each of the vertices of the graph.

2 Write down the total weight of the graph.

3 Hence explain why the postman will not be able to complete his task without walking along at least one street twice.

4 In order to make all of the vertices even, you can join together pairs of odd vertices. Explain why joining a pair of odd vertices (by repeating the road between them) will make the vertices even.

5 Since the odd vertices are B, C, H and E, the postman considers the following strategies for joining the odd vertices:

Pairs to join	Length of first added path	Length of second added path	Total additional length
B & C, E & H	BC = 3	EGH =	
B & E, C & H	BCE = 9	=	
B & H, C & E	= 10	CE = 6	16

Complete the table.

6 You have already found the total weight of the network. Determine which of the three above strategies would add the least additional time to the postman's journey.

7 Redraw the original graph with these routes doubled.

8 Hence find an Eulerian circuit starting and finishing at A.

Exploration 4 follows the steps of the standard solution to the Chinese Postman Problem. It guarantees that you will find the way of doubling routes in a network which adds the least weight though, if there are a lot of odd vertices, you have to be very careful to find all the possible sets of pairs to join and to calculate the shortest added routes carefully.

The method always follows the following steps:

1 Identify the graph's odd vertices.

2 Find all the different ways of partitioning the set of odd vertices into pairs.

3 For each way of partitioning the odd vertices, find the shortest route that joins the given pair of vertices and hence find the total weight that this pairing would add.

4 Choose the set of pairings which adds the least weight overall to the network. If more than one set has the same (least) weight, you may choose either.

Example 1

Determine the length of the shortest Eulerian circuit which traverses the network shown below. State which routes need doubling and one possible Eulerian circuit starting at A.

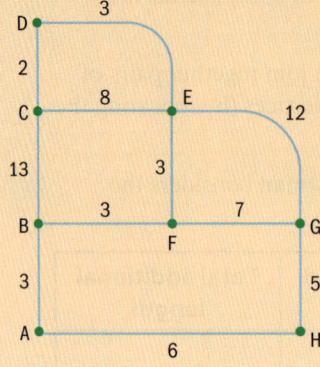

Notice that in this example, the shortest route from C to G was quite a complicated route, requiring four edges. It would be easy to miss this option. There are algorithms that help find the shortest route between two points on a graph: one of them is called Dijkstra's algorithm, and using it would be essential if you were dealing with a very complex network.

The odd vertices are B, C, F and G.

The total weight is $2 + 3 + 8 + 13 + 3 + 3 + 12 + 7 + 3 + 6 + 5 = 65$

In order to make all the vertices even, we could join the odd vertices in pairs as follows:

Possible pairs	Shortest 1st route	Shortest 2nd route	Total extra weight
BC & FG	BC = 13	FG = 7	20
BF & CG	BF = 3	CDEFG = 15	18
BG & CF	BFG = 10	CDEF = 8	18

We rule out BC & FG as a solution.

Since the other options add the same weight, we may pick either. —

In fact, the two other options involve duplicating exactly the same edges, but that doesn't matter.

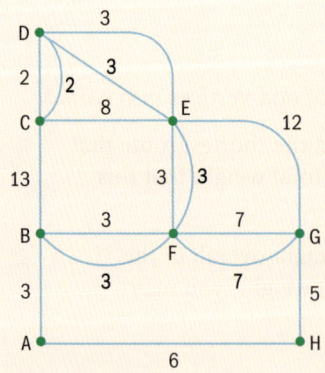

Redraw the graph, duplicating any paths needed for the solution you have chosen.

A possible route is ABFBCDCEDEFEGFGHA.

The total weight of the Eulerian circuit is $63 + 18 = 81$ —

The new total weight is found by adding the weight of the doubled edges to the original total weight.

Practice 2

1   A team of workers are repainting the central lines on a series of roads. The painting machine moves slowly (whether or not it is painting) so they wish to find the shortest route possible which takes in all of the roads, and then return to their start point so it can be loaded back onto their truck. This network shows the configuration of the roads and the weights are the times (in minutes) taken to travel down the road. They park at A.

By determining which roads they should travel down twice, find the minimum time needed for them to complete the task and the routes they need to duplicate. Suggest a possible route that they could take.

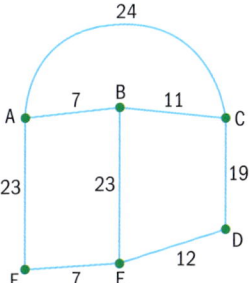

2   As part of her daily exercise regime, a pensioner decides that she will walk along every path in her local park. The paths and the times (in minutes) taken to walk along them are illustrated below. Her walk starts at the gate at A.

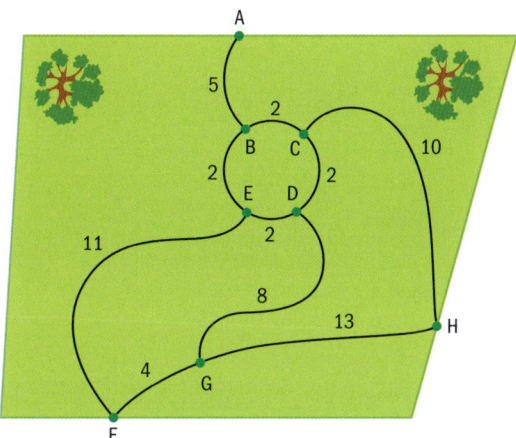

a   Explain why the route AB must be doubled.

b   Identify which other routes should be doubled so that her walk is as short as possible.

c   Find the total duration of her journey.

3 A snow plough is clearing the roads in a mountain village. The length of each section of road, in meters, is indicated below. Given that the snow plough must leave and return to the depot at A, find the length of the shortest possible route it can take around the village so that every road gets cleared.

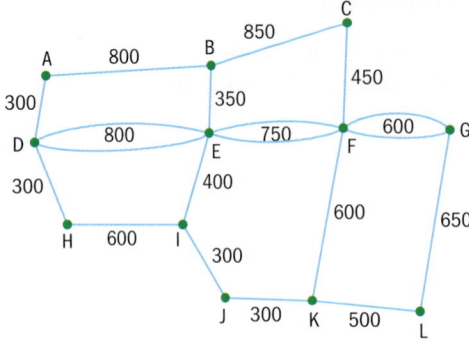

4 A school bus needs to travel at least once down every road of a housing estate. The bus enters and leaves the estate at A on the map below, where the weights represent the lengths of the roads in meters.

```
                        1000
            800        700            1000
         ┌───────────────────────────────┐
  200    │   200        200              │  200
         │800          700          1000 │
         │                               │
  200    │   200        200              │  200
       A●│800          700          1000 │
         │   200        200              │  200
  200    │800          700          1000 │
         │                               │
  200    │   200        200              │  200
         │800          700          1000 │
         └───────────────────────────────┘
                        1000
```

a Determine the total weight of the network.

b By considering the network's odd vertices, determine the minimum distance that the bus must travel if it is to journey down every road on the estate.

5 A child is playing in a playground and wants to walk around a netball court, covering every single line of the court (except the center circle) without leaving the lines at all. The dimensions of the court are as follows:

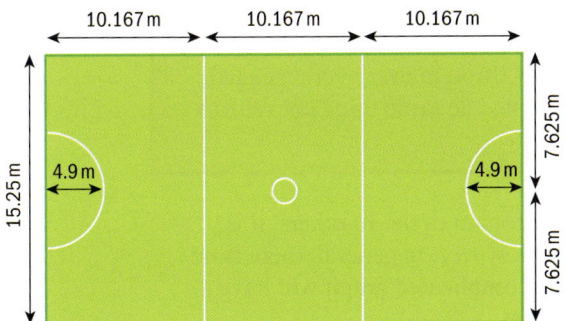

a Find the length of each of the semicircular arcs at each end of the court.

b Find the shortest distance from the semicircular arc to the corner of the court.

c Hence add weights to this graph to create a network showing the distances between different junctions around the court's edge.

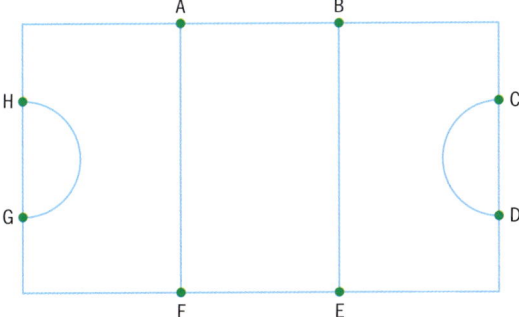

d Explain why at least four edges will need to be doubled in order to complete the journey.

e Write down the four shortest edges in this network along with their weights.

f Hence give an Eulerian circuit of the least weight for this network. Explain how you can be sure that your circuit is of the least weight without testing other possible routes.

D   **Are all network problems solvable?**

- Does the Traveling Salesman Problem facilitate or complicate the optimization of living and working structures?
- What is meant by an exhaustive search?
- What matters more: a quick solution or a perfect solution?

You are already familiar with an Eulerian circuit, a path through a network which travels along every edge.

A **Hamiltonian path** is a path which travels through every vertex exactly once. Furthermore, a **Hamiltonian cycle** does the same thing but returns to its starting vertex.

In some graphs it is very easy to find a Hamiltonian cycle. In others, it is very easy to show that no such cycle exists. However, in general, there is no quick method to determine whether or not a complicated graph will have a Hamiltonian path at all, or to find it if one does.

Exploration 5

1 For each graph, find a Hamiltonian cycle.

a 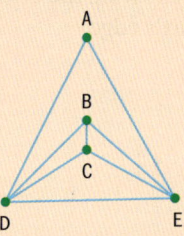 **b** 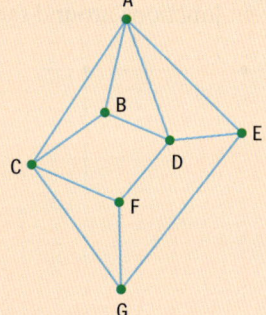 **c**

2 For each graph, explain why no Hamiltonian cycle exists.

a 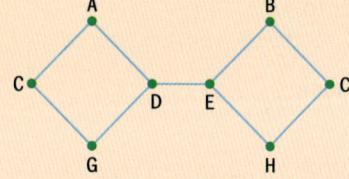 **b**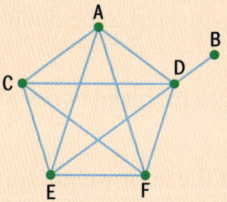

c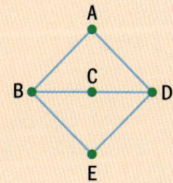

▶ Continued on next page

3 This complete network has three different Hamiltonian cycles.

a Write down the three cycles.

b Find the weight of each cycle.

c Hence find the shortest Hamiltonian cycle for this network.

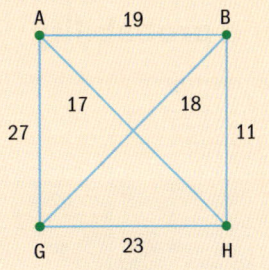

In general, the number of different Hamiltonian cycles for a complete graph with n vertices is given by $\frac{(n-1)!}{2}$. This is a function that grows very quickly as n increases. For example, letting $n = 10$ shows us that there are $181\,440$ different Hamiltonian cycles for a complete graph with 10 vertices. How long do you think it would take you to check all of the different possible cycles to work out which one was the shortest? Probably a very long time! In general, mathematicians try to avoid solutions which involve just checking lots of possibilities because it is time consuming.

Imagine you had tried to solve the Chinese Postman Problem by simply exploring all the possible combinations of edges you could double to see if it happened to create the best solution – it would take a very long time. However, some problems cannot be solved using easier methods than this. One such example is known as the Traveling Salesman Problem. The classic Traveling Salesman Problem considers the following scenario:

> Given a collection of cities, and a means of traveling directly between any given pair of them, what round-trip journey should be made to visit all of the cities whilst covering the least distance? This is the problem of finding the shortest Hamiltonian cycle for a given network.

In general, there no efficient method for solving the Traveling Salesman Problem which will guarantee the most efficient solution, though there are methods which at least guarantee that the solution would be acceptable.

Reflect and discuss 3

- An exhaustive method is one where every case needs to be tried in order to find a solution. What problems in this section have required exhaustive approaches?

- What is more important: getting the best solution to a problem, or getting an acceptable solution quickly?

ATL

Activity: Networks and probability

A coin is dropped into a slot at the top of a machine in an arcade. Its path through the machine is obstructed by a series of walls which force it to bounce either to the left or to the right, at random.

In this case, there are five possible end points for the coin (A–E). Would the coin be equally likely to land in any of them? Or would some outcomes be more likely than others?

1   Use your finger to trace some paths through the machine. By flipping a coin to decide whether to move left or right, generate some journeys at random. Record your results. Suggest whether you think the coin would be equally likely to land in any of the five end points or whether some would be more likely than others.

There are several ways that this machine could be represented using a **directed graph**. A directed graph is one where edges may only be followed in a certain direction.

▶ Continued on next page

2 Here is the beginning of one graph representation of this machine:

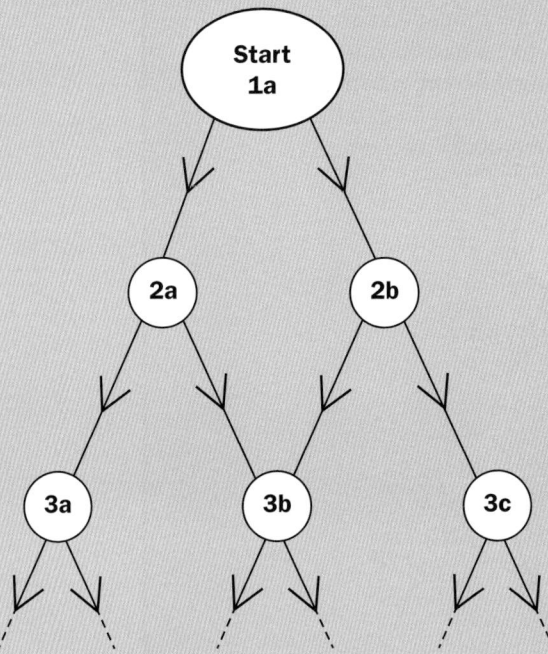

a Create a full representation of the machine. Give yourself enough space to add extra detail to the diagram.

b There is only one way of reaching vertex 2a, and only one way of reaching vertex 2b. Label each of these vertices with a 1.
There is also only one way of reaching each of vertices 3a and 3c. Label these vertices with a 1.
Determine the number of ways of reaching vertex 3b, and add this to your graph.

c Label the rest of the vertices in this manner. Write down anything that you notice about the pattern.

d Explain why the number of ways of reaching vertex 4c is equal to the sum of the number of ways of reaching vertices 3b and 3c.

e By looking at the number of different routes which would take you to each of the end points, find the probability of reaching each of the end points A–E.

▶ Continued on next page

3 Another representation would be to draw a weighted graph showing probabilities on each of the branches, like a tree diagram. By multiplying probabilities together along different branches, and adding together the probabilities where different routes lead to the same place, each vertex can also be labelled with a probability.

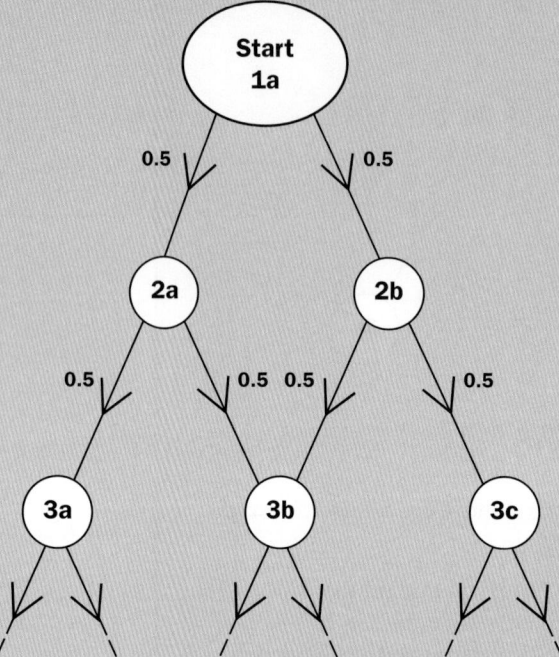

a Explain why the probability of a coin reaching vertex 3a is 0.25.

b Explain why the probability of a coin reaching vertex 3b is 0.5.

c By multiplying and adding, find the probabilities that the coin reaches each of the vertices in the fourth and fifth rows.

d Compare your probabilities to the values that you obtained in question **2**. How are they related?

4 The values for the vertices in question **2** are the same as the values in Pascal's Triangle. Can you explain why this is?

5 Suppose the whole system was tilted, so the probability of a coin going left was 0.6 and the probability of a coin going right was 0.4. Which type of graph do you think would be better evaluating probabilities? Investigate games where the probability of going left is not the same as the probability of going right.

Summary

A **graph** is a collection of points, known as **vertices**.

Those vertices may be joined to each other. The connections are known as **edges**.

The **order** of a vertex is the number of edges connected to it.

A graph is **complete** if every vertex is connected directly to every other vertex by an edge.

A graph is **connected** if every point on the graph may be reached from any other point on the graph, traveling along several edges if needed. If not, it is **disconnected**.

Every edge on a **weighted graph** has a value, or **weight**, associated with it.

Weighted graphs are also known as **networks**.

The **total weight** of the network is the sum of all the weights of the individual edges.

A **walk** is any route through a graph.

A **trail** is a walk which repeats no edges.

A **circuit** is a trail which starts and ends at the same vertex.

A **path** is a route through a graph from one vertex to another which does not pass through a vertex more than once.

A **cycle** is a path which starts and ends at the same vertex, but does not pass through any vertex more than once.

A graph is **traversable** if you can draw it without taking your pen off the paper or retracing your steps.

A connected graph with only even vertices is traversable. It may be traversed starting from any point on the graph and the trail will end where it started. It therefore has an **Eulerian circuit**.

A connected graph with exactly two odd vertices is traversable. Any trail which traverses the graph will start at one odd vertex and end at the other. It therefore has an **Eulerian trail**.

A connected graph with more than two odd vertices has neither an Eulerian circuit nor an Eulerian trail and so is non-traversable.

Mixed practice

1   Copy and complete the table showing the properties of the graphs **a–i**.
    The first row has been completed for you.

Graph	Connected	Complete	Has an Eulerian circuit	Has an Eulerian trail	Non-traversable
a	Y	Y	N	N	Y
b					
...					

 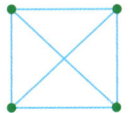  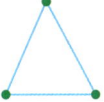

a   b   c

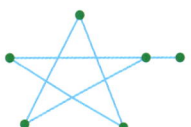 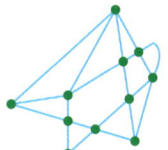 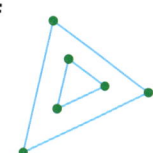

d   e   f

g 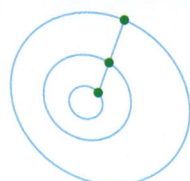   h 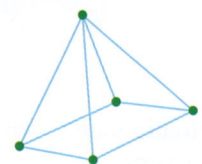   i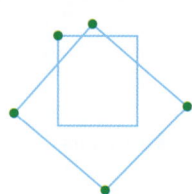

2 An engineer is designing a part to make on a 3D printer. The shape is built in layers, each of which has a cross-section of a regular hexagon with sides 1 cm. The moving head of the printer will follow the lines of the design. For support, some additional lines are added inside the hexagon. The engineer considers two possible designs:

A
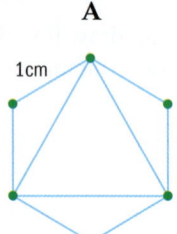
1cm

B
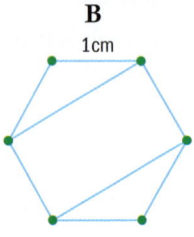
1cm

a **Find** the length of the interior supports.

b **Determine** which design uses more plastic.

c **Show** that one design has an Eulerian circuit but the other does not.

d Assuming the printer head follows the marked lines and heads back to its initial position when finished, **find** the total distance moved by the head for each design.

e Hence **determine** the design which requires less movement overall.

3 A forest warden needs to inspect every path in some woodland to check the safety of the paths. The route is completed on a quad bike, so short cuts through the woods are not possible.

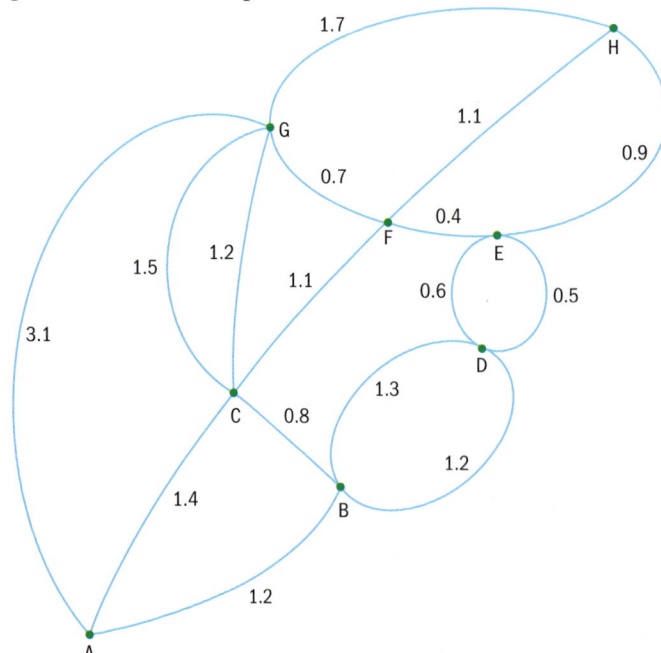

The quad bike is stored in a garage at A, so the inspection route must start and finish here. **Determine** the minimum total distance that the warden must travel to cover all the paths.

4 **Determine** Hamiltonian cycles for each of these networks, starting at A.

a
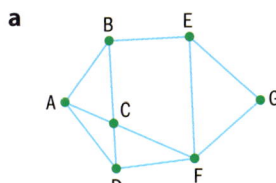

b
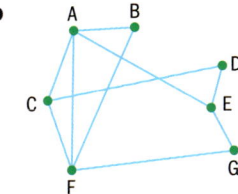

c
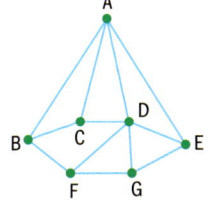

d
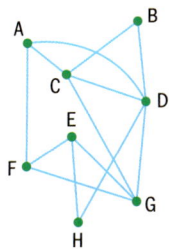

5 A network of four cities are connected by train lines as illustrated. The weights of the edges are the costs, in euros, of tickets to travel along those routes. A tourist wishes to visit all four cities but to spend the least possible amount on tickets. **Determine** the least expensive route, starting and finishing at A.

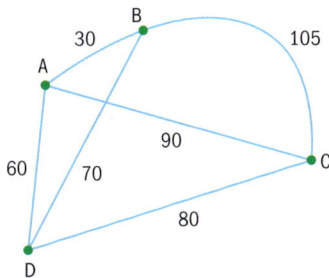

Review in context

A charity raises funds in order to replace the out-dated network cables which connect a group of university buildings. The cables are to run through existing service tunnels, which connect directly to the locations of the server rooms in each building. Because it is a charity-funded project, it is important to keep costs as low as possible.

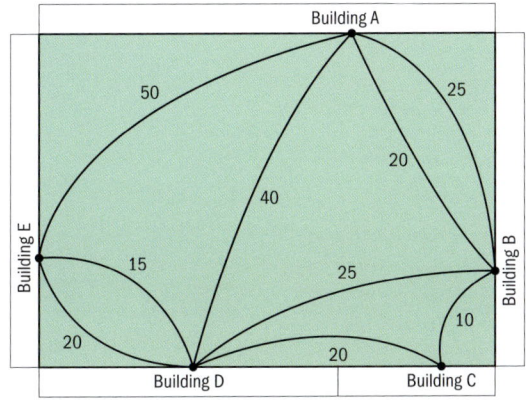

1   The engineer's first task is to inspect all of the tunnels to check that they are suitable for cabling. Transporting the inspection equipment is expensive and so the engineer only wants to enter and leave the tunnel system once.

   a   Suppose that the engineer can start and finish at any point on the network. **Explain** where the start and finish point should be, in order to complete the inspection while traveling the shortest possible distance. **Determine** the total distance that will be covered.

   b   Before starting the process, a colleague tells the engineer that the 20 m tunnel joining A to B is flooded and completely impassable. **Explain** how the engineer should modify the plans in order to travel the least distance whilst inspecting all the tunnels.

   c   On closer inspection, only the access hatch in building C is large enough to allow the inspection equipment into the tunnels. Given that the flooded tunnel is still impassable, **determine** an optimal route to inspect the tunnels, starting and finishing at C, and **calculate** the length of the route.

2   The engineer determines that cabling which follows a Hamiltonian path would be an appropriate way to connect the buildings.

   a   **Explain** why a Hamiltonian path is an appropriate way of connecting the buildings.

   b   **Determine** the Hamiltonian path of least weight for this network, assuming the flooded tunnel cannot be used, and hence find the total length of tunnel which will need to have cables added.

Reflect and discuss 4

Have you explored the statement of inquiry? Give specific examples.

Statement of inquiry:

Using logic to develop patterns and understanding the properties of space can help design models to use resources responsibly and efficiently.

E11.2 Vectors

Global context: Fairness and development

Related concept: Space

Objectives

- Describing translations using vectors
- Adding and subtracting vectors
- Multiplying a vector by a scalar
- Finding the magnitude of a vector
- Finding the dot product of two vectors
- Using the dot product to find the angle between two vectors
- Solving geometric problems using vectors

Inquiry questions

F
- What is a vector?
- How do you find the magnitude of a vector?

C
- How do you perform mathematical operations on vectors?

D
- How do vectors define the spaces in which we live and work?
- How does form influence function?

LOGIC

ATL Critical-thinking

Consider ideas from multiple perspectives

Statement of inquiry:

Using logic to develop patterns and understanding the properties of space can help design models to use resources responsibly and efficiently.

📑 **Launch additional digital resources for this chapter.**

You should already know how to:

find the distance between two points	**1** Find the distance between each pair of points: **a** (4, 7) and (11, 5) **b** (−3, −2) and (1, 1)
solve linear simultaneous equations	**2** Solve the simultaneous equations: $3x + 5y = 5$ $2x + y = 1$
use the cosine rule	**3** Find the size of angle *A*.

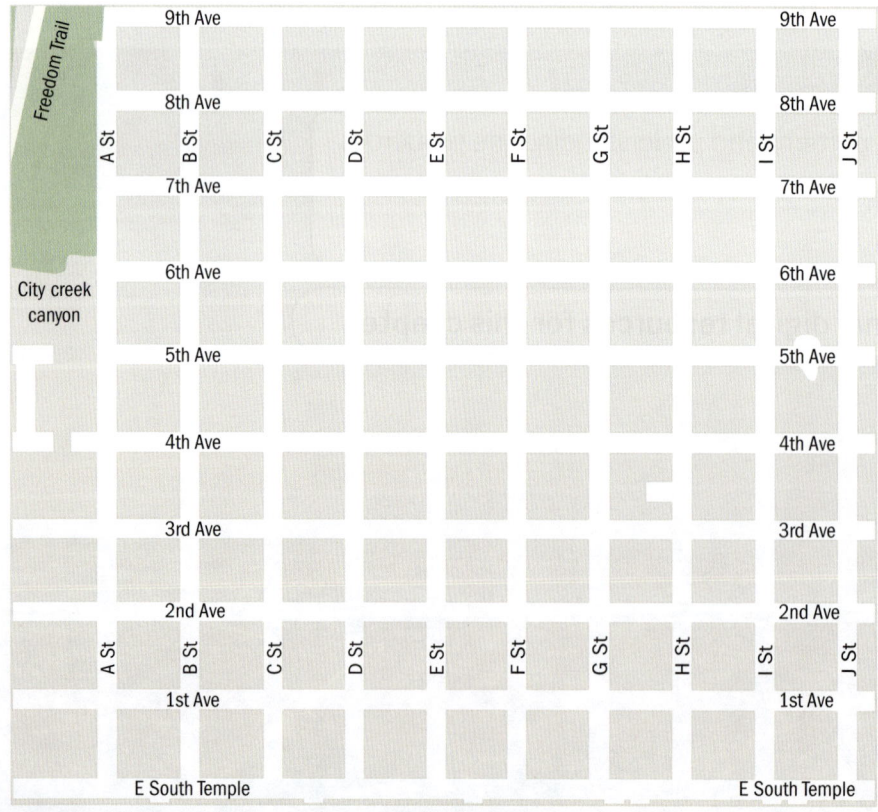

F Introduction to vectors

- What is a vector?
- How do you find the magnitude of a vector?

The map shows part of Salt Lake City, USA, which has a grid layout.

You can give directions in this area of Salt Lake City by giving the number of blocks to travel in an east-west direction, and in the north-south direction.

> A block is the distance between two adjacent intersections.

Exploration 1

1 Using the map of Salt Lake City, write down instructions to get from:

   a the intersection of A Street and 1st Avenue to the intersection of H Street and 3rd Avenue

   b the intersection of D Street and 2nd Avenue to the intersection of G Street and 7th Avenue

   c the intersection of F Street and 3rd Avenue to the intersection of A Street and 6th Avenue.

2 You can use a column vector to represent a translation from one point to another.

   The column vector $\begin{pmatrix} 3 \\ 4 \end{pmatrix}$ means 3 units right and 4 units up.

   Describe these translations in words:

   a $\begin{pmatrix} 1 \\ 3 \end{pmatrix}$ **b** $\begin{pmatrix} 8 \\ 7 \end{pmatrix}$ **c** $\begin{pmatrix} 2 \\ 4 \end{pmatrix}$ **d** $\begin{pmatrix} 4 \\ 2 \end{pmatrix}$

3 The column vector $\begin{pmatrix} -3 \\ -4 \end{pmatrix}$ means 3 units left and 4 units down.

   Using the map, write down the column vector for the journey from:

   a the intersection of A Street and 3rd Avenue to the intersection of C Street and 8th Avenue

   b the intersection of J Street and 4th Avenue to the intersection of B Street and 8th Avenue

   c the intersection of C Street and 8th Avenue to the intersection of G Street and 3rd Avenue.

4 For each vector below, start at the intersection of F Street and 5th Avenue. Write down your final position after a translation of:

   a $\begin{pmatrix} 2 \\ 2 \end{pmatrix}$ **b** $\begin{pmatrix} 3 \\ -1 \end{pmatrix}$ **c** $\begin{pmatrix} 4 \\ 0 \end{pmatrix}$ **d** $\begin{pmatrix} -2 \\ 4 \end{pmatrix}$ **e** $\begin{pmatrix} -3 \\ -4 \end{pmatrix}$ **f** $\begin{pmatrix} 0 \\ -3 \end{pmatrix}$

You will usually use column vectors to describe translations on a coordinate grid.

A **column vector** describes a translation.

A column vector has an x component and a y component: $\begin{pmatrix} x \\ y \end{pmatrix}$

The x component tells you how far to move in the x-direction.

The y component tells you how far to move in the y-direction.

▶ Continued on next page

$\overrightarrow{AB}$ is the vector representing the translation from A to B.

On this grid, $\overrightarrow{AB} = \begin{pmatrix} 3 \\ 1 \end{pmatrix}$

The **position vector** of a point is the vector from the origin O to the point.

On this grid, $\overrightarrow{OA} = \begin{pmatrix} 1 \\ 2 \end{pmatrix}$

$\begin{pmatrix} 0 \\ 0 \end{pmatrix}$ is the **zero vector**. It is the position vector of the origin.

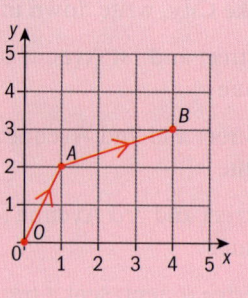

Example 1

A is the point $(4, 9)$ and B is the point $(6, 4)$.

Find $\overrightarrow{AB}$.

$\overrightarrow{AB} = \begin{pmatrix} 6 - 4 \\ 4 - 9 \end{pmatrix} = \begin{pmatrix} 2 \\ -5 \end{pmatrix}$ ———— From A to B you move 2 units right and 5 units down.

Reflect and discuss 1

- How does the vector $\overrightarrow{AB} = \begin{pmatrix} 2 \\ -5 \end{pmatrix}$ relate to the coordinates of points A and B?

- What operation would you perform to find the vector $\overrightarrow{AB}$ if you knew the coordinates of A and B?

- How could you find the vector $\overrightarrow{BA}$ from the coordinates of A and B?

Practice 1

1 **a** Write down the column vectors for these translations on the grid.

   i $\overrightarrow{AB}$ **ii** $\overrightarrow{AC}$ **iii** $\overrightarrow{AF}$

   iv $\overrightarrow{GF}$ **v** $\overrightarrow{OD}$ **vi** $\overrightarrow{OC}$

   b Write down the column vectors for:

   i $\overrightarrow{AD}$ and $\overrightarrow{DA}$ **ii** $\overrightarrow{EG}$ and $\overrightarrow{GE}$

   c Conjecture the relationship between vectors of the form $\overrightarrow{PQ}$ and $\overrightarrow{QP}$.

   d Write down the position vector of:

   i A **ii** B **iii** C **iv** O

   e Write down the point with position vector:

   i $\begin{pmatrix} -1 \\ -1 \end{pmatrix}$ **ii** $\begin{pmatrix} -3 \\ 3 \end{pmatrix}$ **iii** $\begin{pmatrix} 2 \\ -4 \end{pmatrix}$

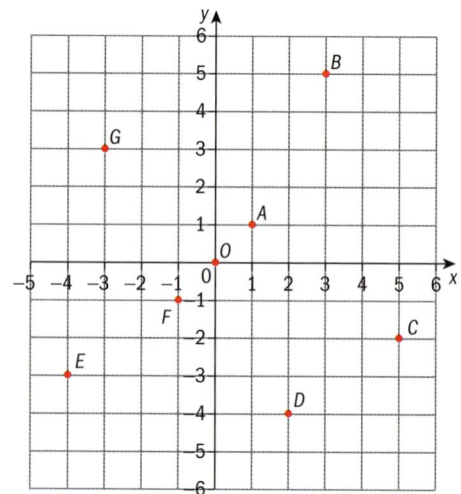

2 On this grid, find two points so that the translation from one to the other is:

a $\begin{pmatrix} 0 \\ 4 \end{pmatrix}$ **b** $\begin{pmatrix} 3 \\ -1 \end{pmatrix}$ **c** $\begin{pmatrix} -5 \\ -1 \end{pmatrix}$ **d** $\begin{pmatrix} 4 \\ -3 \end{pmatrix}$

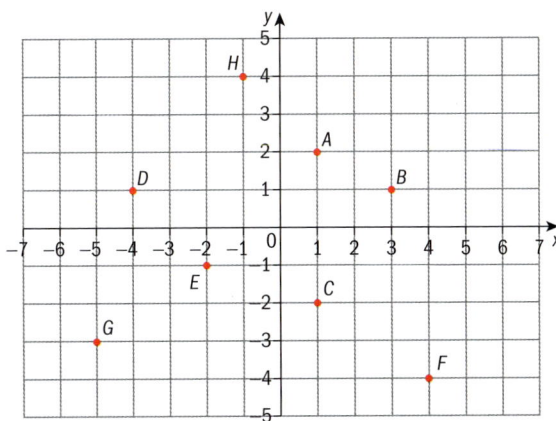

3 On a clean grid, mark the point A with coordinates (3, 4). Write down the coordinates obtained when each of the following translations is applied to A:

a $\begin{pmatrix} 2 \\ 5 \end{pmatrix}$ **b** $\begin{pmatrix} -2 \\ 4 \end{pmatrix}$ **c** $\begin{pmatrix} -3 \\ -1 \end{pmatrix}$ **d** $\begin{pmatrix} 11 \\ -9 \end{pmatrix}$

4 Write down the vector that translates:

a $M(-2, 4)$ to $N(1, 6)$ **b** $P(4, 6)$ to $Q(11, 3)$

c $R(11, -2)$ to $S(7, 5)$ **d** $T(-5, 1)$ to $U(-6, -3)$

Problem solving

5 $\overrightarrow{CD} = \begin{pmatrix} -2 \\ 4 \end{pmatrix}$. Write down the column vector $\overrightarrow{DC}$.

6 Point A has position vector $\begin{pmatrix} 4 \\ 2 \end{pmatrix}$. $\overrightarrow{AB} = \begin{pmatrix} 2 \\ -6 \end{pmatrix}$ and $\overrightarrow{BC} = \begin{pmatrix} -3 \\ 5 \end{pmatrix}$.

a Show points A, B and C on suitable axes.

b Write down the position vector of point C.

7 Write down three pairs of points, where one transforms to the other by the translation $\begin{pmatrix} -5 \\ 3 \end{pmatrix}$.

A journey of $\begin{pmatrix} 2 \\ 2 \end{pmatrix}$ is shown on this section

of the Salt Lake City map.
The length of the journey is 4 blocks.

The larger map, on the next page,
shows different journeys of length 4 blocks.
Each is labelled with a vector: **a**, **b**, **c**, etc.

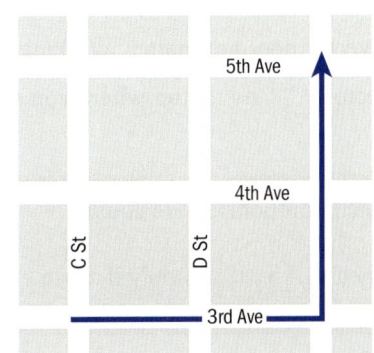

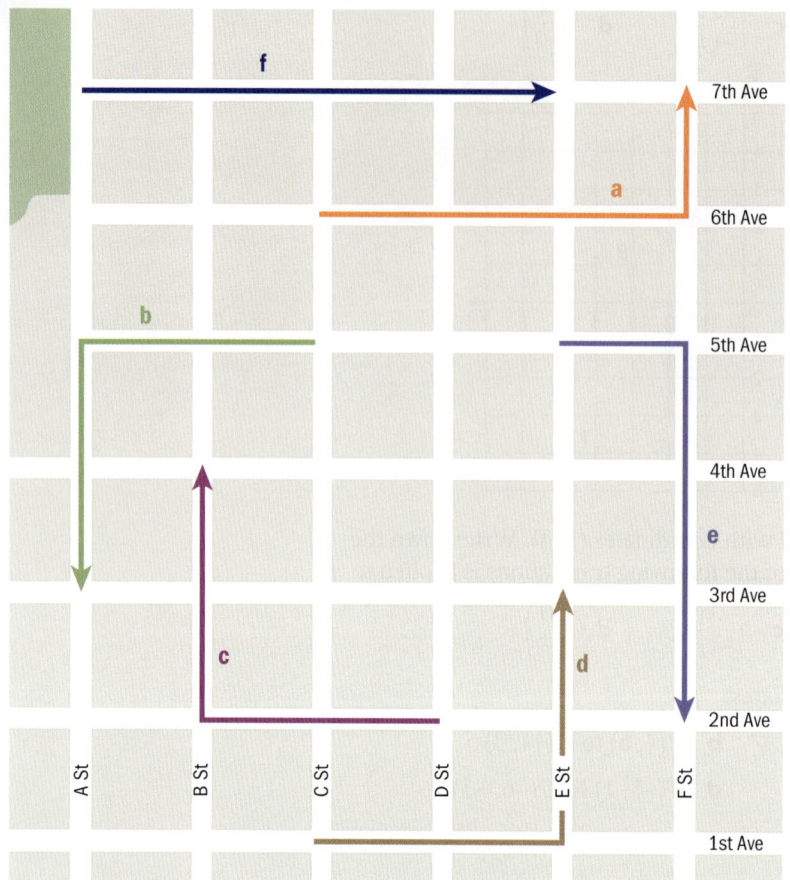

Single letter vectors are printed in **bold**. When writing vectors by hand, in some countries the convention is to underline them, e.g. <u>a</u>, <u>b</u>, and in others they are written with an arrow above, e.g. $\vec{a}$, $\vec{b}$.

ATL

Reflect and discuss 2

- Are any of the journeys shown on the larger map the same as the one on the smaller map on the previous page?

- What does it mean for two journeys to be the same as each other?

Vectors are equal if their components are equal. This means that they are equal if they represent journeys that have exactly the same instructions. Two vectors are not equal if they point in different directions, even if the length of the journey is the same.

The starting position of the vector does not matter. Walking two blocks east and two blocks south has vector $\begin{pmatrix} 2 \\ -2 \end{pmatrix}$, no matter where you start from.

Two vectors are equal if their components are equal.

If $\mathbf{v}_1 = \begin{pmatrix} x_1 \\ y_1 \end{pmatrix}$ and $\mathbf{v}_2 = \begin{pmatrix} x_2 \\ y_2 \end{pmatrix}$ then $\mathbf{v}_1 = \mathbf{v}_2$ if and only if $x_1 = x_2$ and $y_1 = y_2$.

Exploration 2

1 A hiker walks 3 miles due east and then 4 miles due north.

    a Sketch her walk.

    b Write down the total distance she walks.

    c Find the shortest distance between her starting position and ending position.

2 $\overrightarrow{AB} = \begin{pmatrix} 5 \\ -12 \end{pmatrix}$

    The diagram represents the vector $\overrightarrow{AB}$.

    Find the shortest distance from A to B.

3 $\overrightarrow{CD} = \begin{pmatrix} x \\ y \end{pmatrix}$

    a Sketch a diagram to represent this vector.

    b Find the shortest distance from C to D in terms of x and y.

The length of a vector, or the (shortest) distance from one end of the vector to the other, is called the **magnitude** of the vector. The magnitude of vector **v** is written $|\mathbf{v}|$.

The components of a vector represent perpendicular distances, so you can use Pythagoras' theorem to find the vector's magnitude.

$|\mathbf{v}|$, the magnitude of $\mathbf{v} = \begin{pmatrix} x \\ y \end{pmatrix}$, is given by $|\mathbf{v}| = \sqrt{x^2 + y^2}$.

Example 2

$A = (4, 11)$ and $B = (-3, 7)$. Find $|\overrightarrow{AB}|$. Give your answer correct to 3 s.f.

$\overrightarrow{AB} = \begin{pmatrix} -7 \\ -4 \end{pmatrix}$

$|\overrightarrow{AB}| = \sqrt{(-7)^2 + (-4)^2}$ —————————— $|\mathbf{v}| = \sqrt{x^2 + y^2}$

$\qquad = \sqrt{65}$

$\qquad = 8.06 \text{ (3 s.f.)}$

Vectors **a** and **b** both have the same magnitude:

$$|\mathbf{a}| = \sqrt{5^2 + 5^2} = \sqrt{50} \text{ and } |\mathbf{b}| = \sqrt{7^2 + (-1)^2} = \sqrt{50}$$

But **a** and **b** are not equal because they have different components:

$$\mathbf{a} = \begin{pmatrix} 5 \\ 5 \end{pmatrix} \text{ and } \mathbf{b} = \begin{pmatrix} 7 \\ -1 \end{pmatrix}.$$

Even though their lengths are the same, they point in different directions.

Vectors **a** and **c** are parallel, but their directions are opposite. Therefore, **a** = −**c**, or **c** = −**a**.

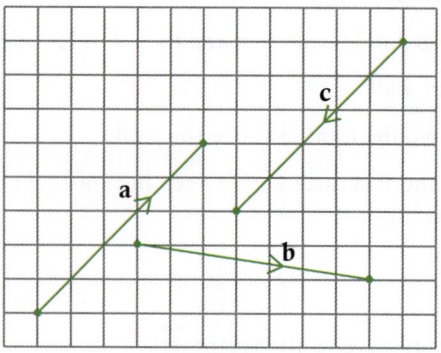

A vector has both magnitude and direction. A scalar quantity does not have a direction. For two vectors to be equal, they must have the same magnitude and direction.

Numbers are scalar quantities. Speed is a scalar quantity, but velocity (defined as speed in a given direction) is a vector quantity. Force is also a vector quantity. The force you experience due to gravity has a size or magnitude (your weight) and a direction (down).

Practice 2

1 Find the magnitude of each vector:

a $\begin{pmatrix} 7 \\ 24 \end{pmatrix}$ **b** $\begin{pmatrix} 3 \\ 4 \end{pmatrix}$ **c** $\begin{pmatrix} 8 \\ -6 \end{pmatrix}$

2 Find the magnitude of each vector. Give your answers in exact form.

a $\begin{pmatrix} -3 \\ 4 \end{pmatrix}$ **b** $\begin{pmatrix} 1 \\ 3 \end{pmatrix}$ **c** $\begin{pmatrix} 2 \\ 4 \end{pmatrix}$

d $\begin{pmatrix} -5 \\ 5 \end{pmatrix}$ **e** $\begin{pmatrix} -5 \\ 12 \end{pmatrix}$ **f** $\begin{pmatrix} 16 \\ 5 \end{pmatrix}$

3 Find the magnitude of each vector. Give your answers correct to 3 s.f.

a $\begin{pmatrix} 4 \\ 5 \end{pmatrix}$ **b** $\begin{pmatrix} 2 \\ -8 \end{pmatrix}$ **c** $\begin{pmatrix} -4 \\ -2 \end{pmatrix}$

d $\begin{pmatrix} 13 \\ -2 \end{pmatrix}$ **e** $\begin{pmatrix} 8 \\ 4 \end{pmatrix}$ **f** $\begin{pmatrix} -6 \\ -11 \end{pmatrix}$

4 For each vector $\overrightarrow{AB}$ find $|\overrightarrow{AB}|$.

a $\overrightarrow{AB} = \begin{pmatrix} 0 \\ -6 \end{pmatrix}$ **b** $\overrightarrow{AB} = \begin{pmatrix} -10 \\ 24 \end{pmatrix}$ **c** $\overrightarrow{AB} = \begin{pmatrix} 24 \\ -7 \end{pmatrix}$

d $\overrightarrow{AB} = \begin{pmatrix} 0.28 \\ -0.96 \end{pmatrix}$ **e** $\overrightarrow{AB} = \begin{pmatrix} 8 \\ -6 \end{pmatrix}$ **f** $\overrightarrow{AB} = \begin{pmatrix} -4 \\ 3 \end{pmatrix}$

5 For each pair of points A and B, find $|\overrightarrow{AB}|$ correct to 3 s.f.

a $A(1, 5)$ and $B(2, -4)$ **b** $A(4, 6)$ and $B(3, 3)$

c $A(-1, -6)$ and $B(2, 7)$ **d** $A(3, 5)$ and $B(5.8, 11.2)$

e $A(11, 4)$ and $B(4.5, 23.8)$ **f** $A(8.7, 5.3)$ and $B(2.1, -14.6)$

Problem solving

6 Four points, $A(1, 7)$, $B(6, 2)$, $C(3, -3)$ and $D(2, 4)$ lie in a plane.

Show that $|\overrightarrow{AB}| = |\overrightarrow{CD}|$.

7 Points A and B lie in a plane, and A has coordinates $(6, -2)$.

Find four possible positions for B such that $|\overrightarrow{AB}| = \sqrt{13}$.

8 The vectors $\mathbf{u} = \begin{pmatrix} 2x \\ y \end{pmatrix}$ and $\mathbf{v} = \begin{pmatrix} 7x - 10 \\ 3 - x \end{pmatrix}$ are equal.

Determine the values of x and y.

9 The vectors $\mathbf{u} = \begin{pmatrix} x^2 \\ 3x \end{pmatrix}$ and $\mathbf{v} = \begin{pmatrix} 7x - 10 \\ x^2 + 2 \end{pmatrix}$ are equal.

Determine the value of x.

- -

C Operations with vectors

- How do you perform mathematical operations on vectors?

The diagram shows two journeys in Salt Lake City:

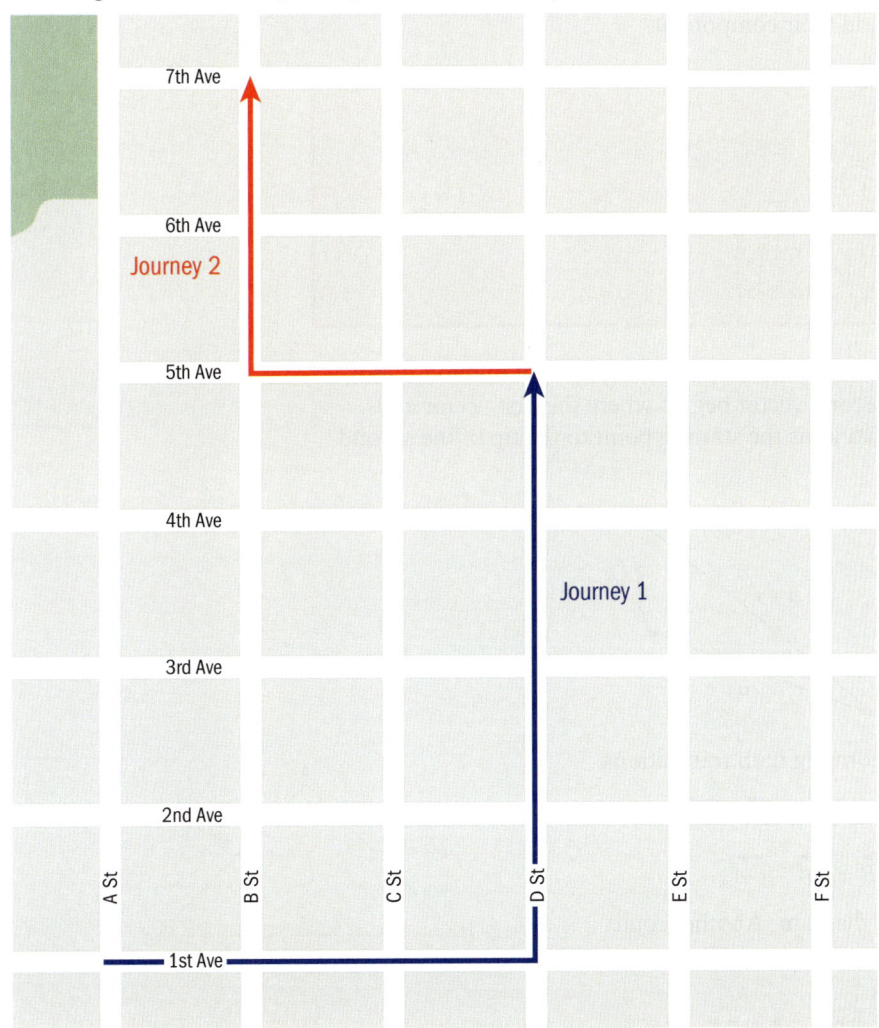

Journey 1 then Journey 2 = Whole journey

$$\begin{pmatrix} 3 \\ 4 \end{pmatrix} \text{ then } \begin{pmatrix} -2 \\ 2 \end{pmatrix} = \begin{pmatrix} 1 \\ 6 \end{pmatrix}$$

Reflect and discuss 3

What do you notice about:

- the relationship between the x components of the LHS and RHS?
- the relationship between the y components of the LHS and RHS?

A translation from A to B followed by a translation from B to C is the same as the translation from A to C: $\overrightarrow{AB} + \overrightarrow{BC} = \overrightarrow{AC}$

$\overrightarrow{AC}$ is sometimes called the **resultant** of $\overrightarrow{AB}$ and $\overrightarrow{BC}$.

To add vectors you simply add their components.

The vector addition law:

If $\overrightarrow{AB} = \begin{pmatrix} x_1 \\ y_1 \end{pmatrix}$ and $\overrightarrow{BC} = \begin{pmatrix} x_2 \\ y_2 \end{pmatrix}$ then

$$\overrightarrow{AC} = \overrightarrow{AB} + \overrightarrow{BC} = \begin{pmatrix} x_1 \\ y_1 \end{pmatrix} + \begin{pmatrix} x_2 \\ y_2 \end{pmatrix} = \begin{pmatrix} x_1 + x_2 \\ y_1 + y_2 \end{pmatrix}$$

You can also draw diagrams to add vectors using a graphical method. Draw the two vectors so that the second vector begins where the first vector ends. The resultant is the vector that joins the starting point to the tip of the second vector:

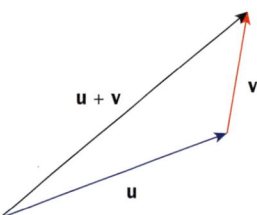

This shows the result of performing both translations.

Using the vector addition law: $\overrightarrow{OA} + \overrightarrow{AB} = \overrightarrow{OB}$.

You can rearrange this to $\overrightarrow{AB} = \overrightarrow{OB} - \overrightarrow{OA}$.

You can also see this on the diagram. Another route from A to B is:

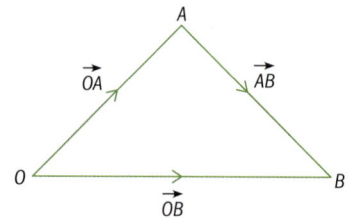

$\qquad$ A to O, then O to B

or $\qquad$ $\overrightarrow{AO} + \overrightarrow{OB} = -\overrightarrow{OA} + \overrightarrow{OB} = \overrightarrow{OB} - \overrightarrow{OA}$

For any two points A and B, $\overrightarrow{AB} = \overrightarrow{OB} - \overrightarrow{OA}$.

Reflect and discuss 4

Explain why $\overrightarrow{AB} + \overrightarrow{BA}$ must be equal to the zero vector.
Hence explain why $\overrightarrow{AB} = -\overrightarrow{BA}$.

Example 3

A is the point $(2, 11)$ and B is the point $(-3, 6)$. Find $\overrightarrow{AB}$.

$\overrightarrow{OA} = \begin{pmatrix} 2 \\ 11 \end{pmatrix}$ $\overrightarrow{OB} = \begin{pmatrix} -3 \\ 6 \end{pmatrix}$ —————————————— Write down $\overrightarrow{OA}$ and $\overrightarrow{OB}$.

$\overrightarrow{AB} = \overrightarrow{OB} - \overrightarrow{OA} = \begin{pmatrix} -3 \\ 6 \end{pmatrix} - \begin{pmatrix} 2 \\ 11 \end{pmatrix} = \begin{pmatrix} -5 \\ -5 \end{pmatrix}$

Example 4

A has coordinates $(a, 3a)$, B has coordinates $(b, b-6)$, and $\overrightarrow{AB} = \begin{pmatrix} 4 \\ -8 \end{pmatrix}$.

Find the values of a and b.

$\overrightarrow{OA} = \begin{pmatrix} a \\ 3a \end{pmatrix}$ $\overrightarrow{OB} = \begin{pmatrix} b \\ b-6 \end{pmatrix}$

$\overrightarrow{AB} = \overrightarrow{OB} - \overrightarrow{OA} = \begin{pmatrix} b-a \\ b-6-3a \end{pmatrix} = \begin{pmatrix} 4 \\ -8 \end{pmatrix}$

$\begin{array}{l} b - a = 4 \\ b - 6 - 3a = -8 \\ b - 3a = -2 \end{array}$ —————————— The components of $\overrightarrow{AB}$ are equal to the components of $\overrightarrow{AB}$ given in the question.

$\begin{array}{l} 2a = 6 \\ a = 3, b = 7 \end{array}$ —————————— Solve the simultaneous equations.

Practice 3

1 Find $\overrightarrow{AC}$ for each pair of vectors:

a $\overrightarrow{AB} = \begin{pmatrix} 3 \\ -1 \end{pmatrix}$ and $\overrightarrow{BC} = \begin{pmatrix} -2 \\ 6 \end{pmatrix}$

b $\overrightarrow{AB} = \begin{pmatrix} -2 \\ 4 \end{pmatrix}$ and $\overrightarrow{BC} = \begin{pmatrix} 10 \\ -5 \end{pmatrix}$

c $\overrightarrow{AB} = \begin{pmatrix} 0 \\ 6 \end{pmatrix}$ and $\overrightarrow{BC} = \begin{pmatrix} -5 \\ 11 \end{pmatrix}$

d $\overrightarrow{AB} = \begin{pmatrix} -9 \\ 12 \end{pmatrix}$ and $\overrightarrow{BC} = \begin{pmatrix} 9 \\ -12 \end{pmatrix}$

e $\overrightarrow{AB} = \begin{pmatrix} -8 \\ -3 \end{pmatrix}$ and $\overrightarrow{BC} = \begin{pmatrix} 2 \\ -1 \end{pmatrix}$

2 Find the vectors $\overrightarrow{AB}$ and $\overrightarrow{BA}$ for each pair of coordinates:

    a $A(0, 7)$ and $B(-1, 0)$ **b** $A(-1, 3)$ and $B(4, 2)$

    c $A(5, -2)$ and $B(-6, 8)$ **d** $A(3, -9)$ and $B(12, -9)$

    e $A(-2, 0)$ and $B(-11, -7)$

3 $\overrightarrow{AB} = \begin{pmatrix} -3 \\ -7 \end{pmatrix}$ and point A is $(-12, 3)$. Find the coordinates of point B.

Problem solving

4 $\overrightarrow{AB} = \begin{pmatrix} -3 \\ -7 \end{pmatrix}$. Find the values of a and b for these coordinate pairs:

    a $A(2a, a - 1)$ and $B(3b, b - 7)$

    b $A(-3a + 1, a + 4)$ and $B(b - 3, b)$

    c $A(2a + 4, 3a - 5)$ and $B(2b + 1, -2b + 3)$

Exploration 3

1 On squared paper, draw the vectors $\mathbf{a} = \begin{pmatrix} 3 \\ 6 \end{pmatrix}$, $\mathbf{b} = \begin{pmatrix} 5 \\ 10 \end{pmatrix}$ and $\mathbf{c} = \begin{pmatrix} 8 \\ 16 \end{pmatrix}$.

State what the vectors have in common.

Draw a fourth vector, $\mathbf{d}$, that has the same property.

2 Explain why for any non-zero vector $\mathbf{v}$, $\mathbf{v} + \mathbf{v}$ must be parallel to $\mathbf{v}$.

3 a Determine which of these vectors are parallel to each other:

$$\begin{pmatrix} 4 \\ 5 \end{pmatrix} \quad \begin{pmatrix} 2 \\ -8 \end{pmatrix} \quad \begin{pmatrix} 26 \\ -4 \end{pmatrix} \quad \begin{pmatrix} 3 \\ -12 \end{pmatrix} \quad \begin{pmatrix} -4 \\ -2 \end{pmatrix} \quad \begin{pmatrix} -16 \\ -20 \end{pmatrix}$$

$$\begin{pmatrix} 13 \\ -2 \end{pmatrix} \quad \begin{pmatrix} 8 \\ 4 \end{pmatrix} \quad \begin{pmatrix} -6 \\ -11 \end{pmatrix} \quad \begin{pmatrix} -5 \\ 20 \end{pmatrix} \quad \begin{pmatrix} 30 \\ 15 \end{pmatrix}$$

    b Hence find which vector is not parallel to any of the others.

4 For any vector $\mathbf{v} = \begin{pmatrix} x \\ y \end{pmatrix}$, $k\mathbf{v} = \begin{pmatrix} kx \\ ky \end{pmatrix}$.

Explain why $k\mathbf{v}$ and $\mathbf{v}$ are parallel to each other.

Scalar multiplication of a vector:

For any vector $\mathbf{v} = \begin{pmatrix} x \\ y \end{pmatrix}$ and any scalar value k, $k\mathbf{v} = \begin{pmatrix} kx \\ ky \end{pmatrix}$.

For any vectors $\mathbf{u}$ and $\mathbf{v}$, if $\mathbf{u} = k\mathbf{v}$ then $\mathbf{u}$ and $\mathbf{v}$ are parallel.

Example 5

Two points have coordinates $A(-1, 4)$ and $B(2b, b+2)$.
$\overrightarrow{AB}$ is parallel to $\mathbf{v} = \begin{pmatrix} 3 \\ 4 \end{pmatrix}$. Find the value of b.

$$\overrightarrow{OA} = \begin{pmatrix} -1 \\ 4 \end{pmatrix} \quad \overrightarrow{OB} = \begin{pmatrix} 2b \\ b+2 \end{pmatrix}$$ — Write the position vectors.

$$\overrightarrow{AB} = \overrightarrow{OB} - \overrightarrow{OA}$$

$$\overrightarrow{AB} = \begin{pmatrix} 2b+1 \\ b-2 \end{pmatrix}$$ — Find the vector $\overrightarrow{AB}$.

$$\begin{pmatrix} 2b+1 \\ b-2 \end{pmatrix} = k\begin{pmatrix} 3 \\ 4 \end{pmatrix}$$ — Parallel vectors are multiples of each other.

$$2b + 1 = 3k$$
$$b - 2 = 4k$$ — Write the system of simultaneous equations and solve for b.
$$b = -2$$

Example 6

Four points, $A(4, 6)$, $B(-2, 16)$, $C(-5, 12)$ and $D(-2, 7)$ lie in a plane.
Show that $ABCD$ forms a trapezoid.

$$\overrightarrow{AB} = \begin{pmatrix} -6 \\ 10 \end{pmatrix} \qquad \overrightarrow{BC} = \begin{pmatrix} -3 \\ -4 \end{pmatrix}$$

$$\overrightarrow{CD} = \begin{pmatrix} 3 \\ -5 \end{pmatrix} \qquad \overrightarrow{DA} = \begin{pmatrix} 6 \\ -1 \end{pmatrix}$$ — Find the vectors for each side of the trapezoid: $\overrightarrow{AB}$, $\overrightarrow{BC}$, $\overrightarrow{CD}$ and $\overrightarrow{DA}$.

$$\overrightarrow{AB} = \begin{pmatrix} -6 \\ 10 \end{pmatrix} = -2\begin{pmatrix} 3 \\ -5 \end{pmatrix} = (-2) \times \overrightarrow{CD}$$ — Look for parallel vectors.

$\overrightarrow{AB}$ and $\overrightarrow{CD}$ are parallel. None of the other sides are parallel.

$ABCD$ has one pair of parallel sides so it is a trapezoid.

Practice 4

Problem solving

1 The vectors $\mathbf{u} = \begin{pmatrix} a-2 \\ a+1 \end{pmatrix}$ and $\mathbf{v} = \begin{pmatrix} a \\ 3a+3 \end{pmatrix}$ are parallel.

Determine the value of a given that $a > 0$.

2 Two points have coordinates $A(2, 5)$ and $B(b-2, 1-b)$.

$\overrightarrow{AB}$ is parallel to $\mathbf{v} = \begin{pmatrix} 1 \\ -3 \end{pmatrix}$. Find the value of b.

In some parts of the world (and in this book) a trapezoid is defined as a quadrilateral with exactly *one* pair of opposite sides parallel. In other parts of the world this is called a trapezium. The confusion dates back to 1795, to a reference in a mathematical dictionary published in the USA that directly reversed the accepted meanings of the day.

3 Two points have coordinates $P(2a, a - 4)$ and $Q(3b + 1, 2a - 3b)$.

$\overrightarrow{PQ} = \begin{pmatrix} -7 \\ 5 \end{pmatrix}$. Find the position vector of the midpoint of the line segment PQ.

> The **position vector** of a point is the vector from the origin O to the point.

4 Four points have coordinates $A(3, 7)$, $B(2, 11)$, $C(15, 3)$ and $D(17, -5)$.

    a Use vectors to show that the lines AB and CD are parallel.

    b Determine if the line segments AB and CD are equal in length.

5 Four points have coordinates $A(4, 6)$, $B(-1, 9)$, $C(1, 1)$ and $D(11, -5)$. Show that $\overrightarrow{AB}$ and $\overrightarrow{DC}$ are parallel.

6 Four points have position vectors:

$\overrightarrow{OA} = 9\mathbf{u} + 9\mathbf{v}$, $\overrightarrow{OB} = 19\mathbf{u} + 14\mathbf{v}$, $\overrightarrow{OC} = 25\mathbf{u} + 5\mathbf{v}$ and $\overrightarrow{OD} = 15\mathbf{u}$.

    a Find $\overrightarrow{AB}$ and $\overrightarrow{DC}$ in terms of $\mathbf{u}$ and $\mathbf{v}$.

    b Hence show that $ABCD$ is a parallelogram.

    c Given that $\mathbf{u} = \begin{pmatrix} 2 \\ 1 \end{pmatrix}$ and $\mathbf{v} = \begin{pmatrix} -1 \\ 1 \end{pmatrix}$, show that $ABCD$ is a rhombus.

7 From the five points $A(-3, 1)$, $B(1, 3)$, $C(4, 3)$, $D(5, 1)$ and $E(-1, -2)$, find two sets of four points, each of which forms a trapezoid.

> Three points P, Q and R are on a straight line if the vectors $\overrightarrow{PQ}$ and $\overrightarrow{QR}$ are parallel.

8 Use vectors to show that the three points $P(5, -4)$, $Q(10, 0)$ and $R(25, 12)$ lie on a straight line.

Reflect and discuss 5

Why does showing that the vectors formed by three points are parallel also show that the three points lie on a straight line?

Exploration 4

1 On suitable axes, draw the points $A(2, 4)$ and $B(6, 1)$.

Label the vectors $\overrightarrow{OA}$, $\overrightarrow{OB}$ and $\overrightarrow{AB}$ on your diagram.

2 The angle between $\overrightarrow{OA}$ and $\overrightarrow{OB}$ is $\angle AOB$.

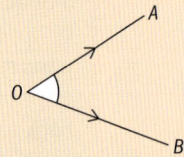

Describe how you could use the cosine rule to find the size of $\angle AOB$.

3 Find $|\overrightarrow{OA}|$ and $|\overrightarrow{OB}|$. Hence find the size of $\angle AOB$, correct to the nearest degree.

4 Use the method in steps **1** to **3** to find the angle between the vectors $\begin{pmatrix} 3 \\ 8 \end{pmatrix}$ and $\begin{pmatrix} 6 \\ 3 \end{pmatrix}$.

▶ Continued on next page

5 The diagram shows vectors **u** and **v**.

Write down an expression for $\mathbf{v} - \mathbf{u}$ in terms of u_x, u_y, v_x and v_y.

$$\mathbf{v} = \begin{pmatrix} v_x \\ v_y \end{pmatrix} \qquad \mathbf{u} = \begin{pmatrix} u_x \\ u_y \end{pmatrix}$$

6 Write down expressions for $|\mathbf{u}|$ and $|\mathbf{v}|$.

Show that $|\mathbf{v} - \mathbf{u}| = \sqrt{u_x^2 + u_y^2 + v_x^2 + v_y^2 - 2u_x v_x - 2u_y v_y}$.

7 Use the cosine rule to show that $-2u_x v_x - 2u_y v_y = -2\sqrt{u_x^2 + u_y^2}\sqrt{v_x^2 + v_y^2}\cos\theta$

and hence that $\cos\theta = \dfrac{u_x v_x + u_y v_y}{|\mathbf{u}|\,|\mathbf{v}|}$

For any two vectors $\mathbf{u} = \begin{pmatrix} u_x \\ u_y \end{pmatrix}$ and $\mathbf{v} = \begin{pmatrix} v_x \\ v_y \end{pmatrix}$, the quantity $u_x v_x + u_y v_y$

is called the **dot product**. It is written $\mathbf{u} \cdot \mathbf{v}$.

From the equation you have formed above, you can see that
$u_x v_x + u_y v_y = |\mathbf{u}|\,|\mathbf{v}|\cos\theta$.

Therefore $\mathbf{u} \cdot \mathbf{v} = u_x v_x + u_y v_y = |\mathbf{u}|\,|\mathbf{v}|\cos\theta$.

> Another name for the dot product is the **scalar product**, because the result is a scalar quantity.

Example 7

Find the angle between the vectors $\begin{pmatrix} 1 \\ 4 \end{pmatrix}$ and $\begin{pmatrix} -2 \\ 5 \end{pmatrix}$.

$|\mathbf{u}| = \sqrt{1^2 + 4^2} = \sqrt{17}$ Find $|\mathbf{u}|$ and $|\mathbf{v}|$.

$|\mathbf{v}| = \sqrt{(-2)^2 + 5^2} = \sqrt{29}$

$\mathbf{u} \cdot \mathbf{v} = |\mathbf{u}|\,|\mathbf{v}|\cos\theta$

$\begin{pmatrix} 1 \\ 4 \end{pmatrix} \cdot \begin{pmatrix} -2 \\ 5 \end{pmatrix} = \sqrt{17}\sqrt{29}\cos\theta$ Substitute in the vectors and their magnitudes.

$1 \times -2 + 4 \times 5 = \sqrt{17}\sqrt{29}\cos\theta$ Use the definition of the dot product.

$\cos\theta = \dfrac{18}{\sqrt{17}\sqrt{29}}$

     Give your answer to a suitable degree of accuracy.

$\theta = 35.9°$

Example 8

Vectors $\mathbf{a} = \begin{pmatrix} 4 \\ 7 \end{pmatrix}$ and $\mathbf{b} = \begin{pmatrix} 2x-2 \\ 2-x \end{pmatrix}$ are perpendicular. Find the value of x.

$\mathbf{a} \cdot \mathbf{b} = |\mathbf{a}|\,|\mathbf{b}|\cos 90° = 0$ The angle between $\mathbf{a}$ and $\mathbf{b}$ is 90°, and $\cos 90° = 0$.

$\begin{pmatrix} 4 \\ 7 \end{pmatrix} \cdot \begin{pmatrix} 2x-2 \\ 2-x \end{pmatrix} = 0$ Substitute in $\mathbf{a}$ and $\mathbf{b}$.

$(8x - 8) + (14 - 7x) = 0$

     Evaluate the scalar product.

$\Rightarrow x = -6$

If two vectors **a** and **b** are perpendicular then $\mathbf{a} \cdot \mathbf{b} = 0$.

Equally, if $\mathbf{a} \cdot \mathbf{b} = 0$ then either $\mathbf{a} = \begin{pmatrix} 0 \\ 0 \end{pmatrix}$, $\mathbf{b} = \begin{pmatrix} 0 \\ 0 \end{pmatrix}$ or **a** and **b** are perpendicular.

Practice 5

1 Find the angle between each pair of vectors, to the nearest degree.

a $\begin{pmatrix} 4 \\ 5 \end{pmatrix}$ and $\begin{pmatrix} 2 \\ -8 \end{pmatrix}$ **b** $\begin{pmatrix} 26 \\ -4 \end{pmatrix}$ and $\begin{pmatrix} 3 \\ -12 \end{pmatrix}$

c $\begin{pmatrix} -4 \\ -2 \end{pmatrix}$ and $\begin{pmatrix} -16 \\ -20 \end{pmatrix}$ **d** $\begin{pmatrix} 13 \\ -2 \end{pmatrix}$ and $\begin{pmatrix} 8 \\ 4 \end{pmatrix}$

2 Show that $\begin{pmatrix} 4 \\ -8 \end{pmatrix}$ and $\begin{pmatrix} 2 \\ 1 \end{pmatrix}$ are perpendicular.

Problem solving

3 Two speedboats are travelling with velocities $\begin{pmatrix} 20 \\ -15 \end{pmatrix}$ m/s

and $\begin{pmatrix} 7 \\ 24 \end{pmatrix}$ m/s respectively, on an east-north coordinate grid.

  a Show that both boats have the same speed.

  b Find the angle between their directions of travel.

4 Triangle ABC has vertices $A(6, 3)$, $B(2, 1)$ and $C(4, 5)$.
Use the dot product to find $\angle ABC$.

5 Vectors **u** and **v** are perpendicular:

$$\mathbf{u} = \begin{pmatrix} -2 \\ 5 \end{pmatrix}, \mathbf{v} = \begin{pmatrix} 3m+3 \\ 2m-2 \end{pmatrix}$$

Find the value of m.

6 Vectors $\begin{pmatrix} a \\ a+2 \end{pmatrix}$ and $\begin{pmatrix} b \\ 2-b \end{pmatrix}$ are perpendicular.

  a Write an equation involving a and b.

  b Explain why you need more information to determine
the values of a and b.

  c Given that $b = 1 - a$, determine the values of a and b.

Problem solving

7 Find three different vectors perpendicular to the vector $\begin{pmatrix} 8 \\ -2 \end{pmatrix}$.

8 Parallelogram $OABC$ has vertices $O(0, 0)$, $A(4, 9)$ and $B(6, 6)$.

  a Find the position vector of C.

  b Find the size of $\angle OAC$.

9 A rhombus $OABC$ has $\overrightarrow{OA} = \mathbf{a}$ and $\overrightarrow{OC} = \mathbf{c}$. $\angle AOC = 120°$ and $|\mathbf{a}| = 4$.

Find the value of $\mathbf{a} \cdot \mathbf{c}$.

10 For the vectors $\mathbf{a} = \begin{pmatrix} 3 \\ 5 \end{pmatrix}$, $\mathbf{b} = \begin{pmatrix} 2 \\ -2 \end{pmatrix}$ and $\mathbf{c} = \begin{pmatrix} 5 \\ 1 \end{pmatrix}$, verify that

$\mathbf{a} \cdot (\mathbf{b} + \mathbf{c}) = \mathbf{a} \cdot \mathbf{b} + \mathbf{a} \cdot \mathbf{c}$

11 Consider the vectors $\mathbf{a} = \begin{pmatrix} a_x \\ a_y \end{pmatrix}$, $\mathbf{b} = \begin{pmatrix} b_x \\ b_y \end{pmatrix}$ and $\mathbf{c} = \begin{pmatrix} c_x \\ c_y \end{pmatrix}$.

Prove that $\mathbf{a} \cdot (\mathbf{b} + \mathbf{c}) = \mathbf{a} \cdot \mathbf{b} + \mathbf{a} \cdot \mathbf{c}$ for any 2D vectors $\mathbf{a}$, $\mathbf{b}$ and $\mathbf{c}$.

D Vector geometry

- How do vectors define the spaces we live and work in?
- How does form influence function?

You can use vectors in geometric problems even when you do not know their components. Remember that you can add vectors pictorially.

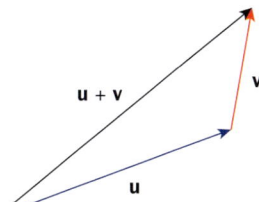

Exploration 5

1 The diagram shows a pair of vectors $\mathbf{a}$ and $\mathbf{b}$.

Copy the diagram and draw the vectors:

  a $3\mathbf{a}$ **b** $2\mathbf{b}$

  c $\mathbf{a} + \mathbf{b}$ (the resultant vector of $\mathbf{a}$ and then $\mathbf{b}$)

  d $\mathbf{a} - \mathbf{b}$ **e** $-\mathbf{a} + \mathbf{b}$ **f** $-\mathbf{a} - \mathbf{b}$

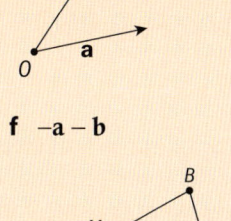

> Start with a new copy for each diagram.

2 In this diagram, M is the midpoint of AB and N is the midpoint of AC.

  a Given that $\overrightarrow{AM} = \mathbf{a}$ and $\overrightarrow{AN} = \mathbf{b}$, explain why $\overrightarrow{AB} = 2\mathbf{b}$ and write down a similar expression for $\overrightarrow{AC}$.

  b Explain why $\overrightarrow{MN} = \mathbf{b} - \mathbf{a}$. Form a similar expression for $\overrightarrow{BC}$.

  c Hence show that $MNCB$ is a trapezoid.

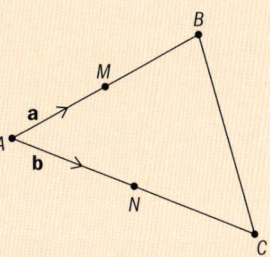

> Remember that $\overrightarrow{MN} = \overrightarrow{MA} + \overrightarrow{AN}$.

▶ Continued on next page

3 Four points A, B, C and D have position vectors $\mathbf{a} + \mathbf{b}$, $\mathbf{a} - \mathbf{b}$, $-\mathbf{a} - \mathbf{b}$, and $-\mathbf{a} + \mathbf{b}$ respectively, where $\mathbf{a}$ and $\mathbf{b}$ are non-parallel non-zero vectors.

   a This sketch shows one possible pair of vectors $\mathbf{a}$ and $\mathbf{b}$.
      Copy the sketch and draw points A, B, C and D on the diagram.

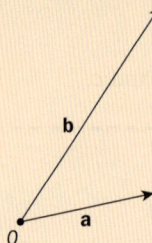

   b This sketch shows another possible pair of vectors $\mathbf{a}$ and $\mathbf{b}$.
      Copy the sketch and draw points A, B, C and D on the diagram.

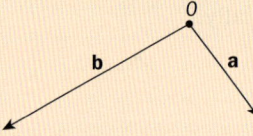

   c Find expressions for $\overrightarrow{AB}$ and $\overrightarrow{DC}$.

   d Hence show that $ABCD$ is a parallelogram.

4 This diagram shows points A, B, C and D.

$\overrightarrow{AD} = \mathbf{a} + \mathbf{b}$

$\overrightarrow{BD} = 2\mathbf{b} - \mathbf{a}$

$\overrightarrow{BC} = 3\mathbf{a}$

   a Find $\overrightarrow{AB}$.

   b Find $\overrightarrow{DC}$.

   c Hence show that $\overrightarrow{AB}$ and $\overrightarrow{DC}$ are parallel.

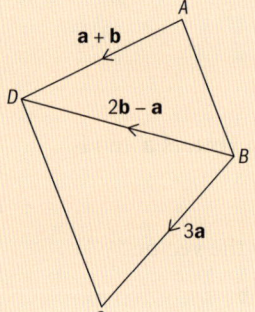

The word 'vector' was originally a Latin word, meaning 'to carry'. You can think of a vector in mathematics as something that carries you from one place to another. We also use the word in other contexts: mosquitos and some other insects are referred to as vectors because they transmit disease from one organism to another. In sociology, a vector is a person that passes folklore on from one generation to the next. And in aeronautics, a vector is a set of appropriate headings to guide an aircraft in flight.

Reflect and discuss 6

- How does your answer to Exploration 5, step **3c** show you that $ABCD$ is a parallelogram regardless of the direction of vectors $\mathbf{a}$ and $\mathbf{b}$?

- Why was it necessary in step **3** to state that $\mathbf{a}$ and $\mathbf{b}$ were non-zero?

- Why was it necessary to state that $\mathbf{a}$ and $\mathbf{b}$ were not parallel?

Practice 6

1 Using the diagram, express the vectors below it in terms of **u**, **v** and **w**:

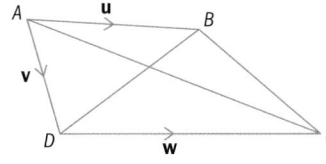

a $\overrightarrow{BD}$ **b** $\overrightarrow{CA}$ **c** $\overrightarrow{BC}$

Problem solving

2 The diagram shows a regular hexagon *ABCDEF*.

Find in terms of **a** and **b**:

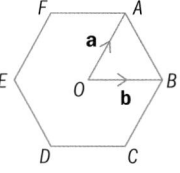

   a $\overrightarrow{AB}$ **b** $\overrightarrow{OC}$ **c** $\overrightarrow{FO}$ **d** $\overrightarrow{AC}$ **e** $\overrightarrow{DB}$

3 Points *P*, *Q* and *R* form a straight line and have position vectors

p, **q**, and **r** respectively. $|\overrightarrow{QR}| = 4\,|\overrightarrow{PQ}|$.

a Express **r** in terms of **p** and **q**.

b Hence show that $\mathbf{q} = \dfrac{1}{5}\,(4\mathbf{p} + \mathbf{r})$.

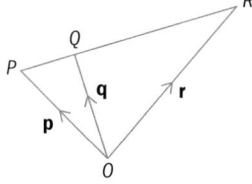

4 Points *S*, *T* and *U* form a straight line and have position vectors **s**, **t** and **u** respectively, where $|\overrightarrow{SU}| = 3\,|\overrightarrow{TU}|$.

Express **s** in terms of **t** and **u**.

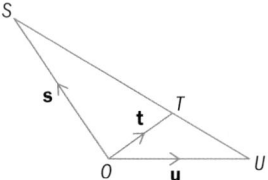

5 In this diagram, *M* is the midpoint of *AB*. $\overrightarrow{OA} = 3\mathbf{a}$ and $\overrightarrow{OB} = 2\mathbf{b}$.

   a Find $\overrightarrow{OM}$.

   b The point *N* has position vector $\overrightarrow{ON}$ where $\overrightarrow{ON} = 2\overrightarrow{OM}$.

Show that $\overrightarrow{AN} = 2\mathbf{b}$.

   c Given that $|\mathbf{a}| = |\mathbf{b}|$ and $\mathbf{a} \cdot \mathbf{b} = 0$, fully describe the quadrilateral *OANB*.

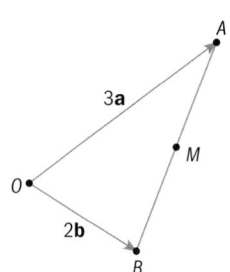

Summary

A **column vector** describes a translation.

A column vector has an x component and a y component: $\begin{pmatrix} x \\ y \end{pmatrix}$

The x component tells you how far to move in the x-direction. The y component tells you how far to move in the y-direction.

$\overrightarrow{AB}$ is the vector representing the translation from A to B.

The **position vector** of a point is the vector from the origin O to the point.

$\begin{pmatrix} 0 \\ 0 \end{pmatrix}$ is the **zero vector**.

Two vectors are equal if their components are equal.

If $\mathbf{v}_1 = \begin{pmatrix} x_1 \\ y_1 \end{pmatrix}$ and $\mathbf{v}_2 = \begin{pmatrix} x_2 \\ y_2 \end{pmatrix}$ then $\mathbf{v}_1 = \mathbf{v}_2$ if and only if $x_1 = x_2$ and $y_1 = y_2$.

The **magnitude** of a vector is its length.

$|\mathbf{v}|$, the magnitude of $\mathbf{v} = \begin{pmatrix} x \\ y \end{pmatrix}$, is given by

$|\mathbf{v}| = \sqrt{x^2 + y^2}$.

A vector has both magnitude and direction.

A scalar quantity does not have a direction.

For two vectors to be equal, they must have the same magnitude and direction.

A translation from A to B followed by a translation from B to C is the same as the translation from A to C: $\overrightarrow{AB} + \overrightarrow{BC} = \overrightarrow{AC}$

$\overrightarrow{AC}$ is sometimes called the **resultant** of $\overrightarrow{AB}$ and $\overrightarrow{BC}$.

The vector addition law:

If $\overrightarrow{AB} = \begin{pmatrix} x_1 \\ y_1 \end{pmatrix}$ and $\overrightarrow{BC} = \begin{pmatrix} x_2 \\ y_2 \end{pmatrix}$ then

$$\overrightarrow{AC} = \overrightarrow{AB} + \overrightarrow{BC} = \begin{pmatrix} x_1 \\ y_1 \end{pmatrix} + \begin{pmatrix} x_2 \\ y_2 \end{pmatrix} = \begin{pmatrix} x_1 + x_2 \\ y_1 + y_2 \end{pmatrix}$$

For any two points A and B, $\overrightarrow{AB} = \overrightarrow{OB} - \overrightarrow{OA}$ and $\overrightarrow{AB} = -\overrightarrow{BA}$.

Scalar multiplication of a vector:

For any vector, $\mathbf{v} = \begin{pmatrix} x \\ y \end{pmatrix}$ and any scalar value k:

$k\mathbf{v} = \begin{pmatrix} kx \\ ky \end{pmatrix}$

If $\mathbf{u} = k\mathbf{v}$ then $\mathbf{u}$ and $\mathbf{v}$ are parallel.

For any two vectors $\mathbf{u} = \begin{pmatrix} u_x \\ u_y \end{pmatrix}$ and $\mathbf{v} = \begin{pmatrix} v_x \\ v_y \end{pmatrix}$, the quantity $u_x v_x + u_y v_y$ is called the **dot product**.

$$\mathbf{u} \cdot \mathbf{v} = u_x v_x + u_y v_y = |\mathbf{u}|\,|\mathbf{v}| \cos \theta$$

If two vectors $\mathbf{a}$ and $\mathbf{b}$ are perpendicular then $\mathbf{a} \cdot \mathbf{b} = 0$.

Equally, if $\mathbf{a} \cdot \mathbf{b} = 0$ then either $\mathbf{a} = \begin{pmatrix} 0 \\ 0 \end{pmatrix}$, $\mathbf{b} = \begin{pmatrix} 0 \\ 0 \end{pmatrix}$ or $\mathbf{a}$ and $\mathbf{b}$ are perpendicular.

Mixed practice

1 **Write down** column vectors that represent:

   a a translation of 5 right and 4 up

   b a translation of 2 left and 3 up

   c a translation from (4, 5) to (7, 9)

   d a translation from (9, 14) to (−2, −5).

2 **Find** the vectors $\overrightarrow{AB}$ and $\overrightarrow{BA}$ given the points:

   a $A(1, 3)$ and $B(−2, 0)$

   b $A(4, 2)$ and $B(−3, 5)$

   c $A(−7, 1)$ and $B(−4, −4)$

   d $A(−2, 7)$ and $B(11, −7)$

3 **Find** $\overrightarrow{AC}$ given:

   a $\overrightarrow{AB} = \begin{pmatrix} -2 \\ 4 \end{pmatrix}$ and $\overrightarrow{BC} = \begin{pmatrix} -1 \\ -7 \end{pmatrix}$

   b $\overrightarrow{AB} = \begin{pmatrix} 0 \\ -8 \end{pmatrix}$ and $\overrightarrow{BC} = \begin{pmatrix} 9 \\ 2 \end{pmatrix}$

   c $\overrightarrow{AB} = \begin{pmatrix} -1 \\ -3 \end{pmatrix}$ and $\overrightarrow{BC} = \begin{pmatrix} 4 \\ -2 \end{pmatrix}$

   d $\overrightarrow{AB} = \begin{pmatrix} -6 \\ 15 \end{pmatrix}$ and $\overrightarrow{BC} = \begin{pmatrix} 4 \\ 0 \end{pmatrix}$

4 Given that $\overrightarrow{AB} = \begin{pmatrix} 2 \\ -1 \end{pmatrix}$, **find** the values of a and b given the coordinates:

  a $A(a-3, 3a+2)$ and $B(-b, 2b-1)$

  b $A(2a, -4+a)$ and $B(-2b, b)$

  c $A(a-6, -2a+10)$ and $B(2b+9, b+3)$

  d $A(-3a, a-2)$ and $B(11+b, 2b+1)$

5 **Find** the magnitude of each of these vectors, giving your answer in exact form.

  a $\begin{pmatrix} 5 \\ 2 \end{pmatrix}$ **b** $\begin{pmatrix} -4 \\ 3 \end{pmatrix}$ **c** $\begin{pmatrix} 12 \\ 15 \end{pmatrix}$ **d** $\begin{pmatrix} 13 \\ -16 \end{pmatrix}$

6 $M(-3, 2)$ and $N(2, 5)$.

  Find a $\overrightarrow{ON}$ **b** $\overrightarrow{MN}$ **c** $\overrightarrow{NM}$

7 **Find**, correct to the nearest degree, the angle between:

  a $\begin{pmatrix} 3 \\ 7 \end{pmatrix}$ and $\begin{pmatrix} -2 \\ 1 \end{pmatrix}$ **b** $\begin{pmatrix} 1 \\ 1 \end{pmatrix}$ and $\begin{pmatrix} -4 \\ 5 \end{pmatrix}$

  c $\begin{pmatrix} 3 \\ -2 \end{pmatrix}$ and $\begin{pmatrix} 2 \\ 4 \end{pmatrix}$

: **Problem solving**

8 From the list of nine vectors below, **select** pairs of vectors which are parallel to each other.
Determine which vector is not parallel to any of the others.

$\begin{pmatrix} -6 \\ 20 \end{pmatrix}$ $\begin{pmatrix} 16 \\ 20 \end{pmatrix}$ $\begin{pmatrix} 12 \\ -18 \end{pmatrix}$ $\begin{pmatrix} 36 \\ 45 \end{pmatrix}$ $\begin{pmatrix} 9 \\ -30 \end{pmatrix}$

$\begin{pmatrix} 15 \\ 25 \end{pmatrix}$ $\begin{pmatrix} 5 \\ 8 \end{pmatrix}$ $\begin{pmatrix} -9 \\ -15 \end{pmatrix}$ $\begin{pmatrix} -4 \\ 6 \end{pmatrix}$

9 **Show that** the vectors $\begin{pmatrix} 1 \\ 4 \end{pmatrix}$ and $\begin{pmatrix} 8 \\ -2 \end{pmatrix}$ are perpendicular to each other.

Problem solving

10 The vectors $\mathbf{u} = \begin{pmatrix} 5a+2 \\ a-4 \end{pmatrix}$ and $\mathbf{v} = \begin{pmatrix} a+7 \\ 8-2a \end{pmatrix}$ are parallel.

  Determine the possible values of a.

11 For the points with coordinates $A(-3, 2)$ and $B(2b+1, b-4)$:
$\overrightarrow{AB}$ is parallel to $\mathbf{v} = \begin{pmatrix} -2 \\ -9 \end{pmatrix}$. **Find** the value of b.

12 The diagram shows five points O, A, B, C and X.
$\overrightarrow{OX} = \overrightarrow{XB} = \mathbf{a}$ and
$\overrightarrow{CX} = \overrightarrow{XA} = \mathbf{b}$

  Show that $OABC$ is a parallelogram.

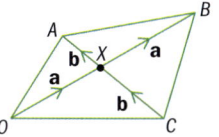

Problem solving

13 The diagram shows a quadrilateral $OABC$.
$\overrightarrow{AB} = \mathbf{a}$, $\overrightarrow{OC} = 2\mathbf{a}$ and $\overrightarrow{OA} = \mathbf{b}$. Lines OB and AC intersect at X.

  a **Explain** why $OABC$ is a trapezoid.

  b **Show that** $\overrightarrow{OB} = \mathbf{a} + \mathbf{b}$.

  c **Find** $\overrightarrow{AC}$.

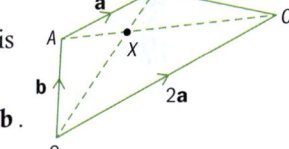

  d Use the fact that X lies on OB to **explain** why $\overrightarrow{OX} = k(\mathbf{a}+\mathbf{b})$ for some constant k.

  e By considering $\overrightarrow{OA} + \overrightarrow{AX}$, **show that** $\overrightarrow{OX} = \mathbf{b} + m(2\mathbf{a} - \mathbf{b})$ for some constant m.

  f Hence **find** $\overrightarrow{OX}$ and **determine** the ratio in which X divides $\overrightarrow{AC}$.

Review in context

Objective D: Applying mathematics in real-life contexts
ii. select appropriate mathematical strategies when solving authentic real-life situations

Think about how magnitude, direction, the dot product, etc. relate to the questions being asked.

In these questions, a floor cleaning robot has been placed on the floor of a large room. It measures its progress across the floor in 10 cm units, so the vector $\begin{pmatrix} 1 \\ 0 \end{pmatrix}$ represents a movement of 10 cm in the x-direction.

1 **Show that** if the robot travels on a vector of $\begin{pmatrix} 3 \\ 4 \end{pmatrix}$, it covers a distance of 50 cm.

2 **Find**, correct to the nearest centimeter, the distance travelled by the robot as it moves on each vector.

a $\begin{pmatrix} 3 \\ 7 \end{pmatrix}$　　**b** $\begin{pmatrix} 2 \\ -4 \end{pmatrix}$　　**c** $\begin{pmatrix} 6 \\ 3 \end{pmatrix}$

d $\begin{pmatrix} 9 \\ -3 \end{pmatrix}$　　**e** $\begin{pmatrix} -15 \\ 25 \end{pmatrix}$　　**f** $\begin{pmatrix} 40 \\ -20 \end{pmatrix}$

3 In a rectangular room, the robot is positioned so that the x-and y-directions are the edges of the room.
The robot starts in one corner at $(0, 0)$, travels on $\begin{pmatrix} 25 \\ 0 \end{pmatrix}$ until it reaches another corner and then on $\begin{pmatrix} 0 \\ 60 \end{pmatrix}$ until it reaches a third corner.

a **Find** the area of the room in m^2.

b **Write down** the vector which would return the robot to its starting point.

c In total the robot travels along two sides of the room and then straight back to the start. **Find** the total distance travelled.

4 The robot is put in the L-shaped room below, $ABCDEF$. It starts at O, which is somewhere inside the room. Its x-direction is parallel to AF, BC and DE and its y-direction is parallel to AB, CD and FE.

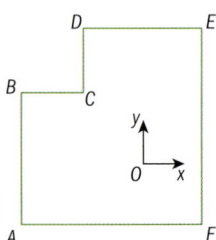

In its mapping process, the robot determines that $\overrightarrow{OA} = \begin{pmatrix} -14 \\ -30 \end{pmatrix}$, $\overrightarrow{OC} = \begin{pmatrix} -2 \\ 15 \end{pmatrix}$ and $\overrightarrow{OE} = \begin{pmatrix} 22 \\ 25 \end{pmatrix}$.

a **Find** vector $\overrightarrow{AE}$ and the distance from A to E.

b **Find** the position vector $\overrightarrow{OF}$.
Hence **find** the distance from C to F.

c **Determine** which is longer, AC or CE.

d **Calculate** the perimeter and area of the room.

Reflect and discuss 7

Have you explored the statement of inquiry? Give specific examples.

5 The robot is placed in another room, $PQRS$, but its axes are not lined up with the sides.

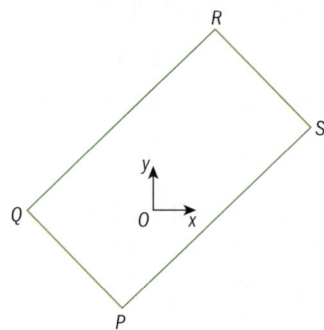

The robot finds the location of the room's corners to be as follows:

$$\overrightarrow{OP} = \begin{pmatrix} -10 \\ -30 \end{pmatrix} \qquad \overrightarrow{OQ} = \begin{pmatrix} -34 \\ 2 \end{pmatrix}$$

$$\overrightarrow{OR} = \begin{pmatrix} 25 \\ 45 \end{pmatrix} \qquad \overrightarrow{OS} = \begin{pmatrix} 50 \\ 15 \end{pmatrix}$$

a **Find** $\overrightarrow{PQ}$ and $\overrightarrow{PS}$.

b **Show that** walls PQ and PS are perpendicular.

c **Find** $\overrightarrow{SR}$.

d **Determine** whether SR and PQ are parallel. Hence **determine** whether the room is rectangular. **Justify** your answer.

6 The robot is placed at O, somewhere in a four-sided room. It finds the four corners of the room, U, V, W and X.

You are given the following vector information:

$$\overrightarrow{OW} = \begin{pmatrix} 15 \\ -25 \end{pmatrix} \qquad \overrightarrow{OV} = \begin{pmatrix} 40 \\ 0 \end{pmatrix}$$

$$\overrightarrow{OX} = \begin{pmatrix} -32 \\ 22 \end{pmatrix} \qquad \overrightarrow{UX} = \begin{pmatrix} -50 \\ 0 \end{pmatrix}$$

a **Find** $\overrightarrow{UV}$ and $\overrightarrow{XW}$.

b Hence **show that** the room is a trapezoid.

c **Show that** $\overrightarrow{VW}$ is perpendicular to both $\overrightarrow{UV}$ and $\overrightarrow{XW}$.

d **Find** the area of the room.

e **Find** the size of $\angle VUX$.

Statement of inquiry:

Using logic to develop patterns and understanding the properties of space can help design models to use resources responsibly and efficiently.

Index